TELECOMMUNICATIONS, MEDIA & TECHNOLOGY (TMT) FOR DEVELOPING ECONOMIES

How to Make TMT Improve Developing Economies in Africa and Elsewhere for the 2020s

H SAMA NWANA

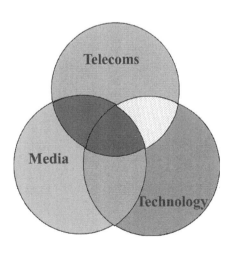

~ How to Make TMT Improve Developing Economies in Africa and Elsewhere for the 2020s ~

Futura Formare Prospicere Melius

(It is better to *shape* the future than to try and *foresee* it.)

In the context of this volume, it is better to shape the future of the TMT sector than just to try and foresee it.

Published by GIGALEN PRESS
Telecommunications, Media & Technology (TMT) for Developing Economies
H Sama Nwana,

First Published in the United Kingdom in 2014 by Gigalen Press
c/o Atlantic Telecoms & Media,
Suite 604, Crown House Business Centre,
North Circular Road,
Park Royal, London,
NW10 7PN
United Kingdom

ISBN: 099282110X
ISBN-13: 9780992821104

Version 1.0
Printed by CreateSpace, a DBA of ON-Demand Publishing Ltd

TABLE OF CONTENTS

PRAISE FOR TMT FOR DEVELOPING ECONOMIES

An anonymous reviewer of this book wrote:

"The book is successful in its objectives. This complete examination of the TMT sector for Africa and developing economies has left no stone unturned. Those involved in the process will no doubt refer to the book again and again. Readers who are TMT novices will discover an in-depth "textbook" that will guide them through this complicated subject. The book is an authority on the topic because of the extensive research and the author's personal involvement."

Professor William Webb, FIET is CEO of the Weightless SIG and President-Elect of the IET[1] wrote:

"H Nwana has a unique and impressive background. He has operated at senior Ministerial and Business levels within Europe and across Africa. His role as Group Director at Ofcom UK – one of the world's leading Communications Regulators – has provided him with a unique opportunity to experience all aspects of Telecommunications, Media and related Technologies. This background combined with his African roots has enabled him to propose an equally unique TMT

---

1   The Institution of Engineering and Technology (The IET – www.theiet.org) is the professional society for the engineering and technology community, with more than 150000 members in 127 countries.

Vision for the African Continent and Emerging Economies that guarantees Accessibility and Affordability of TMT services at its very heart.

Making use of a high level of evidence and data throughout, the book is an outstanding blend of information on key areas of the TMT world, and how they can be applied specifically to the case of Developing Economies including Africa. He makes many insightful recommendations for Governments, Industry, Regulators and associated entities that have the potential to dramatically improve the wealth and infrastructure of much of the African continent and beyond.

There are not many books that offer the possibility of changing the world, but this is one of them. It should be obligatory reading for all those involved in this exciting TMT area."

Dr Ernest Ndukwe, Chairman of Openmedia Group (Nigeria) and ex-CEO of the Nigerian Communications Commission (NCC) for 10 years, wrote:

"It has indeed been a pleasure to read the book. There is no doubt this is a major achievement by a respected authority in the field of Telecom, Media and Technology.

Nwana is a real talent and this work is a valuable contribution to knowledge in the TMT sector for developing economies"

Another anonymous reviewer writes:

"Nwana in this volume argues forcefully, cogently and unapologetically that emerging economies must think of a single TMT sector as the singular "nerve centre" of their economies; indeed, he offers a blueprint for it. He also argues that the TMT sector must be proactively *shaped*, rather than just foreseen – in order to optimize the benefits to consumers and citizens. The book is a "how to" book written by someone who has been an active participant and player in the sector; it contains hundreds of recommendations across contemporary TMT areas. It covers the case for TMT, its anatomy and geography, a TMT blue print, spectrum, auctions, TV Whitespaces for rural broadband, Digital Switch Over, broadcasting, regulation and affordable and widespread TMT services including mobile voice, mobile data, AM/FM radio, digital TV, other media and fixed Internet".

Tara Jones, Createspace Editor writes:

"The book is organized extremely well. Each chapter has a clearly stated purpose that is systematically addressed. The numerous headings provide a useful map for navigating the material. These headings also make it easier for readers to go back and locate needed information. Very well done!"

ACKNOWLEDGMENTS

This was difficult book for a single author to write given the sheer breadth and depth that it covers, and I obviously take responsibility for all its many flaws. I clearly did not fully think this through when I started it. I only hope its contributions and insights to such a key and emerging sector—TMT—in Africa and other emerging countries is greater than its flaws. Like most authors, I regretted at several junctures ever having started it. This book was motivated through various keynotes and training assignments I have done all across Africa, Caribbean and some other emerging market countries (in my spare time) over the years, and some of my students and trainees pressed me to write my ideas down and publish. However, it was specifically in 2011 when a very senior telecommunications executive who attended a keynote lecture and Q/A session I gave in South Africa came to me afterwards. He said there was - and still is - a gaping hole in the market for a book that current and future TMT decision makers in emerging economies including himself (as well as entrepreneurs and other practicing TMT professionals) would devour to better understand the emerging TMT sector. He flattered my "talent", "experience from developed markets" and "your unique ability to powerfully translate your experience" to emerging economies. These underserved flattery clearly worked because it was the seed of this volume - TMT for Developing Economies. I acknowledge my TMG Consultancy[2] colleagues, particularly Drs. Sam Atungsiri, Sako Burnley and Charles Nche who, in a convoluted way, also inspired this volume.

---

2 www.tmgcmr.org (accessed December 2013).

I am heavily indebted to so many I have had the honour of working and collaborating with in industry, academia, and regulatory—who have all taught me so much. I cannot list them all as they are so numerous. However, I would like in particular to single out and thank all my ex-colleagues at Ofcom, the esteemed UK communications regulator. I would not have been able to pen such a volume without my four years of education there. The influence Ofcom has had on me is clear to see in this volume, and its website was a key source of information that underpins this volume. I cannot overstate how indebted I am to all my ex-directors, ex-SPG staff, ex-executive/board peers, and all ex-colleagues who I worked so closely with at Ofcom—too many to name. Thank you to you all.

I acknowledge the support of Impact Broadband Ltd (via Peter Henderson)towards the costs of publishing of this book.

Andin, my dear wife, has been exceedingly patient with me writing almost nonstop for four to five months between frequent flights in and out of Africa and Asia—and for that I thank her immensely. Her support too has been invaluable.

This insignificant work is dedicated to my amazing parents, Elias and Odilia Nwana, who have just celebrated fifty years of marriage this past December, and who have taught, and continue to teach, all my siblings, grandchildren and myself so much. It is also dedicated to the memory of my late twin—Protus Sama Nwana as well as to Bambot Peter Sama.

H. Sama Nwana
January 2014

PREFACE

*"Whatever you do will be insignificant, but it is
very important you do it."*
— *Mahatma Gandhi*

This book is insignificant, but it is very important that I—who is even more insignificant—wrote it! I bet you have never read such an honest admission at the beginning of a book before. It is simply just true. However, the hope of such an insignificant book in itself is that it falls into the hands of a few slightly more significant *current* key decision makers and entrepreneurs or *future* decision makers and entrepreneurs and that these people get stimulated about what *could be*, rather than *what is*. Beyond this, as they say, the world is our oyster.

I am lucky to have had the unique honour of seeing firsthand, but perhaps even more importantly, of having been an *active participant* for twenty-five years (albeit an insignificant one) in the TMT revolution that swept Europe and other parts of the developed world.

TMT in the context of this book, and it is not of my invention, is short for telecommunications, media, and technology. Combined, they increasingly count as one sector—indeed, *arguably* the most important sector of any modern economy. You should just get used to this short form of this key sector—TMT. It is used throughout the book.

Any country, or even state, region, or province in some cases, which does not take TMT seriously is creating significant opportunity costs for itself, but in the case of a developing or emerging country, it is committing national *hara-kiri* for its citizens. It could not be over-stated how much developing economies (e.g., in Africa, some Asian, Caribbean, and Latin American countries too) need to get this sector right and for their governments, policy makers, and other stakeholders to set it up for success. The idea of letting the sector creep up on us, i.e., just *foreseeing* it rather than *shaping* it, is fraught with so many risks, such as the holding back of the sector, the wrong assignment of scarce resources like spectrum, the emergence of monopolies which are ultimately not in the interest of the consumer and citizen, or severe lack of necessary investment.

Unfortunately, for reasons both understandable and otherwise, many emerging economies just do not set their TMT sectors up for success, particularly in our *digital Internet age*. Benjamin Franklin's maxim "By failing to prepare, you are preparing to fail" is particu-larly apt here. Many emerging economies, even in the second decade of the twenty-first century AD, particularly in Africa, have not even begun to truly prepare for TMT and so are doomed to fail. How else do you explain the power supply gap in so many African and emerg-ing economies wherein the rate of power consumption in sub-Saharan Africa (excluding South Africa) is barely 1 percent of that in high-income countries, according to the World Bank (World Bank, 2010)? Sorting out these power shortage challenges is *sine qua non* for any TMT economy.

Telecommunications, particularly mobile voice telecommunications—where there will be in this decade more mobile/cellular phones than people on the African continent—has undoubtedly changed many a developing economy for the better. However, in general, this has been no thanks to many of the impediments in making this happen in these countries, like power challenges, poor or nonexistent legislation and regulation, and so on. A significant number of mobile transmission sites on the African continent run on diesel generators[3] which need to be replaced often. So to run many a mobile voice or data business in much of Africa is to also run a logistics and security business. The CEO worries more about the following, and arguably rightly so too, than about his/her customers:

---

3 Typically, there are two generators per site.

- power cuts
- the logistics of getting diesel to his or her transmission sites right
- theft of the diesel (and even theft of diesel generators)
- vandalism of telecommunications equipment, fibre cuts, etc. euphemistically termed "community issues" in Nigeria
- physical security of these sites' power backup

The CEO has such impediments which should not be there in the first place and more. The important point though is that these all introduce costs into the industry that these economies could do without, as these costs add to the inefficiency of such a vital sector of the economy. Inefficiency means higher prices to customers and citizens of these emerging economies. Yes, the inefficiencies (or is it ineptitude?) of power problems or poor roads in most African economies add to prices of the telecommunication services and more on the continent. Many African leaders fail to realize this.

The next phase is mobile data to enable the Internet for the masses in developing countries. This will be even more difficult because the economics of mobile data is much more challenging than that for voice. Voice has always been the killer application in the mobile business, and practically everyone needs it as a basic service.

The media subsector in most developing countries, particularly in Africa, is just moribund, bedeviled by analogue-era thinking, and failed thinking at that. For example, many developing countries are still working to develop their detailed plans—and not just technical plans, but more importantly plans for the media sector that will come after it—to switch from obsolete analogue television (which neither never really worked properly in most of these countries anyway nor provided for "universal access"[4] and "universal service"[5]) to digital. Taking the same failed attitude seen with analogue television into the

---

4 Universal access policy refers to the implementation of the policy for the benefit of every person in society, including those in rural areas.

5 Universal service refers to the specific service that is delivered to all in society. For example, it could be the main channel from the state broadcaster that broadcasts news.

digital world (dominated by wireless and the Internet) carries such large opportunity costs to both citizens and potential new entrepreneurs in these countries. Imagine the opportunity costs of missing out on the jobs, the creativity, the innovation, the emergence of a true advertising industry, the tax receipts, etc., that come from forty to eighty digital channels compared to having one or two nonfunctional analogue television channels. Of course, the issue of where the decent content on these many channels in these countries come from is a critical one, which yet again demonstrates the opportunity to plan and execute for a digital-world content industry in most countries.

The technology subsector too in most developing countries is equally still very much in its infancy. Indeed, infancy in some African, Caribbean and Asian countries is being optimistic—in some of these countries, the technology sector has been stillborn. How many of their senior government officials do you see with business cards bearing Yahoo, Hotmail, Gmail, etc., domain names? Also imagine, as we did earlier, the opportunity cost of *not* having Internet for the masses *for another decade or more* such that the continent misses out on a whole new array of businesses based on Internet technology. Truly unfathomable—is it not? However, you do not get there without planning and superb execution, not something the continent of Africa (or some other emerging market countries) is known for. Local businesses would emerge because local EBay markets will emerge that allow for local trading of good or services. Schools would be tethered to an information pool such as mankind has never witnessed before. Why should we disadvantage African and other developing economies' children in a globalized world? This is literally tantamount to sending them out to the world in blindfolds. Imagine them missing out on all *zeitgeists.*

These issues and more are bad enough. Much worse is the fact the stewards of these sectors in many a developing economy do not recognise that they are in trouble with their directing of such a key sector to the economy. If most of these stewards were aircraft pilots, they would want to ask themselves how many of their citizens would fly in their planes. The famous Cambridge professor Stephen Hawking warns that "the greatest enemy of knowledge is not ignorance—it's the illusion of knowledge." Stewards of such a key sector as TMT in Africa and other developing economies must *not* put themselves in a position where they are accused of displaying the illusion of knowledge. This book is here to start helping them.

In this book, I explain why the TMT sector is so invaluable to developing economies, particularly in Africa. This bit should be self-evident, but illustrating the costs of doing little, or not thinking through carefully what needs to be done, is most important—and is one of the goals of this book. After describing the architecture of the TMT sector, I also attempt to explain practically how to address some of the many tricky and intertwined challenges of delivering a *bona fide* TMT sector which creates jobs, wealth, innovation, and opportunities for entrepreneurs whilst also allowing for fair competition and, subsequently, more choice to consumers and citizens at affordable prices. Squaring this circle is tricky at the best of times even in developed economies where we have also made many errors (just consider some of the causes of the crisis of 2007/8 in the developed economies). A key point of this book is that we do not have to repeat them in our TMT sectors.

The book unapologetically uses many examples from Africa to illustrate key points and messages. This is because the challenges on the African continent are more profound in many cases than in most other emerging economies this book addresses. I contend (or hypothesise) that the lessons in all the chapters will apply to other emerging economies in Asia, Latin America, and the Caribbean—as they apply in Africa. For example, many of the TMT issues in Asian economies like Myanmar (i.e., Burma), Cambodia, Bangladesh,and Pakistan - or in Papua New Guinea and Haiti - are, in many cases, as challenging as those in Africa. As of 2013, Myanmar only has a 10 percent teledensity[6] much lower than most African countries, and it is around 80 percent rural, just like Uganda. Therefore, the recommendations in all chapters would apply to other emerging economies too.

---

6 Teledensity, or telephone density, refers to the number of phone connections for every hundred individuals residing within an area.

Hence the stewards of TMT in developing economies must with *humility* realise when they need help—in almost *all* cases they do— and who to seek this help from, and even better, to *execute* on the good advice. TMT can help unleash such societal benefits, that by not enabling it, it is almost criminal. This is why I admire what is happening in the ICT sector in Rwanda, one of the smallest countries[7] on the African continent. Small sometimes is indeed beautiful: this country should be a good case study of what can be achieved by planning a sector properly and even executing better. Rwanda is rolling out a fourth generation (4G) LTE (up to 100 Mbps) wireless network to complement the more than 3,000 kilometres of fibre optic cable, national backbone laid down in 2010 across this small country. Rwanda aims for 90 percent of Rwandans to access 4G LTE broadband by the end of 2014/15. Being small in geography is also beneficial to this outcome. Rwanda has an even bigger and clearer outcome in mind— that of being a middle-income status country by 2017. Who will doubt them? They have just tripled their GDP in ten years, growing to GDP per capita of circa $US644 in 2012, up from just $206 in 2002.[8] The government passionately believes broadband and ICT will be a key enabler to make this happen. For a country leaving behind its awful war and genocide past of the 1990s, Rwanda is well on its way to realising the sort of ICT sector that all other African countries should aspire to. However, even Rwanda needs to realise TMT, as covered in this volume, is a problem that's larger by whole scale.

In this vein, this book is deliberately *not* written in the form of an academic treatise with dense and numerous citations which largely makes them impenetrable to the average reader. I have written my fair share of academic papers and books when I was an academic whose readership and citations were just by me and my collaborators. This is no good for such an important area as the structure/future of TMT in Africa and emerging economies.

As it is aimed at government officials, state officials, governors, government and state ministers and commissioners, policy makers,

---

7 Rwanda is a very small country in Africa in terms of geographical area.

8 See http://www.gov.rw/Rwanda-s-GDP-per-capita-in-2012-rises-to-USD-644-from-USD-593-in-2011 (accessed July 2013).

regulators, investors, entrepreneurs, academics, students, and other key *practicing* professionals,[9] the book emphasises good outcomes (and warns of the dangers of bad ones). It unashamedly encourages how to strive for the good outcomes whilst mitigating against the sub-optimal ones.

There is a lot of inevitable jargon, new lingo, and acronyms to absorb. You will understandably be confused in places, so there is a simple Jargon Buster at the end of this book that should hopefully help for reference, and there are plenty of footnotes. For these reasons too and more, the tone of the language in the book—as you have hopefully evidenced in this preface—is also deliberately informal, provoking, questioning, and direct for easier readability, accessibility, and to fully engage this wide intended readership. Hopefully, some of my passion comes through too, and it may also help with readability and accessibility to get through the volume.

It will take significant policy (and commercial) *planning* and *implementation*—and leadership—for the rest of this decade and early on in the next for Africans (and other emerging economies) to get the TMT sectors they deserve for the 2020s—hence the subtitle *How to Make TMT Improve Developing Economies in Africa and Emerging Markets for the 2020s*. It can be done. It should be done. It must be done. To coin a phrase: yes, we can.

Earlier in this preface, I noted I have been an *active participant* for twenty-five years in the TMT sector in Europe. Indeed, I have, in several guises: executive roles running businesses or divisions in Europe; as a very senior regulator responsible for large swathes of TMT policy areas with one of the most esteemed TMT regulators in the world; as a venture capitalist investor, albeit for short time; as a multiple-award-winning TMT technologist/researcher/senior manager; and as a senior academic in TMT areas. I make no apologies if you hear a smorgasbord of all these "voices" in these pages, but you are obviously the ultimate judge.

---

9   This will include other key stakeholder communities related to TMT, including lawyers, economists, TMT consultants, technologists, researchers, etc.

This volume is one long argument—perhaps more accurately a series of smaller arguments—based on evidence pilfered from as many *reputable* sources as possible. Some of the evidence is historic, but what are emphasized too are the trends. You are also warned that I express some strong and forthright views and recommendations in much of this volume on the grounds this is a "how to" professional book and that it is better you have something to disagree about rather than having none at all or a bland set of recommendations. This book is 500+ pages of proven and practical know-how. Readers who want a hype-filled, superficial TMT introductory book should look elsewhere. On the other hand, if you want a comprehensive and realistic guide to TMT for emerging economies in Africa, Caribbean, Latin America, Asia and elsewhere, this volume is for you.

If you like what you read, ensure another "insignificant"[10] being other than yourself does read it too. Ensure it is used as a tool to debate and generate true collective and shared TMT knowledge in your country, province, or region—and that such true knowledge replaces the *illusion* of knowledge which Stephen Hawking implies is worse than ignorance. This way, the "network effect"[11] which is a core and important presence in the TMT sector takes hold, and this insignificant book may not be that insignificant after all.

H. Sama Nwana
January 2014

---

10 Of course, no reader of this book is insignificant! The reader should read this euphemism in the context of the great Mahatma Gandhi's quote which started this book's preface.

11 The network effect—sometimes known as network externality—refers to phenomenon wherein the value of a product or service is dependent on the number of people using the service. A world with only one telephone is pretty useless—no one else to phone! A world with a thousand telephone lines is more valuable as each can telephone 999 others. This is clearly more valuable. A network of one hundred million numbers is clearly exponentially more valuable—this is the essence of the network effect. Google, which makes most of its revenues from advertising, is wholly dependent on the network effect of so many "eyeballs" using Google's search services.

SECTION I

AN INTRODUCTION TO TMT

CHAPTER 1

THE CASE FOR TMT IN AFRICA AND EMERGING ECONOMIES — AND FOR A NATIONAL TMT BUSINESS PLAN

If the modern economy were a human body, clearly the financial sector constantly circulating money around the economy is the blood (or circulatory) system. The primary and food sectors are key parts of the energy system. TMT is the nerve (or nervous) system. Without the nerve system, the body is literally lifeless. Without a well-functioning TMT sector, the modern economy neither has life nor soul.

Perhaps you believe the above to be a bit of a hyperbole. Perhaps you think it is not. Or perhaps you do not care. What matters is that you decide for yourself at the conclusion of this chapter, if not this book, whether you should care and what you believe.

A quote from Deloitte[1] to start off this chapter:

As in 2011, this year's Prediction report is published as a single report rather than three separate ones.

---

1   Deloitte, *Technology, Media and Telecommunications Predictions*, 2012, http://www.deloitte.com/assets/Dcom-Australia/Local%20Assets/Documents/Industries/TMT/Deloitte_TMT_Predictions_2012.pdf (accessed July 2013).

Deloitte's view is that developments in each sub-sector[2] are now so inter-linked and interdependent that TMT executives need to be cognizant of key trends across all sectors.

The quote above relates to Deloitte, the Big 4 accounting and consulting firm, which from 2011 stopped publishing their well-respected TMT Predictions as three separate predictions reports covering the three subsectors. Instead, it now publishes it as a single "converged" report. As the quote notes, "each sub-sectors are now so inter-linked and interdependent that TMT executives need to be cognizant of key trends across all sectors." I completely agree—and go further to argue that decision makers on the African continent and in other emerging economies should start thinking "TMT" first and its constituent subsectors second. In the next five to ten years, if not already, separate ministries of telecommunications or communications—of ICT (information and communications technologies), of post, of broadcasting, etc.—will no longer make sense in a converged TMT sector. Similarly, separate industry regulators for the broadcasting sector, for the telecommunications sector, and for the Internet are increasingly obsolete in favour of a single converged regulator for the entire sector. We return to this many times later on in the book.

---

2 Read: the subsectors of telecommunications, media, and technology.

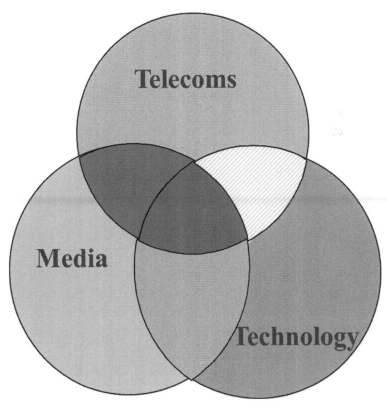

Figure 1—TMT as a Single Sector of the Economy
(all three subsectors are so interlinked and interdependent)

This chapter makes the case for TMT, why it is arguably the most important sector of the modern economy. It impresses on why decision makers (i.e., presidents, governors, mayors, ministers of communications, ministers of IT, etc.) must have a *credible* TMT plan. Without one, they are committing national *hara-kiri* for their citizens. Any such plan must not be the typical plans that sit of shelves in various government ministries across Africa and some other emerging countries in Asia and Latin America, literally gathering dust. It must be one that people can see evolving in front of their very eyes. It must be a *living plan* as in Rwanda. It must be specific, measurable (as in there are metrics to measure progress), actionable (and being put into action), realistic, and timely—or SMART for short. It is also different from the ICT plan which most African countries have but whose implementation is, on the whole, perfunctory across the continent. Calandro *et al.* (2010) provide a truly excellent analysis of some of the reasons why.[3] Whilst in countries like Rwanda, its ICT plan[4] is being rolled out in a SMART fashion, in most other countries it's less so. However, the point here is that the TMT plan is different from the ICT plan. Both are invaluable. The ICT plan is more relevant to the technology subsector of TMT. In this vein, the ICT plan is a subset of the TMT plan.

Why—you may ask—should the case for TMT be made? Is this not obvious? The answer is simple and in two parts. Firstly, there are literally no credible TMT plans on the African continent today, and in many other emerging economies too. There are ICT plans, but as noted earlier, these are different. In any case, they are hardly implemented in many countries anyway. Secondly, it must be acknowledged that decision makers have tough choices to make with very limited financial and nonfinancial resources. They have to allocate resources to health and hospitals, to defence, to roads, to power, to education, public safety, etc. These are tough choices, and TMT needs to make its case to be heard.

1.1 The Case for TMT in Africa and Emerging Economies

We make the case for TMT in Africa and emerging economies from several vantage perspectives which hopefully corroborate each other:

- By keeping in mind that mobile telecommunications infrastructure on the African continent is in relative good shape and improving. This makes for a good start and not from a hopeless position.

---

3 Enrico Calandro, Alison Gillwald, Mpho Moyo, and Christoph Stork (2010), *Comparative Sector Performance Review 2009/2010: Towards Evidence-based ICT Policy and Regulation*, Volume 2, Policy Paper 2, researchICTafrica.net

4 *National ICT Strategy and Plan NICI*, Rwanda Development Board, www.rdb. rw, (accessed July 2013).

- By boldly stating that due to the latter, telecommunications in Africa has had a greater impact on true growth[5] on the continent over the past fifteen years than any other sector of the African economy.

- By noting that whilst mobile voice telecommunications is going strong, the real challenges ahead, that of mobile data (and the mobile Internet), are just humongous. This needs real planning for. We will not be cabling fixed Internet to any significant African homes anytime soon. So the last mile will almost certainly be via radio in most countries, barring some areas of the diversified economies of perhaps Egypt, Morocco, South Africa, and Tunisia. We have lost both the race and the will to build robust fixed-line infrastructure on the continent, particularly to the majority of homes. Africa has the lowest fixed-line penetration rates in the world at mostly less than a woeful 2 percent[6] as is shown in chapter 10.

- By noting that for TMT, whilst the telecommunications subsector is relatively mature on the continent, the media and technology subsectors of TMT are still very nascent. For example, the advertising sector on the continent is so nascent that it represents a real opportunity which only a credible TMT plan will unearth.

- By noting that broadcasting on the continent, particularly digital terrestrial broadcasting for the masses, is unlikely to have an investable business case standing alone. However, looked at collectively as TMT, the industry "surpluses" in voice communications could "pay" for the losses in mass broadcasting.

---

5 It must be acknowledged that the continent's natural resources fetching buoyant prices can also be thanked for the sustained 5 to 7 percent growth rates across the continent.

6 Enrico Calandro, Alison Gillwald, Mpho Moyo, and Christoph Stork (2010), *Comparative Sector Performance Review 2009/2010: Towards Evidence-based ICT Policy and Regulation*, Volume 2, Policy Paper 2, researchICTafrica.net, http://www.researchictafrica.net/publications/Policy_Paper_Series_Towards_Evidence-based_ICT_Policy_and_Regulation_-_Volume_2/Vol_2_Paper_5_-_Comparative_ICT_Sector_Performance_Review_2009_2010.pdf, accessed July 2013.

- By revisiting TMT's contributions to a major Western city to better illustrate the potential size of the TMT opportunity to decision makers on the continent.
- Lastly, by noting that there is a real golden opportunity to design (or redesign) the entire TMT sector in most African countries, as well as the other emerging countries in Asia, the Caribbean, and Latin America. This is afforded by the switch-off of analogue television (TV) signals across these continents and migrating to digital terrestrial TV, in addition to planning for the next round of 4G spectrum releases on the continent to enable the mobile Internet and Internet for the masses. Add in the case of Africa, with all the new submarine cable landings and the new fibre backbones, these truly and implicitly should drive convergence thinking within the TMT sector on the continent—or it should.

These different vantage points aim at providing a more holistic case for TMT. We look at these perspectives individually.

1. Telecommunications has benefited from significant investment over the past fifteen years on the continent—and the climate to maintain such investment must be maintained. Indeed, it must be continuously improved.

"Telecommunications is the only sector in Africa where there is no infrastructure gap." —Tim Harrabin[7]

As you read the Harrabin quote above, I can see the head scratching you're doing. Africa has no infrastructure gap in telecommunications? Nonsense, perhaps you say. It is sometimes good to start a section of this nature with a quote which is arguably polemical. However, the point Harrabin is making is an important one. In relative terms, mobile

---

7 Tim Harrabin previously led global telecoms investment, strategy, and M&A for Vodafone, including Safaricom (Kenya) from its inception in 2000 until 2012 and the transformation of Ghana Telecom into Vodafone Ghana.

telecommunications in Africa has seen no infrastructure gap vis-à-vis other sectors, such as roads, railways, power, water, buildings, and so on over the past fifteen years. A longer version of a similar quote from Harrabin is perhaps more helpful: "There is no infrastructure gap in telecoms across Africa—since 2000 [up until 2013], over US$150bn has been invested in licence fees, mobile infrastructure, subsea cables, national fibre optic and mobile money platforms across Africa."[8]

Which other sectors in Africa have had such levels of investment at US$150 billion? The results have been startling and there for all African consumers and citizens to see. Even better, none of the monies that have made such a difference today in African telecommunications is aid monies. Is this not just great? This demonstrates that entrepreneurship and the private sector are ultimately the only answers to poverty on the continent.

If we are honest, much of this investment came in despite many impediments: the erstwhile climate of virtually inelastic corruption, totally nonexistent or unliberalised regulatory regimes which provided for

- no predictability
- weak local banks
- primitive power systems which were incredibly much worse than they are today[9]
- inane public officials
- an incredible lack of modern telecommunications skill sets on the continent (another major challenge for the TMT sector even today), and
- a much worse political climate with coup d'états (which is gladly no longer the case today)[10]

---

8 Tim Harrabin—at the Fourth Annual TMT Finance & Investment Africa Conference in London, June 20, 2013, www.tmtfinance.com/africa (accessed August 2013).

9 The power problem on the continent is still very bad, and a key brake on growth on the continent.

10 In 1979, there were only three democracies on the continent. In 2013, there are circa twenty-eight, depending on how you count them. The recent coup in Mali or the instability in the Central Africa Republic in 2013 is truly depressing.

Reading these, it is arguably fortuitous or miraculous that such investment occurred in the first place.

It is up to decision makers on the continent to continue to improve on all these factors that ensure TMT investments in the sector no longer face such hurdles. These decision makers must acknowledge with humility that much of these US$150 billion are foreign monies seeking better returns. In this context, portraying a climate wherein the continent's or country's resources continue to be pillaged whilst our people wallow in poverty is not conducive to further investment.

2. Telecommunications in Africa has had a greater impact on growth over the past fifteen years (to 2013/14) than any other sector, including in broader social value. We will not maintain the same growth rates, but the TMT sector in Africa should aim for high teens[11] percentage contributions to GDP.

This is a deliberately bold statement. McKinsey evidence notes that access to telecommunications grew exponentially from a nonexistent 2 percent of the population of the continent in 2000 to 37 percent in 2008.[12] The position as of the end of 2011 was even much better at 65 percent. Take Nigeria for example, the most populous nation on the continent. Ndukwe notes that the percentage share of gross domestic product[13] (GDP) from the telecommunications sector in Nigeria rose from 0.06 percent in 1999 (yes, you read that right, i.e., less than 0.1

---

11 That is, sixteen (16 percent), seventeen (17 percent), eighteen (18 percent) of GDP by 2025.

12 *Lions on the move: The progress and potential of African economies,* McKinsey & Company: McKinsey Global Institute, June 2010, http://www.mckinsey.com/insights/africa/lions_on_the_move (accessed July 2013).

13 GDP is the total market value of all officially recognised finished goods and services in an economy of a country over a specified period of time. Much of the other goods or services in a country's economy are not officially recognised, and this is what is typically referred to as the "informal sector." It is often noted anecdotally that the size of the informal sector is typically almost as large as that of the formal sector in many African countries.

percent) to 3.5 percent by 2011.[14] Ndukwe notes that the growth in the telecommunications sector had resulted (by the end of 2011) in the creation of over sixteen thousand direct jobs in the telecommunications subsector of TMT in Nigeria, and several millions more are informally employed through the sector. From only 400,000 lines in 1999, today, there are 114.76 million[15] lines in Nigeria as of July 2013, creating a teledensity of 82 percent.

Not many people will realize that the biggest and most sold commodity today on the African continent is "airtime," thanks to mobile communications. In Kenya, telecommunications—courtesy of Safaricom—has yielded arguably the biggest mobile payments platform certainly on the continent of Africa in M-PESA.[16] In 2012, US$10.4 billion was transacted through the M-PESA platform.[17] By mid-2013, 35 percent of the national GDP of Kenya and 20 percent in Tanzania were transferred through M-PESA and were growing. These are truly phenomenal side effects of the telecommunications networks on the continent. This telecommunications growth effect can be replicated all across Africa. Then to this "formal" growth add on the effect of telecommunications on growth in the informal sector: the value accretion from the fact that you can now speak to your grandmother in the village anytime you like without her being taken for miles to the nearest fixed line which rarely worked. Or that the farmer can transact

---

14 Source: Ministry of Communication, Nigeria, as quoted by Dr. Ernest Ndukwe in *The Telecommunication Revolution in Nigeria*, 2011 Igbinedion University Convocation Lecture, December 2, 2011. Dr. Ndukwe was executive vice chairman and CEO of the Nigerian Communications Commission (NCC) from February 2000 to March 2010. He, along with his chairman for his ten-year stint at the helm of NCC, Alhaji Ahmed Joda, should be credited with turning around the fortunes of the telecommunications sector in Nigeria over the past fifteen years, to 2013–14.

15 Source: NCC website, http://www.ncc.gov.ng, accessed September 2013.

16 Wikipedia defines M-Pesa as follows: "(M for mobile, *pesa* is Swahili for money) is a mobile-phone based money transfer and microfinancing service" for Safaricom and Vodacom, the largest mobile network operators in Kenya and Tanzania.

17 Source: Presentation, *Promoting innovation through enabling regulations*, by Joseph Tiampati ole Musuni, principal secretary, Ministry of Information, Communications and Technology, Republic of Kenya, CTO Forum, Abuja, Nigeria, October 2013.

and trade his coffee with buyers in the city without leaving his village. Or the informal value generated from all the money transfers happening in Africa on these telecommunications networks. We could go on. In economics terms, this is called the *broader social and citizen value,* or broader social value, that immeasurable value that accrues from you not being anxious about your grandfather/father who is a hundred kilometres or three thousand miles away in the village because you can get in touch with him or are able to transfers monies to him.

This telecommunications-inspired growth in GDP including secondary—particularly including informal growth and broader social value—has not been measured accurately by anyone yet, not even by McKinsey, though some estimates are mentioned in a couple to several pages from this one. . Most Africans living on the continent will regale you with numerous but true anecdotes of communications before the mobile era and what they experience now: about how it has made all their lives so much more efficient. In economics, what we are getting at here is sometimes called the *multiplier effect.* This, in layman's terms, is the change in real GDP divided by the quantum of the original investment that has gone in in the first place.

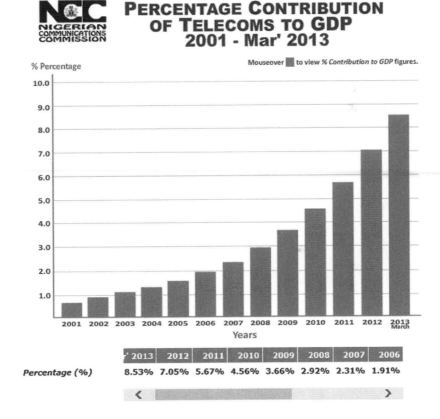

Figure 2—Percentage Contribution of Telecoms to GDP in Nigeria[18]

Let us consider Nigeria again, Africa's biggest telecommunications economy having overtaken South Africa as far back as 2008.[19] Ndukwe[20] notes that by the end of September 2011 (from August 2001), about US$18 billion of "private sector investment in licensee fees, building infrastructure, development of local manpower, empowerment of local companies that provide support services, etc." As at the

18 Source: NCC, http://www.ncc.gov.ng (accessed August 2013).
19 Enrico Calandro, Alison Gillwald, Mpho Moyo, and Christoph Stork (2010), *Comparative Sector Performance Review 2009/2010: Towards Evidence-based ICT Policy and Regulation*, Volume 2, Policy Paper 2, researchICTafrica.net, p. 17.
20 Dr. Ernest Ndukwe in *The Telecommunication Revolution in Nigeria*, 2011 Igbinedion University Convocation Lecture, December 2, 2011, Nigeria, pp. 14–15.

end of June 2013, the total investment flow into Nigeria's telecom's sector since liberalisation in 2001 had been US$32 billion, including $7 billion of investment inflow from 2010 to 2013.[21] According to the NCC,[22] the telecommunications sector in Nigeria is, as of the end of April 2013, 8.53 percent of the Nigerian GDP (see figure 2). In fact, Nigeria has been ranked the fastest growing telecommunications market in the world by the ITU for the last five years running to 2012.

From less than 1 percent in 2001, the telecommunications contribution to the GDP of Nigeria is self-evident. This can be replicated across many countries in Africa. Overall, the mobile industry in Africa contributes circa US$56 billion to the regional economy, equivalent to 3.5 percent of total GDP.[23] So Nigeria at 8.3 percent of GDP is well above average and is reflective of the $US32 billions of investment than has gone into Nigeria.

Sustainability? Resource Drawdown

	Remaining Years of Hydrocarbon Reserves
Nigeria	41
Gabon	41
Chad	36
Angola	21
Equatorial Guinea	19
Congo Republic	18
Others	27

Figure 2a—Remaining Years of Hydrocarbon Reserves[24]

---

21 "Nigerian Banks, telecom operators forge flourishing partnership," *Africa Telecom & IT*, October 2013, p. 30.

22 Source: Nigerian Communications Commission (NCC), http://www.ncc.gov.ng.

23 Source: ICT in Africa: Trends and Investment Opportunities, in *Africa Infrastructure Investment Report 2013*, Commonwealth Business Council, March 2013, p. 160, http://www.cbcglobal.org (accessed August 2013).

24 Source: Dr. Jonathan Thomas, Senior Economist, Lloyds Bank, UK, based on World Bank Data.

Overall, in terms of sub-Saharan Africa (SSA), GSMA and Deloitte (2012)[25] report these economies have benefited considerably from the growth of the mobile sector. In 2011, they reported on estimates of mobile operators and their associated ecosystems:

- a direct year impact of US$32 billion, including paying $12 billion in taxes
- associated with creating 4.4 percent of SSA's GDP after adding the effects of mobile technology on workers' productivity
- created more than 3.5 million full-time equivalent (FTE) jobs across both the formal and informal sectors; this both includes some of the highest paid formal employment on the continent, plus airtime resellers and informal small-scale shops selling, repairing, and recharging mobile handsets
- supported the development of more than fifty technology hubs, labs, incubators, and accelerators across SSA

Do you now believe telecommunications in Africa has had a greater impact on growth in Africa over the past fifteen years (to 2013) than any other sector apart from the natural resources sector? And do you believe the claims for the latter are arguable? These are particularly believable if you include broader social value too. Can you think of any other sector that comes close, just looking at the evidence from Nigeria above?

It is undoubtedly true that buoyant commodity prices in oil in particular, but also Africa's minerals and metals, are the key drivers to the continent's sustained 5 percent to 6 percent growth rates. This fact notwithstanding, the following points are relevant to telecommunication's cause for having had the greatest impact on growth (along with highest growth rates) on the continent over the past decade and a half.

First, admittedly, telecommunications GDP growth started from an extremely low base—in the case of Nigeria, as can be seen from figure 2 above, from circa 0.6 percent to 8.53 percent as of April 2013.

---

25 GSMA Intelligence (2012), *Sub-Saharan Africa Mobile Observatory 2012*, http://www.gsma.com/publicpolicy/wp-content/uploads/2013/01/gsma_ssamo_ full_web_11_12-1.pdf (accessed September 2013).

No other sector has matched such a year-on-year growth in thirteen years.

Second, there is a strong argument for excluding the extractive sector in such comparisons. This is because such resources are by definition finite, and reliance on such revenues in perpetuity makes little economic sense. In financial accounting terms, there will be no terminal value in a discounted cash flow model after the oil, gas, or mineral is predicted to dry up. Figure 2a shows the predicted remaining years of hydrocarbon resources, and clearly these reserves run out in the lifetimes of today's (2013/14) teenagers and those in their twenties.

Third, and admittedly slightly facetiously, the oil, gas, diamonds, etc., in themselves have not "grown" as they were always there in the first place but had not been "discovered" and/or extracted.

Subscribers (who pay real revenues) have grown on the continent from literally no subscribers to 619,800,290 by the end of 2011.[26] Indeed, the continent's mobile penetration in terms of SIM cards sold reached 65 percent at the end of 2011, compared to a penetration rate of 20 percent in 2005.[27] These numbers are higher as of end of Q2 2013 at 781 million, according to Ericsson,[28] and growing by the day. And these are sustainable revenues which the telecommunications sectors will retain in perpetuity barring an unforeseen major industry crash.

Fourth, though almost 90 percent of Nigeria's GDP is from the extractive sector, it only employs 3 percent of the workforce.

There has indeed been—as Ndukwe calls it—a telecommunications revolution, not only in Nigeria but across the African continent, and its effect so far has been so huge, and not fully quantified in GDP terms, and possibly unquantifiable. And the multiplier effect of this

---

26 GSMA Intelligence, *African Mobile Observatory 2011: Driving Mobile and Social Development through Mobile Services*, GSMA, http://www.gsma.com (accessed August 2013).

27 Nevertheless, this 65 percent number corresponds to circa 35 percent human penetration in 2011 after discounting for the string trend in having multiple SIM cards on the continent. This is also good news in that there is still more people penetration to be achieved on the continent.

28 Source: Communications Africa, http://www.communicationsafrica.com/mobile/ericsson-predicts-mobile-phone-subscription-in-africa-to-rise (accessed November 2013).

investment, particularly from the extremely low base of near zero GDP percentage contribution back as recently as 1999, is incalculable.

More importantly, I believe most countries in Africa—perhaps with the exception of what McKinsey's Lions of the Move Report classifies as the diversified economies of Egypt, Morocco, South Africa, and Tunisia—can aim for GDP contributions from TMT in the range of 16 to 18 percent, if not 20 percent. The TMT plan for each country can realistically aim for this. Who would have forecasted a growth from sub 0.1 percent in Nigeria in 1999 to 8.53 percent in 2013? And this is only for telecommunications, excluding technology and media subsectors. The media and technology sectors in 2013/14 are arguably where we were back in 1999. Looking at it from this perspective, 20 percent may not be that ambitious after all.

3. Delivering the mobile Internet in Africa and emerging economies, already difficult in the Western world, will be so much harder. The problem is called the "naked mobile" problem.

I have met many a decision maker on the continent of Africa and from some Asian, Latin American and Caribbean economies who "forgivably" believes that just as international finance flooded into the African continent and some poorer Asian or emerging market countries to enable the mobile voice communications revolution happen, so it would happen too for the mobile data/Internet revolution on the continent. This next bit is unashamedly aimed at disavowing all of this misguided view. The problem is one which has come to be known as the "challenge of naked mobile." Figure 3 (below) illustrates it.

The problem can be described as follows. First, we had the killer application[29] in telecommunications which is undoubtedly voice communications. As human beings we all like to talk to each other. We are psychologically wired to communicate (and typically orally),

---

29 Killer application—or killer app for short—is a marketing term which refers to the product or service *most*, if not all, customers buy. This is what substantially drives sales. Mobile voice is the runaway killer app in the telecommunications sector.

be it to family, friends, work colleagues, school alumni, etc. One of the core commercial reasons US$150 billion has gone into this sector on the African continent was because this killer app of voice was clearly proven elsewhere in world, and the bet was Africa would be no different. That said, it is a fact that telecommunications analysts were still dubious about its take-up in Africa. I have it on good authority that Vodafone was warned by analysts and more about how Kenya was the fourth most corrupt country on the planet back in the early 2000s and that Vodafone would never achieve any more than half a million mobile subscribers ever in Kenya. As of Q3 2012, Kenya had over 30 million subscribers, a mobile penetration of 78 percent.[30] I have also learnt MTN achieved the first five to six years of its then business plan in Nigeria within eighteen to twenty-four months of full operation in the country. Whilst these are salutary lessons about how much analysts sometimes get it swashbucklingly wrong, it is also very illustrative of the thinking that goes on before investment decisions are made.

---

30   Communications Commission of Kenya, http://www.cck.go.ke (accessed September 2013).

THE "NAKED" MOBILE PROBLEM

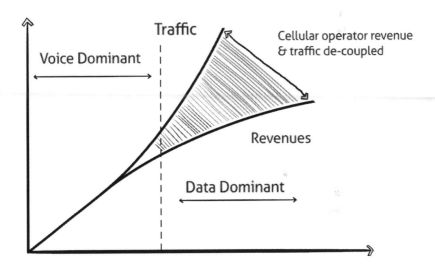

Figure 3—The "Naked" Mobile Problem

Returning to the "naked mobile: problem, all the aforementioned impediments aside, there was a fair amount of optimism that voice communications would thrive since it is the killer app, and it had been the case everywhere else. This bet has turned out to be, of course, true. Take MTN, the largest telecommunications operator on the African continent as well as the Middle East (covering more than twenty countries) with EBITDA[31] more than double that of its peers. The breakdown of its revenue composition for the years 2009, 2010, and 2011 shows voice as still the major top line and profit contributor at 86 percent, 83 percent, and 83 percent respectively, with SMS at circa 10 percent and data at only 7 percent.[32]

---

31 The EBITDA of a company provides a clear view of the profitability of the operational business. It stands for earnings before interest, tax, depreciation, and amortisation are subtracted.

32 Source: MTN Annual Reports.

As figure 3 depicts, with the voice communications killer app, there is a linear relationship between voice traffic and revenues whilst voice is dominant. Simplistically, you can work out the revenues from voice communications by multiplying the minutes by some average tariff-per-minute. If voice dominates, as can be seen on figure 3, this straight line relationship between traffic and revenues holds true. Mobile network operators like Vodacom, MTN, Bharti Airtel, Safaricom, Sonatel (Senegal), ETC (Ethiopia), Tunisiana (Tunisia), etc., love this straight line relationship, as it makes them immensely profitable. This is because the revenue-per-bit[33] of voice traffic yields a very high number: the operators are handsomely paid for voice, yet voice consumes very little bits of traffic on their networks. Understand that the voice speech is carried digitally as bits of zeroes and ones.

---

33   A bit is shorthand for "binary digit." Communications on networks, at its most basic level, are a series of these binary digits of zeroes and ones which transmit all the voice and data information on these networks. So a bit is the most basic measure of capacity of this network.

Using mobile to browse the Internet

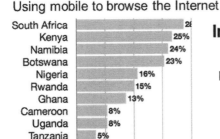

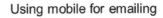

Internet use among mobile phone owners: Social networking more popular than email in some countries

Using mobile for Facebook etc.

Using mobile for emailing

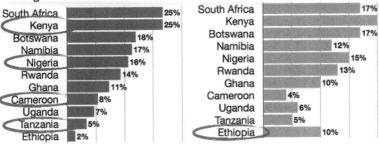

Figure 4: How Africans Are Increasingly Using Their Mobiles
(Source: Research ICT Africa, Professor Alison Gillwald;[34]
reproduced with permission of the copyright owner.)

The problem is as these networks' traffic start carrying more data[35] traffic as opposed to voice, this relationship between traffic and revenues breaks downs. You can see the clear bifurcation on figure 3 with the amount of bits of traffic growing exponentially whilst the revenues earned flattens off. Figure 4 shows why, by depicting how Africans are increasingly using more and more data via e-mails and social networking like Facebook and browsing the Internet. As such data starts dominating, as it is (or will be) across most countries on the continent, the revenue-per-bit of traffic drops off a cliff, and revenues

---

34 From Presentation at the CTO Forum, Abuja, October 2013, *Innovation, Policy & Regulation*, by Prof. Alison Gillwald, Research ICT Africa, http://www.researchictafrica.net/presentations.php.

35 This is increasingly the case with communications traffic generated by applications such as Google, Facebook, Twitter, e-mails, eBay, and Apple iTunes for music and ringtones. These are not voice traffic.

flatten off (as shown in figure 3). This is the problem of the "naked" mobile. It is metaphorically as if the high-margin voice revenue is rendered "naked," i.e., it is unclothed for what it really is: just the pricing of "capacity"[36] on these operators' networks by the operators. Some refer to this phenomenon as the commoditisation of voice, or indeed the commoditisation of telecommunication services.

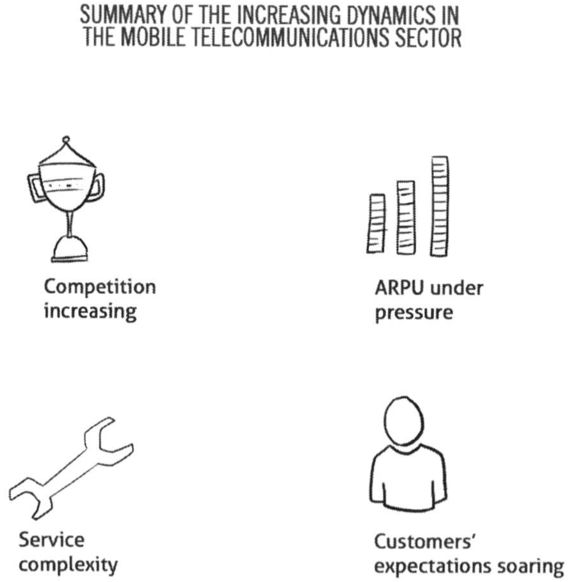

SUMMARY OF THE INCREASING DYNAMICS IN
THE MOBILE TELECOMMUNICATIONS SECTOR

Competition
increasing

ARPU under
pressure

Service
complexity

Customers'
expectations soaring

Figure 5—Summary of the Increasing Dynamics in the Mobile
Telecommunications Sector

Ultimately, telecommunication networks provide capacity to carry voice and data. Would they rather use the capacity for a killer app service which generates high margins (in this case mobile voice) or for another with quite lower margins (mobile data/Internet)? Using a shop

---

36 One can think of an analogy of road capacity. Trucks, large cars, small cars, and motorcycles all use the same roads, but they are not that discriminated and disproportionately charged for using this road capacity, i.e., a truck does not pay for using the road capacity one hundred times what the car pays. So why should it be different for network capacity?

analogy, will you fill your shelves in your small store (with limited capacity) with products that sell in volume and with good margins, or will you stock them with products that sell sparingly and with low margins? Any shopkeeper knows the answer to this question. This is the crux of the naked mobile problem which all mobile network operators across Africa (and the rest of the world) are increasingly contending with. Where the naked data problem truly bites is with coverage of mobile data/Internet networks. As the revenue-per-bit economics falls, the coverage of mobile data networks would be far less than the coverage for mobile voice networks. In other words, if a voice network profitably extends to, say, 80 percent of the population, the mobile data/Internet network may only extend to half of the voice population, i.e., 40 percent.

Figure 5 summarises the dynamics currently faced by many operators on the continent. It shows the following:

- Even though there is still some road to go on subscriber growth across the continent as well as across other emerging economies, competition is increasingly driving lower margins on voice traffic. There are typically two to four operators per country, with most markets now having at least three. Three or more typically leads to healthy competition if the regulatory regime in the country is working as it should do. In many countries, it could be much better, as Enrico Calandro *et al.* (2010) point out. Nevertheless, fierce competition is eating away at margins in most countries whilst increasing penetration.

MTN Nigeria – Local revenues and growth, %

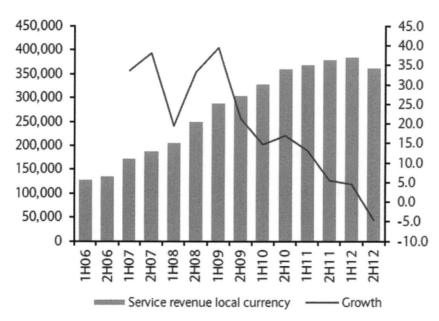

Figure 6—Illustrating Lower and Lower Revenue Growth Levels (MTN Nigeria)
(Source: Barclays Capital)[37]

- Traditional revenue growth is flattening (as figure 3 postulates) as data begins to grow and/or dominate and dilute the revenues. This must be the mathematical result of African network traffic projected to grow 400 percent from 2012 to 2016 (according to research house Informa Telecoms & Media)[38] or 85 percent per year (according to Deloitte) whilst revenues are virtually flat (year-on-year) as revenue-dilutive incremental subscribers add to networks. Mobile markets are definitely moving towards *lower* revenue growth levels, as telecommunications services become increasingly commoditized. The graph for MTN (figure 6) illustrates this trend clearly. There are other key reasons which contribute markedly to decreasing profitability. Expanding mobile coverage

---

37 *CEEMEA Telecom Services, Barclays Equity Research*, March 15, 2013.
38 Informa Telecoms & Media, http://www.informatandm.com.

to underserved rural areas is expensive with lesser returns and hence is an earnings dilutive exercise, due to increasing costs and decreasing marginal revenues. Economics limits and constrains mobile data coverage. Setting up new mobile base stations sites in these rural areas with no or insufficient electricity, necessitating dependence on diesel generators, all drive up costs.

- Customer expectations are soaring—they want more but simultaneously pay less.
- The mobile business is becoming more and more complex as they diversify into many nonvoice services[39] to drive up both revenues and margins. Complexity in business means costs, and costs mean reduced profits and margins.

Figures 3, 4, 5, and 6 and the rest of this subsection above should tell you the returns on investment (RoI) for mobile data will *not* only be much lower than for the killer application mobile voice, but it will almost certainly take a much longer time too to achieve these returns. This is not very attractive to international investors, or any other investors for that matter. Therefore, there is a very strong case in this context that the beneficiaries of the mobile data/Internet revolution (i.e., Africans or nationals of emerging Asian, Caribbean and Latin American economies, such as the cases of countries like Haiti, Bangladesh and Colombia respectively) should take more of the risk on mobile data/Internet. Bluntly, African investors would have to do more of the investments to make the mobile revolution happen in the case of Africa. African banks and their bond and equity markets must be strengthened to take on more of the mobile data/Internet revolution risk.

As noted earlier, the naked mobile problem also has an even worse side—mobile data coverage. Mobile voice networks tend to cover almost all the main population centres, including many minor ones. This means that villages get coverage, and you can travel into some

---

39 These include Facebook, SMS, basic Internet, e.g., search, mobile broadband, money transfer, mobile apps, premium content, etc.

hinterland towns, villages, and hamlets across the continent and still get mobile coverage, albeit patchy in many places. In other words, there has been (and is) competition for coverage with voice. And when there are not spots,[40] telecommunications regulators in a significant number of African countries have set up Universal Service Access Funds[41] to strive towards universal access for voice at least. This is because it is clearly highly desirable for social and economic reasons to have widespread availability of such services, for broader social value reasons as noted earlier.

The geographical and population coverage for mobile data—without regulatory intervention—is highly *unlikely* to get beyond the major population centres on the African continent and elsewhere. This is because, as figures 2 and 3 show, the revenues for data tend to be flat, and so it is cheaper and makes economic sense to only provide mobile data/Internet service in the major cities. Africa is a mostly rural. Rolling out networks beyond these urban cities will lose buckets of money for mobile network operators, which rational businesses do not do! Therefore, the risk of the emergence of a society of "haves" and "have-nots" with mobile data and/or mobile Internet is extremely high on the continent of Africa as well as other emerging economies. The operators like MTN, Bharti Airtel, mCel (Mozambique), RwandaTel (Rwanda), etc., cannot be compelled to do what is patently uneconomical and uncommercial. And yet, we also want the schools in the rural areas to have access to the Internet in just the same way as the schools in urban areas like Douala, Ndjamena, Addis Ababa, Lagos, etc. The omens are very poor for mobile Internet on the continent with the African population being some 60 to 70 percent rural.

Add to the fact that there will be little fixed Internet on the continent any time soon, and the economics of mobile Internet only works

---

40 Mobile hot spots are areas where people cannot access mobile services due to lack of coverage.

41 "Universal Service," e.g., for voice, historically means every household in a country has the access to telephone service. The term "universal" also connotes several other elements, including availability, affordability, and accessibility. Operators are typically taxed a certain percentage, typically less than 1 percent, of their annual revenues, which go into this fund. Such funds can be "tapped" to build and subsidise communications to uneconomic areas.

for the major conurbations, decision makers need to think carefully about how to square this circle.

4. Whilst the telecommunications subsector of TMT is relatively in its early teenage years, the media and technology subsectors are still infants, in many countries *stillborn* at that.

This is a yet another deliberately bold statement. We have covered in some detail the telecommunications sector above. Sadly, there is much less to cover on technology and media, hence a significant opportunity too for entrepreneurs. The media and technology subsectors still do not even register in any official GDP statistics in most African countries for different principal reasons.

For the technology subsector, the *nonmobile* ICT infrastructure does not exist yet. It had started meandering its way there in 2013/14 via national backbone networks—though certainly not $150 billion worth of it like in the case for mobile telecommunications. Internet penetration in Africa (i.e., access) was only about 11.5 percent in 2011, with mobile broadband penetration at only 3.79 percent, whilst fixed broadband was merely at 0.2 percent.[42] You can see where the "infant" metaphor originates. It is arguably worse: ICT and the technology subsector have been stillborn in African towns and cities. Practically just about every school on the continent outside the diversified economies of South Africa, Egypt, Morocco, and Tunisia has no access to the Internet.

This is catastrophic if it persists. This is why I am heavily involved in introducing a new low cost approach to rural broadband called *white spaces*[43] *technology*, which I believe Africa desperately needs in order to make some significant bridging across this Internet chasm

---

42   Source: ICT in Africa: Trends and Investment Opportunities, in *Africa Infrastructure Investment Report 2013*, Commonwealth Business Council, March 2013, pp. 161, http://www.cbcglobal.org (accessed September 2013).

43   This is a technology and approach pioneered by Google and Microsoft and others which promises affordable broadband to the masses using frequencies currently reserved for TV.

on the continent. Many trials and pilot programs have already proven the technology across the world, even in Africa in Cape Town (South Africa) and Nanyuki (Kenya). Bet you have never heard of Nanyuki unless you are Kenyan. Understandable, but this is the point. Nanyuki is a market town in the central east Rift Valley of Kenya, the main air-base of the Kenyan Air Force. It is a very rural town, and white space technology is ideal for rural areas like these where the economics of mobile broadband will not allow the operators to cover soon. This approach and technology is covered in chapter 6.

The success of nonmobile ICT initiatives on the continent is truly perfunctory. This puts the brakes on the growth of the technology subsector on the continent, which means jobs are not being created when we badly need them. It's so bad that Microsoft, the world's largest software maker, launched a new strategy to expand Internet access across the continent, positioning it to grow its business which it can see is halting in Africa due to the paucity of ICT.[44] If this is bad enough for schools and companies, the ICT situation on the continent is positively disastrous for small and medium enterprises (SMEs). SMEs are the beating hearts of most economies employing the vast majority of employees. As e-commerce is enabled by ICT, there is hardly any of it on the continent. In the United Kingdom in 2011, £1 in every £5 of sales took place online or through electronic means driven by purchases made on Amazon and eBay and business-to-business online purchases by SMEs and big businesses.[45] I recently provided some lectures to seven middle-class and cash-rich managers of a prominent African regulator, and not one of them had ever shopped online up until July 2013. It was not obvious to us collectively how soon they would be able to do so.

When the ICT subsector aren't planned and executed properly, the opportunity costs to SMEs are genuinely incalculable. Decision makers should really take note of this. They should start by looking at the woeful state of the regional and national backbone infrastructure

44 Under the '4Afrika' Initiative, Microsoft has announced that it will invest $75M over the next 3 years (2013-2015) in broadband infrastructure, bringing 1 million small and medium enterprises online.
45 ICT activity of UK businesses, Office of National Statistics, 2011.

across the continent. This is a massive brake towards the development of broadband Internet of the continent. *Coordination failure* looms large here,[46] and even the large operators on the continent cannot solve this one. Even if they do so in patches, they will solve the problem for themselves and not principally for African consumers and citizens.

Turning to the media subsector on the continent, there is much less to write about outside South Africa and a few other economies like Kenya, Egypt, Tunisia, and Morocco. Outside South Africa, which hosts a giant-like Naspers,[47] and Nation Media Group[48] and Zuku[49] in Kenya, there are few other media firms of note to talk about. This is a substantial opportunity for entrepreneurs on the continent. The African media sector is frankly in the doldrums. Though there are pockets of some brilliance, the following all contribute to a pretty moribund media subsector on the continent:

- no ICT infrastructure
- few national terrestrial TV channels
- no (mobile) Internet
- no true cross-platform media operators of scale

The media industry should play a key role in enabling a knowledge economy through providing access to information through several means, including broadcast, books, newspapers, magazines, and advertising, all typically generated and consumed through digital platforms. So if the digital platforms do not exist in the first place, there is no scope for content generation or consumption.

---

46 Coordination failure here refers to the inability of countries, states, provinces, and the private sector to coordinate their efforts to deliver regional and national ICT backbones across Africa. Even in countries where there should be a "central command," many stakeholders are watching for others to lead. In most countries, there do not appear to be any coordinated broadband infrastructure implementation programmes—yet alone across national boundaries.

47 www.naspers.com

48 www.nationmedia.com

49 www.zuku.co.ke

Justin Bieber was a Canadian teenager who started playing songs on YouTube. Today he is a major superstar. Without the Internet and YouTube, this would not have happened. Without the Internet on the continent, so many talented "Justin Biebers" on the continent of Africa just waste away. What an opportunity cost yet again for not planning and executing on all TMT platforms and infrastructure on the continent.

A later section (in a page or two) illustrates some of these opportunity costs more.

5. True broadcasting to the masses is unlikely to have an investable business case in most African and emerging market countries. Seen as an entire TMT sector, broadcasting becomes investable.

Mass broadcasting is also important for the continent of Africa. Broadcasting is certainly not "valued" by consumers and citizens as much as voice communications. Another way of articulating this same message is by noting that people are far more likely to do without their radio/TV sets than to do away with their mobile phones. Thanks to this simple proposition, mobile companies can monetize their services far more than broadcasters can. For this simple reason as well, broadcasters—particularly terrestrial broadcasters who do not have the coverage that satellites do—certainly struggle to have solid cases to build viable broadcasting businesses. However, does this mean that broadcasting via TV/radio is not as important for a nation's development as mobile and data communications? This is certainly arguable to many people, but I argue strongly in this volume that broadcasting via radio/TV is equally as important to Africa's development and cohesion as mobile voice/data communications.

Many South Africans were brought together by the TV coverage of the Nelson Mandela funeral no matter what part of the world they were in. The key difference in this context is that profits can be "extracted" from mobile communications relatively easily compared to from broadcasting, and so the latter resorts to seeking different means to pay for its operations, typically via sponsorship and advertising. This is covered more in some detail in chapter 8.

Take news provision, for example. Ofcom, the esteemed UK communications regulator, noted in 2007 that no form of television news in the United Kingdom currently pays its own way and that it is even worse for regional news. If this is true for a mature United Kingdom, it is likely to be starker in Africa and other emerging markets unless it is *not* a mass proposition. Does this mean that news and regional news should not be available on TV/radio? Surely not! The reason is that much of the "value" in broadcasting is in the broader social value. Broader social value includes intangible aspects like "access and inclusion"—where true mass broadcasting enables a country's citizens to feel included in that country and helps them feel they belong to that society. True mass broadcasting—as is covered in chapter 8—informs, entertains, and educates. It fosters culture and enables an informed democracy. Do most citizens go out their way to pay for these? Sadly, they do not. Is it, however, important that it is paid for somehow? Definitely yes—in my view at least. Mass broadcasting is unaffordable on its own. Collectively, as part of media—the latter which itself is part of TMT—mass broadcasting may/would become affordable. If "cash-rich" telecommunications has to "subsidise" "cash poor" mass media (which delivers significant broader social value) to make it investable in most countries, so be it, assuming sponsorship and advertising revenues do not make it profitable.

6. Illustrating the potential gains from establishing a TMT sector—the case of London, England.

It is also illustrative as the case is made for TMT in Africa to "benchmark" with some of the top-of-the-class TMT cities elsewhere in the world which African (or other emerging market) cities and countries can choose to strive to emulate. It is arguably better to strive towards a best-in-class city rather than a country, because it offers provinces and states in African and other emerging economies the opportunity to see promotion of TMT as their goal too, in just the same way as they should for ICT. Indeed, there is a strong case that all the capital and/or economic capital cities on the African continent and elsewhere should strive to have thriving TMT sectors. Cities on the African continent like Kinshasa, Maputo, Douala, Lagos, Accra, Dakar, Nairobi, Johannesburg, Cape Town, Cairo, and more are all cities ripe to be TMT hubs. They all have young, educated, and dynamic citizens with rich cultural backgrounds as well as other unique assets. For example, Lagos is already known for its thriving Nollywood[50] industry thought to be a \$500 million a year industry already, shooting and distributing high quality digital movies using an analogue era distribution system. Nollywood's output is allegedly second in the world in terms of volume of output after Bollywood (Nwulu *et al.*, 2010), which has overtaken Hollywood. Nollywood productions come in English (44 percent) and in indigenous Nigerian languages subtitled in English too (Yoruba: 31 percent; Hausa: 24 percent; and Igbo: 1 percent) according to Nwulu.

If Nigeria is this creative, Democratic Republic of Congo (DRC) would be too. Kinshasa is simply one of the key untapped cultural jewels of the African continent whose bountiful culture will burst at its seams once DRC gets its act together. Douala in Cameroon has a small but thriving content sector, sometimes referred to as Collywood. Douala is known for some very bilingual (in English/French, typically Anglophones) and talented directors who produce the equivalent of Nollywood productions. One suspects not many Africans have heard of Collywood—but that is exactly the point. Given a chance of a half-decent TMT sector in Cameroon, most Africans will hear of it pretty quickly, thanks to the power of social media. Nairobi is an African hub and has a similarly highly educated, young, and dynamic population with so much talent to give to the TMT sector. I could go on. For someone like me who has spent a long time in London (England), where young and talented people under forty around Soho and Chiswick are the backbone of the media sector as producers, creative directors, illustrators, actors, designers, etc., it is an incredible truism that so much similar creativity is being literally stifled on the African continent.

---

50 Nollywood is the metonym for Nigeria's movie and cinema industry, adapted from Hollywood and Bollywood, metonyms for the United States' and India's movie and cinema sectors.

So, what is the prize for these cities to emulate? London, England—I postulate—is a city worth emulating for its TMT prowess. London is a city of just over eight million people, not too dissimilar from the population of Lagos State in Nigeria. London-based telecommunications, media, and technology (TMT) firms contribute £125 billion (or US$190 billion as of September 2013) a year to the United Kingdom, equivalent to 8 percent of the United Kingdom's GDP, according to consultants Deloitte.[51] Furthermore, TMT employs over 440,000 in London, or around one in ten jobs in the capital, according to Deloitte. Nearly 50 percent of UK media employment is in London, and 28 percent of its total TMT employment is in Greater London.

TMT Subsector (s)	Layer	Examples
Media	Services Layer	Content, services, and applications
Technology	Active Infrastructure Layer	Electronic equipment like servers, active equipment on base station sites, OSS, BSS, design/customisation of ICT infrastructure
Telecommunications	Passive Layer	Trenches, ducts, dark fibre, regional backbone, national backbone, mobile base station sites, satellite links

Figure 7—The Simplistic TMT "Layers" View

---

51 *London—Enabling a World Leading Digital Hub*, Deloitte, July 2013, www.deloitte.com (accessed August 2013).

Even more revealing, perhaps surprising, is a breakdown of the 440,000 TMT jobs across its three subsectors. The Deloitte analysis shows only 40,000 of this is telecoms, 185,000 for technology, and 208,000 for media. You may need to do a double take on reading this breakdown. However, a bit more thinking about it explains why.

Figure 7 shows a simplified TMT layers structure. Telecommunications provide for the "base" passive layer, including trenches, ducts, poles, fibre, base station sites, etc. This layer is more concentrated amongst less than a handful of players typically. Technology encompasses more of the "active infrastructure layer" covering active transmission equipment, servers, and platforms like operational support systems (OSSs), business support systems (BSSs), customer relationship management systems (CRMs), billing systems, etc. These are large and complex technology platforms, and there are typically more platform competitors here including consultancy organisations that consult on and implement all these platforms. Media encompasses content, services, applications, apps, etc., i.e., the "services" layer. Media provides that value-added and creative layer.

Is this now a prize worth going for? How would you as a decision maker or entrepreneur like having five to six times as many media jobs as there are telecommunications jobs in Cairo, Nairobi, or Lagos? Or four to five times as many technology jobs as telecoms in Douala, Tunis, Casablanca, or Kinshasa?

The point of these data is not to draw parallels between London and Cairo or Nairobi or Kinshasa. Rather, it is to illuminate and *illustrate* the art of the possible and how these different strata truly generate jobs and release creativity. Who would have known that telecommunications would be 8.53 percent of the GDP of Nigeria from almost zero in 1999? The TMT sector will need to be meticulously planned for, but the prize is worth going for, particularly when the case for doing it is igniting the innate creativity of Africans who are so richly blessed with so many diverse cultures. And even better: the promise of multiplying five-fold the number of jobs in media as there are in telecoms.

7. There is a real golden opportunity to design (redesign) the entire TMT sector in most African and emerging economies: analogue to digital switchover of television, submarine fibre landings (including national fibre backbones), and 4G[52] spectrum auctions and Internet for the masses.

I submit to you that over the next five to ten years, we do have some golden opportunities afforded by international obligations and customer demand on the ground in Africa and other emerging economies to design/redesign our TMT sectors. This is afforded by

- the switching off of analogue television (TV) signals across the continent;
- switching to digital terrestrial TV;
- the next round of spectrum releases on the continent to enable the mobile Internet;
- the submarine cable landings delivering oodles of international connectivity capacity which need distribution via national backbones.

Furthermore, universal access obligations (and other self-imposed declarations, e.g. see the Indaba declaration at the beginning of chapter 7), legally and morally compel decision makers to ensure Internet/mobile data for the masses truly happen, and not just for those in the cities. Let us briefly look at this in turn. Then there are other miscellaneous issues which we have touched on in this chapter.

The *first opportunity* is that of switching off analogue television across the continent of Africa. You may find some of the following arcane and esoteric, but suffice to say in common with other countries in

---

52   4G refers to fourth generation mobile phone technology standards which succeeds second generation (2G) and third generation (3G). 2G and 3G, which have been deployed in Africa today, were mainly designed for killer application voice. 4G differentiates itself in that it is designed for data—i.e., to enable the mobile Internet.

ITU[53] Region 1,[54] all African countries undertook in the Geneva 2006 agreement to complete the transition from analogue to digital terrestrial TV broadcasting by June 2015 for southern African countries and 2020 for the rest of Africa, indeed thirty countries.[55] Confused? You should be. If not, you are unfortunately as nerdy as some of us. We can unpack this some more and more in chapter 9.

All African countries, in theory, have analogue *terrestrial*[56] television transmissions on air right now in 2013/14. Terrestrial television is a mode of broadcasting television using radio waves from land-based transmission sites, transmitting and receiving via antennas and television antenna aerials, respectively. It does *not* primarily involve fibre, satellite transmission, or cables. So for example in South Africa before switchover, there are three analogue SABC[57] terrestrial channels from the state broadcaster (SABC-1, SABC-2, and SABC-3) as well as other independent or private ones like eTV. In Cameroon before switchover, there is just one terrestrial channel from CRTV,[58] which just covers 40 percent of the population. Yes, Cameroon has some private broadcast TV transmissions on air in some cities like Douala and Yaounde, but they are hardly national. Angola similarly has three analogue channels: TPA-1, TPA-2, and TPA-3 from state broadcaster TPA.[59] There is also a private channel, TV Zimbo. Nigeria has two NTA[60]

---

53 International Telecommunications Union (ITU) is a specialised agency of the United Nations responsible—amongst many other things—for coordinating the shared use of global radio spectrum and the shared use of satellite orbit slots in the skies, and it works to improve telecommunications infrastructure in the developing world.

54 The ITU splits all the nations of the world in three different geographical regions. Region 1 comprises Europe; Africa; the Middle East west of the Persian Gulf, including Iraq; the former Soviet Union; and Mongolia.

55 Specifically, June 2015 is the deadline for UHF analogue TV protection via the ITU, whilst June 2020 is for VHF. These terms are explained later in chapter 4. UHF stands for ultra high frequency spectrum bands, whilst VHF connotes very high frequency bands.

56 There are of course numerous satellite channels on air on the continent.

57 South African Broadcasting Corporation, http://www.sabc.co.za.

58 Cameroon Radio and Television, http://www.crtv.cm.

59 Televisão Pública de Angola

60 NigeriaTelevision Authority

national terrestrial channels on air in 2013/14. Kenya has two main terrestrial and national TV stations by KBC,[61] the state broadcaster, and KTN,[62] the leading independent Kenyan broadcaster. The point of these country examples is to illustrate that most African countries do not offer more than a handful of TV channels on their analogue terrestrial platforms and in many cases, like in Cameroon, only one. Furthermore, the coverage of these terrestrial platforms is rather limited: 40 percent in Cameroon and Tanzania only had a paltry 22 percent of the population covered by analogue TV transmissions before they started turning on their digital transmissions in December 2012.

So let us return to the arcane issues of the ITU and Region 1. Another key point is, of course, there are satellite channels in these countries, but they are not controlled *by* the TMT sectors in African countries concerned by definition *for* the African sector. Only terrestrial networks will truly afford African entrepreneurs and the public sector the control of their *national* broadcast and media sectors. Satellite birds are owned by big multinationals like SES Astra, Intelsat or Avanti from Europe. That said, I must state that I am a big proponent of plurality of platforms (satellite, terrestrial, Internet, cable, etc.) as they offer consumers and citizens more choice.

The Regional Radiocommunication Conference (RRC-06) (organised by the ITU in Geneva in 2006) set June 17, 2015, as the deadline for eastern and southern African countries mostly using UHF for their analogue TV transmissions, and 2020 for thirty other African countries (who mostly use VHF) to migrate from analogue to digital terrestrial broadcasting technologies.[63] It is, therefore, mandatory for all countries worldwide. Beyond these dates, the ITU will no longer guarantee the protection from interference of these analogue signals.

---

61 Kenya Broadcasting Corporation

62 Kenya Television Network

63 The thirty countries on the 2020 list include Algeria, Benin, Burkina Faso, Cameroon, Central African Republic, Chad, Congo, Democratic Republic of Congo, Egypt, Equatorial Guinea, Eritrea, Ethiopia, Gabon, Ghana, Guinea, Guinea-Bissau, Ivory Coast, Liberia, Madagascar, Mali, Morocco, Mauritania, Niger, Nigeria, Sao Tome and Principe, Sierra Leone, Somalia, Sudan, Togo, and Tunisia.

Frankly, this does not necessarily amount to much for most of Africa as there is not much analogue TV on air to protect anyway. More important is the fact that analogue technology is getting obsolete and inefficient. Most important is that the real driver is one of spectrum efficiency: for the same amount of frequency as one of the analogue channels mentioned above in all these countries, at least eight (8) and up to twenty (20) new digital and better quality channels can be delivered. This way, more valuable spectrum can be freed up for other uses on the continent.

So, more channels and more choice, better quality and cheaper up-to-date technology all make this an easy decision subject to the economics working out. Every country can now control their TV platforms more, with more channels, and more local and more private sector involvement in the TV and media sector, have less reliance on satellite only, and foster the emergence of a true local advertising sector with these local and national channels. This affords the opportunity to revisit and redesign the whole TV and media landscape of a country. Even for the leading countries like Tanzania who will be completing their switchover soon,[64] there is still an opportunity for them to think strategically about how to use these released analogue frequencies along with other extant projects for the benefit of their consumers and citizens.

This leads us nicely to the *second opportunity*, which provides for the redesign the sector—the coming 4G auctions on the continent. The United Kingdom concluded its digital switchover—one of the biggest switchovers ever—switching over 1,150 transmission sites and relays from analogue to digital in October 2012. It is important though to be clear on what the real prizes for this effort were. *The first prize* was moving from only five analogue free-to-air channels to fifty standard definition (SD) digital channels, twenty-four digital radio stations, and four high-definition (HD) TV channels.[65] So the TV platform also

---

64 Tanzania already completely switched off its analogue TV signals in its capital, Dar es Salam, on December 31, 2012, and most of country will have been done by late 2014.

65 Simply, HD provides for much higher quality resolution than SD, making for much better looking pictures, particularly on big flat screen TVs.

carries radio! The second and key prize was that some of those cleared frequencies which were used for analogue TV—remember one analogue channel can now hold typically eight digital ones—were sold off in the United Kingdom's biggest auction of frequency in more than a decade, raising £2.37 billion. This auction concluded in February 2013, and I was privileged to have led it at the United Kingdom's communications regulator Ofcom, in addition to leading a significant part of the digital switchover for some channels in the United Kingdom. I digress.

More important is the fact that these frequencies[66] have now been auctioned to be used for mobile broadband or mobile Internet. Indeed, mobile broadband will extend as far as 98 percent (indoors) of the population of the United Kingdom using 4G[67] technology. So the *second key prize* stems from the fact that that many African and emerging markets now need more spectrum for mobile Internet, or 4G spectrum, just as the United Kingdom and most of Europe and America have already done. I cannot overemphasise how urgently more spectrum for broadband is needed on the Africa continent, as well as in other emerging economies.

So what have these got to do with an opportunity to design or redesign the TMT sector in most African, Caribbean and emerging market countries, like some Asian and Latin American ones?

Figure 8 captures the sector design/redesign opportunity diagrammatically. Digital switchover from analogue is mandated by the ITU for 2015 for eastern and southern African countries, and 2020 for thirty other countries. Most African countries though— even those on the 2020 list either by ignorance of the 2020 deadline for them or by design—have opted voluntarily for the 2015 deadline. Kenya (with some luck), Uganda, and Zambia will all be done by

---

66 This is called the 800MHz band of frequencies, ranging from 790MHz to 862 MHz.

67 4G refers to fourth generation mobile phone technology standards that succeed second generation (2G) and third generation (3G). As of 2013/14, 2G (and 3G more sparingly) that has been deployed in Africa today was mainly designed for the killer application of voice. The way 4G differentiates itself is that it is designed for data—i.e., to enable the mobile Internet.

the end of 2015; Tanzania switchover to digital had already mostly happened by December 31, 2012, as the first mainland sub-Saharan country to do so. Mauritius is already complete and Malawi and Rwanda are almost there too in December 2013. Frankly however, many others will not meet this 2015 deadline, not least because they neither have good plans in place nor are they concerned with the risk to their current analogue transmissions being interfered with. These risks are low as they do not have that many channels on air, as we saw earlier.

The *third opportunity* is all about new international fibre connectivity. So much terabytes of fibre capacity are being landed on the continent, and this capacity is being distributed via various national and international backbones. This is indeed a game changer on the continent. International capacity costs (per megabyte) have already dropped like a stone in many countries as satellite VSAT no longer maintains its stranglehold on international connectivity across the continent. Satellite capacity has dropped from circa US $5000 per megabyte per annum to circa $500 in just several years. As the landed submarine capacity is further distributed within every country via national fibre backbones (to major cities and other hinterlands)—and as African countries link their backbones to one another—a real opportunity emerges to rethink and redesign the entire TMT sector across Africa and other emerging economies.

TMT SECTOR REDESIGN FROM ALL THESE ACTIVITIES OR "MUDDLE THROUGH" AS SEPARATE PROJECTS?

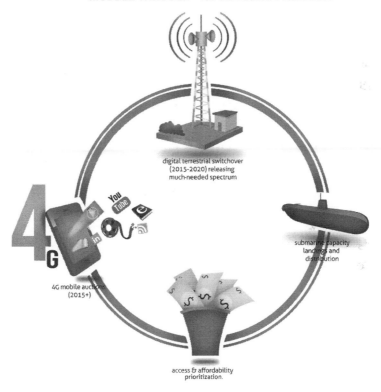

Figure 8: TMT Sector Redesign from All These Activities or
"Muddle Through" as Separate Projects?

The *fourth opportunity* is all about affordable rural *communications* services covering voice, broadband Internet, radio, TV, and other media. It is critical that all these terabytes of international connectivity are for the many, not the few! It is critical that *access and affordability* is top-of-mind for all policy makers on the continent to ensure the 2020s deliver for all and not just for the elite, as is the case with several services today, like satellite TV, TV in general, etc.

Let us exemplify these four opportunities with the example of affordable rural broadband. As noted, many countries are currently landing submarine capacity and rolling out fibre, along with planning out national and regional backbones to distribute this landed fibre capacity and enabling the Internet. There is also already mounting pressure from operators in many African countries to start releasing new 4G spectrum for mobile Internet. In addition to all these, there are concerns about coverage as covered in this chapter to pre-empt creating the haves and the have-nots for mobile Internet, particularly for rural broadband. So unlike in the United Kingdom, where I and my colleagues at Ofcom were able to impose a population coverage obligation of 98 percent on one of the five winning licensees of the 4G auction, this would be a disproportionate step for most African countries. This is due to the naked data problem discussed earlier and also because, as chapter 3 shows, Africa is a truly massive continent. This is why I have also mooted white spaces technology as a candidate approach and technology for *affordable Internet for the rural masses* in Africa. Therefore another real prize Africa must design for up front is widespread and affordable Internet, indeed widespread and affordable digital services in general.

Competition concerns are already beginning to emerge in the telecommunications sector with findings of dominance against the likes of MTN in Nigeria, and there are significant concerns too about the likes of Safaricom in Kenya. All of these projects, as shown in figure 8, are very interlinked, and most of them are *not* well funded, and their execution is patchy. The mind-set that TV broadcasting is independent of the mobile Internet, which in turn is independent of mobile voice, is sheer nonsense. Even with a one-to-many broadcast, having a "return path" for interactive communication between a home and the service provider should be a key part of the thinking for a new TMT sector in Africa. Therefore, a digital terrestrial or satellite TV set-top box could/should have such a return path for just such an instant interaction where a user sees an advert on TV and can proceed to buy on his/ her TV. This links TV broadcasting policy (and implementation) with broadband policy thinking (wireless or fixed).

So figure 8 demonstrates the opportunity to look at all of these separate activities "in the round" or holistically in order to take stock and design for the sort of TMT sector Africa (and elsewhere) can evolve (and needs). Or will many countries choose to pretend these projects are all separate and working to different timescales when they all patently are not? This is a golden opportunity to design or redesign our TMT sectors and fund it appropriately for the long term. This is a *marathon* of a task—designing a critical sector of African and other emerging market economies—not a *sprint*. Careful up front planning will pay massive dividends downstream. This is one of the many clear lessons from Europe. We cover these in other chapters of the book (see chapters 3, 6, 7, 8, 9, 10 and 11.

Furthermore, looking at separate policy areas holistically has paid dividends elsewhere in the developed world. For example, it was a hallmark of the Digital Britain report.[68] This report was a policy document published in 2009 which defined the UK government's strategic vision to help ensure the country continues to be at the leading edge of the global digital revolution. This was a joined-up policy document sponsored by the then UK minister for communications, technology and broadcasting, Lord Stephen Carter.[69] You should note here that the UK minister for this sector oversees communications (including telecommunications), technology, and broadcasting (more broadly the media). Therefore one minister oversees UK TMT—not two or three ministers or ministries. I digress. Substantively, the joined-up policy document's recommendations covered:

- next generation broadband: funds to invest in next generation broadband networks, particularly fibre rollout to uneconomic areas
- universal access to broadband by 2012
- the modernisation of wireless radio spectrum holdings: this included the liberalisation of 3G spectrum
- a digital future for radio: where the policy document recommended moving from analogue radio today in the United Kingdom to just digital radio, as has happened with TV

---

68   The Digital Britain Final Report, Building Britain's Future, June 2009, http://www.official-documents.gov/uk/document/cm76/7650/7650.pdf (accessed September 2013).

69   Stephen Carter was also the first CEO of the United Kingdom's esteemed converged communications regulator, Ofcom.

- a new deal for digital content rights: this included support for public service content partnerships
- enhancing the digital delivery of public services: this included a three-year plan to enhance and boost digital participation
- consultation on how to fund local, national, and regional news
- a "more robust system" for video games classification
- enhancing the role of one of the United Kingdom's key publicly owned but commercially funded broadcaster, Channel 4

There are several points to be made here. First, you can see from the abridged list above that the UK policy document covered recommendations across TMT in a holistic and converged manner. This was deliberate. Secondly, this policy set of recommendations resulted in the UK's Digital Economy Act 2010, which came into force in June 2010. Therefore, it became a binding enacted piece of legislation which even a subsequent change of government has (and had) to enforce. Thirdly, not all the recommendations necessarily happened when it was envisaged they would happen. For example, universal access to broadband did not happen by 2012 as envisaged, but importantly, there is a clear plan in place to make this happen. I can attest that in my four years at UK communications regulator, Ofcom, much of what I led and achieved were prescribed in the Digital Britain report.

When this report was initially published as a draft, Lord Stephen Carter wrote:

> The innovation, creativity and vitality of our communications industries rightly demand clarity from Government on its role and a framework for the future. Delivering Digital Britain will depend upon a smart industry, working with a committed Government to produce lasting solutions.

Yes, African and other emerging market governments too need to provide "clarity" on their role and framework towards a digital Africa, and governments need to be "committed" to produce lasting solutions. If this prescription is good enough for Britain, it must be good for

Africa and other emerging economies. The next section on the case for national and regional TMT business plans unashamedly emulates and draws from the lessons from the Digital Britain Report. The ethos that underpins this next section is the same basic ethos that underpinned the Digital Britain report.

1.2 The Case for National and Regional TMT Business Plans—Towards a Digital Africa

The case for most African countries having national TMT business plans seems clear-cut in the second decade of the twenty-first century. The reasons include the following:

- It is best practice—particularly for governments and civil servants who are not wealth creators[70]—to have clearly developed and credible business plans to base any significant government spending on. It is not obvious how reputable audit firms on the continent of Africa provide unqualified audit reports on government departments who rarely produce credible business plans for projects worth tens to hundreds of millions of US dollars.
- Figure 8 summarises the size and the quantum of several key projects currently going on in most countries today. The last section made a cogent case (hopefully) for looking at all these projects in the round as they are so interlinked. Unless a business plan approach is taken wherein all the key assumptions and interdependencies for all the various projects are clearly articulated, the taxpayers of the countries are likely to be paying for some activities twice or more times over.
- Figure 8 and the rest of this chapter have—with any luck—demonstrated that one does not set up a key sector of the

---

70 Indeed, it is salutary to remind government and civil servants in Africa in particular that, in economics terms, they are rent seekers. That is, they thrive on the taxation and revenues from the wealth-creating sectors of the economy. Many a time, they act as if they are the wealth-generating entrepreneurs.

economy like TMT without a good plan. Like building your dream home, you will not dare start without an architect's plan and, furthermore, dare not live and abide by that plan. How much more for one of the most important sectors of any modern economy?

- Most governments on the continent have not been able to secure budgets for all these key projects out of their meagre budgets. Be it the projects for national backbones to distribute fibre within a country, be it the analogue to digital switchover projects or projects to improve mobile coverage to noneconomical parts of the countries—all these projects need significant sums of monies associated with them. And if all of the projects all come along in the same budget or government cycle, it is even more important to look at all of them in the round with a solid business case.

- Furthermore, governments arguably need true private sector partners who are prepared to stand "shoulder to shoulder" with some of our governments for over a decade or more. The digital switchover and digital TV platform in the United Kingdom—Freeview—has been partly financed by the private sector monies in exchange for contracts extending to 2034! It can be done, but it must be done transparently and with much due diligence.

- Regional business plans also make eminent sense when it comes to rolling out regional fibre backbones for example. The risks of coordination failure are large, but this is where the benefits and experience of funding agencies such as the World Bank and the Africa Development Bank (ADB) come into their element. They will certainly be demanding credible business plans.

- I can think of no better plan than to securitize future (almost guaranteed) revenues from natural resources (oil, gas, minerals, and metals) in many countries in Africa against such business plans which develop and invest in key future growth sectors like TMT and infrastructure projects like energy and transport. Having credible business cases which are bought into and invested in by long-term private external and national investors must be strongly encouraged for Africa's development.

As if the reasons above are not enough to motivate the production of business cases for TMT, also consider the following rule of thumb findings which may also be considered to make TMT business cases even stronger.

- Deloitte and GSMA Intelligence[71] seminal 2005 analysis reported from a sample of fifty-seven developing countries that a 10 percent increase in mobile penetration leads to a 1.2 percent (in comparison to 0.6 percent in developed countries) increase in the *annual* growth rate in GDP. The World Bank estimates that African economies grow by 1.4 percent for every 10 percent growth in broadband penetration.[72] Furthermore, as the mobile sector continues to expand and develop a new service, its contribution to GDP is likely to further increase. According to McKinsey, the total economic impact of wireless mobile is the sum of three key elements: the direct impact from mobile operators, the indirect impact from other companies in the wireless ecosystem (hardware and software vendors, handset vendors, etc.), and a second form of indirect impact, the surplus enjoyed by end users.
- Indeed, a more recent 2012 report from Deloitte[73] measured the impact of "simple" mobile on a country's total factor productivity (which is a measure of economic productivity that reflects an economy's long-term technological dynamism). They found a 10 percent increase in mobile penetration increases

---

71 Deloitte and GSMA Intelligence Report (2005), "Tax and the Digital Divide—How new approaches to mobile taxation can connect the unconnected."

72 World Bank (2009), Information and Communication for Development: Extending reach and increasing impact, Chapter 3, http://siteresources.worldbank.org/EXTIC4D/Resources/IC4D_Broadband_35_50.pdf (accessed October 2013).

73 Deloitte Report, November 2012, http://www.gsma.com/publicpolicy/wp-content/uploads/2012/11/gsma-deloitte-impact-mobile-telephony-economic-growth.pdf (accessed August 2013).

total factor productivity in the long run by an astonishing 4.2 percentage points.

- There is also a clear benefit to move from older mobile technology like 2G to new technologies like 3G or 4G. The same November 2012 Deloitte research of a panel of ninety-six developed and developing markets quantifies that for a given level of total mobile penetration, a 10 percent substitution from 2G to 3G penetration increases GDP per capita growth by 0.15 percent.
- The same 2012 report also found by analyzing fourteen countries that a doubling of mobile data use leads to an increase in the GDP per capita growth of half a percentage point. GSMA Intelligence (2012) extrapolate this half percent for sub-Saharan Africa and conclude that GDP could increase by US$40 billion over the next four years, representing approximately 0.5 percent of total GDP of this region over that period subject to some constraints being swept away, principally spectrum.
- Another 2011 study by Ericsson and Arthur D. Little[74] found that both broadband availability and speed of broadband are strong drivers in an economy. They concluded that for every ten-percentage-point increase in broadband penetration, GDP increases by 1 percent. Furthermore, if speeds are doubled, then GDP increases by one-third percentage point. Given that by definition these research findings were derived from developed economies (as most African countries do not have any meaningful broadband as yet), these growth figures—like the 1.2 percent vs. 0.6 percent above—would likely be double for African and some emerging market economies.

A key part of the case for TMT in Africa is plainly simple. It makes economic sense to first broadband connect the vast African unconnected, and second, then up the broadband speeds!

---

74 Source: http://www.telecompaper.com/news/doubling-broadband-speed-leads-to-03-gdp-growth-in-oecd--829373 (accessed June 2013).

1.3 Breakdown of the Rest of the Book and How to Read the Book

Below is breakdown of the rest of the book. It consists of seven broad sections:

I. *Introductory:* **Section I** includes this introductory chapter and a further one, chapter 2. Chapter 2 describes the anatomy and geography of TMT so that all readers can achieve a shared understanding of the evolving new telecommunications, media, and technology sector. Chapter 2 is slightly technical in places, as it delves into the anatomy of the various parts of the TMT subsectors, but you must not be scared off at all. It is, hopefully, a gentle introduction. An important goal of this volume is to demystify and critique some of the technicalities of the sector—enough to draw out the key messages and opportunities that decision makers, policy professionals, and entrepreneurs should be concerned about.

II. *Blueprint:* **Section II** consists of just a single chapter (chapter 3), which proposes a blueprint for TMT for Africa and elsewhere. To arrive at the blueprint set of recommendations, the key drivers for the TMT sector are listed and explained, and the recommendations are categorized under these key drivers. The recommendations draw from the overview and critiques of the chapters in the introductory section.

III. *Towards Widespread Availability of Affordable, High-Quality Mobile Voice, Mobile Data, and Mobile Internet:* Section II concludes and proposes several broad-themed desired outcomes that the rest of the volume expands upon—the first being how to achieve widespread and affordable mobile voice, mobile data, and mobile Internet for the masses. **Section III** consists then of four chapters which concern themselves with these broad desired outcomes. Widespread mobile voice, data, and Internet would not be achieved without spectrum airwaves, so chapter 4 provides a gentle introduction into this important subject, and more spectrum must be released to the market on the African continent, fast. It then proceeds to emphasise key concerns and recommendations that policy makers and others should worry about towards achieving these three widespread services. Chapter 5 picks up from chapter 4 to discuss awards and/or auctions of spectrum to ensure mobile voice, data, and Internet can be achieved given that spectrum is the true oxygen of wireless communications. Chapter 6 proposes that countries seriously consider a new evolving approach/technology called TV white spaces to help ensure true universal access of Internet services in urban and rural areas alike. Chapter 7 is a "catchall" chapter which "rounds out" and completes section III's goal of achieving affordable, high-quality voice, data, and Internet on the African continent and elsewhere for the 2020s.

IV. *Towards Widespread Availability of Affordable Audio Radio, Digital TV, and Other Media:* **Section IV** consists of two chapters. Chapter 8 begins with an excursion of what current African media as of 2013/14 entails, covering and introducing (in some detail) the history and anatomy of audio radio, analogue and digital TV, and newspapers. After reviewing the core drivers for these media, the chapter proceeds to explore where this general media sector is heading. After some lessons for African media from the rest of the world, the chapter concludes with clear recommendations towards widespread availability of audio radio, digital TV, newspapers, and other media. Chapter 9 covers the important subject of the basis and praxis of analogue to digital switchover of television. This is an important project that all countries on the continent of Africa and other emerging markets would have to conclude. An important message of the chapter and the section is that the analogue to digital switchover of TV should not just be an exercise in technocracy. It argues that it should and must be exploited as an opportunity to light the burners of the new multichannel, multimedia, more interactivity, and more social new media sector. There are also clear recommendations on how to achieve a successful TV switchover project.

V. *Towards Better Availability of Affordable Fixed Line and Fixed Internet:* **Section V** consists of just the one chapter, which tackles the most difficult challenge of the TMT sector on the continent—how to crack the fixed line and fixed Internet problem for a continent where the fixed problem is truly Herculean. The chapter argues for and makes clear recommendations for some "baby" steps towards better availability of affordable fixed Internet in the medium term, recognizing fully that widespread and affordable fixed is a problem of a much longer term.

VI. *Regulation as a Critical Success Factor:* A volume of this nature must cover regulation, and so the single chapter in **Section VI** does just that. Regulation is such a critical success factor for the TMT sector that its pivotal role can hardly be overstated. After covering what is TMT regulation and its goals, it proceeds to cover why converged and independent regulation—and what these really mean as well as how they are achieved. Uniquely, this chapter also introduces the legal and economic bases of economic regulation—areas that many regulators in Africa and emerging economies do not tend to fully appreciate. Regulation is both a science and an art, which are covered. It concludes with some clear recommendations towards better TMT regulation and regulators in Africa and other emerging economies.

VII. *TMT and Neighbouring Sectors and Conclusions:* The last section of the book—**Section VII**—consists of just one chapter. The key and substantive rationale for chapter 12 is simple: to ensure all the readers of this volume appreciate how much TMT is *gating* other key "neighbouring" sectors of the economy, particular in a digital, information, and knowledge economy. TMT is not an island. Therefore, any delays (e.g., spectrum delays) or missteps by the TMT sector have significant repercussions elsewhere: mobile financial services, mobile/e-commerce, mobile/e-health, mobile/e-education, and mobile/e-agriculture to name several. These are neighbouring sectors literally waiting on TMT, which require significant collaboration between them (i.e., these neighbouring sectors and TMT) in both policy and implementation in order to change the lives of Africans and other emerging economies' citizens for the 2020s. Recommendations are made on such cross-sector collaborations. Chapter 12 then proceeds to round out the book by mentioning other activities, such as incubation services, returning to the power problem, training, and capacity building, etc.—all prerequisites to a successful TMT sector in Africa and elsewhere for the 2020s.

The sections are written to be self-contained, and they can be read in any order once the reader has read the introductory chapters. However, within each section with more than one chapter, it is recommended they are read sequentially.

Frankly what matters more is for you to be inspired enough to read all the chapters in the book in whatever order you chose.

CHAPTER 2

THE GEOGRAPHY AND ANATOMY OF TMT AND LESSONS FOR THE TMT SECTOR

"The purpose of geography is to provide 'a view of the whole' earth by mapping the location of places."

—Ptolemy, 150 AD

Anatomy "is the branch of science concerned with the bodily structure...as revealed by dissection and separation of parts."

—Oxford Dictionary

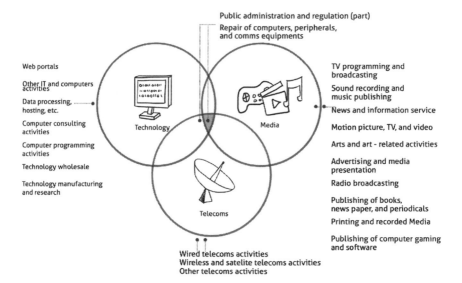

THE TMT SECTORS AND SOME OF
THEIR KEY AREAS (SOURCE: DELOITTE)

Public administration and regulation (part)
Repair of computers, peripherals,
and comms equipments

Web portals

Other IT and computers
activities

Data processing,
hosting, etc.

Computer consulting
activities

Computer programming
activities

Technology wholesale

Technology manufacturing
and research

Technology

Media

Telecoms

TV programming and
broadcasting

Sound recording and
music publishing

News and information service

Motion picture, TV, and video

Arts and art - related activities

Advertising and media
presentation

Radio broadcasting

Publishing of books,
news paper, and periodicals

Printing and recorded Media

Publishing of computer gaming
and software

Wired telecoms activities
Wireless and satelite telecoms activities
Other telecoms activities

Figure 9: The TMT Sectors and Some of Their Key Areas
(Source: adapted from Deloitte)[1]

Ptolemy had it right two millennia ago about what *geography*'s purpose is. This chapter attempts bravely is provide "a view of the whole" of TMT by mapping its various parts. TMT's anatomy, on the other hand, is about *dissecting* and *separating* those parts, as the *Oxford Dictionary* defines.

It is important to have a shared understanding of the basic geography and anatomy of the TMT sector that this book purports to describe. This chapter is extremely mindful of the intended readership of this book too, and so it does *not* focus on describing the nerdy details of various technologies. Having a shared understanding of the *geography* of the TMT sector in addition to a top-level description of the *anatomy* of its key regions or parts is an essential prerequisite for the remaining chapters and sections of the book too.

---

1 *London—Enabling a World Leading Digital Hub*, Deloitte, July 2013, www. deloitte.com, Appendix C.

As this geography and anatomy of the forthcoming African and emerging market TMT sector is described, it is also opportune to highlight some key lessons towards laying the right foundations for it. Some of implications of these lessons will obviously differ from country to country. The chapter also attempts to demystify some of the technicalities whilst helping decision makers, entrepreneurs, policy makers, executives, etc., to better realise what *really* should concern them about TMT—like competition issues, coverage issues, costs, coordination failures in the sector, financing issues, regulation, regional development issues, etc.—and less so the technicalities of how Cisco switches or routers work.

Figure 9 shows the three core TMT areas and some of their key constituent parts. We take each of the parts or subsectors in turn, dissect and describe its key activities, and provide some top-level details of the constituent parts.

2.1 The Geography, Anatomy and Lessons for the Telecommunications Subsector

As figure 9 depicts, we describe the three telecommunications subsector activities, namely:

- wired telecommunications activities
- wireless and satellite telecommunications activities
- other telecommunications activities

2.1.1 Wired Telecommunications Activities

Wired or fixed telecommunications activities refer to services provided over communications networks which serve *fixed* locations. Wired services are distinguished from mobile (or wireless) services which can be used whilst on the move. Examples of wired or fixed networks include fixed access networks using copper or optical fibre or cable networks.

Drawing from the themes of geography and anatomy, we describe two key scenarios:

- First, a scenario which traces how someone sitting at a home or office in Lagos, Nigeria, is accessing information sitting on a Google or Bing server in California over fixed telecommunications lines.
- Second, a scenario where the same person is placing a call over his/her fixed line from the home or office to someone in California.

FIXED NETWORK LINK FROM A HOME OR OFFICE IN AFRICA ACCESSING A GOOGLE SERVER IN CALIFORNIA OR SOMEONE CALLING CALIFORNIA

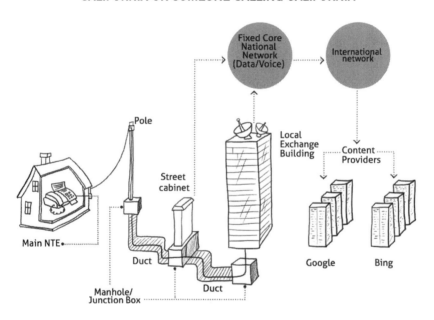

Figure 10: Fixed Network Link from a Home or Office in Africa Accessing a Bing or Google Server[2] in California or Someone Calling California

---

2 A server is a computer that holds digital information shared between many users who can connect to it across the Internet or other networks.

In describing how both these scenarios work, we describe the top-level details *only* of the various types of networks and some of their essential characteristics.

Figure 10 shows the main aspects of the geography of wired tele-communications networks covering both these scenarios and salient issues.

The Fixed Access Network

The access network covers, *inter alia*, access to network elements within the end user's house or office and other associated facilities (which may involve the connection of equipment) by fixed access to physical infrastructure, including buildings, poles, ducts, and masts Everything in figure 10, from the home/office all the way to the exchange, is part of the *access network*. So the main network termination element (NTE), the end socket in the home/office, the poles that the fixed telephone and broadband router are plugged into, the ducts, the street cabinet, manholes, and junction boxes up to the exchange building are all part of the access network.

The voice or data of the person who is calling California (or accessing the Internet there) has to travel, firstly, over this access network via the copper, coaxial, or fibre lines which run in the ducts and poles via the street cabinet into a local exchange building. In some cases, the data goes directly into the fixed core data network via the street cabinet without going via the local exchange, as is shown in figure 10.

There are access networks evolving sometimes haphazardly on the continent of Africa and in other emerging market countries. States, provinces, councils, or some other form of local government typically have control over fixed ducts and poles through which data and voice signals or bits flow—assuming there are fixed access networks, of course.

The following are some key lessons of note about access networks that are of relevance to what is happening on the continent and elsewhere that decision makers should worry about, presented both for information and as recommendations:

1. *Monopolies typically exist with fixed access networks, and so they have to be regulated:* There is typically only one fixed access network, i.e., there is typically only one pole or duct through which the coaxial, copper, or fibre are threaded going to a single home or office. There could be more in places, but typically there is usually just the one. There is typically, as well, only one fixed voice or data line into the house. This means the company who owns the line to that home has a monopoly on *originating or terminating* all calls to that home using that line, assuming that home has a fixed line, of course. This is because all calls originating and terminating in that premises has to use that fixed line. This gives that company that owns that line immense power, which means without regulation, they can charge whatever they like. Regulation takes the form of the national regulator[3] actually finding that the owner of the line into that home has *market dominance* for the line, and it therefore proceeds to *impose* some *remedies*. Remedies in this case will typically involve the regulator implementing *price controls* that the company owning that line into the house can charge other companies (and even itself) for having access to that line. This is the *access charge* or *monthly line rental* costs. The regulator also imposes further price controls on how much the company owning that line can charge other companies for terminating calls onto a line that it owns. This is the first introduction of the concept of regulation in the book so far. It's a key presence in the telecommunications sector because there are so many *bottleneck* points in a network where one company commands dominance.

2. *Competition needs to reign—others having access to access networks need to be designed in order to encourage competition. States, councils, countries, and provinces need to design*

---

3 Nigerian Communications Commission (NCC) in the case of Nigeria. Communications Regulator of Namibia (CRAN) in the case of Namibia. National Communications Authority (NCA) in the case of Ghana. Bangladesh Telecommunication Regulatory Commission (BTRC) in the case of Bangladesh, etc.

competition into all access networks being built in towns and cities: The previous point crept very quickly into competition issues. Competition is vital because wherever there is true competition, generally, prices are low, quality improves, consumers have more choice, and there is usually much innovation. These are all good outcomes that consumers and citizens demand, and regulators want to achieve these. Therefore, as councils, states, provinces, or authorities allow private operators access to existing public ducts and poles, or even get into PPP[4] relationships with private operators to design and build new ducts/poles spines in the city, they must do so fully mindful of competition concerns. This is because new access networks are being built which will be owned by monopolies. The authorities are unlikely to have several pole/ducts spines in the city, not least because so many companies would be digging up all streets at the same time in this case!

3. *Coverage of the access network is important:* If new ducts and poles are being specified and developed, or the old ones are being extended/refurbished, the coverage of the access network should be properly planned up front to ensure all key population nerve centres of a city are covered. It is unlikely homes will be fibred to, but key regions of cities must be. The access network, if it is fibre, may also need to be extended to locations where major traffic will be generated, like current or proposed locations of shopping centres, TV transmission stations, Internet cafes, and transmission and receiving stations for TV or mobile. Planning coverage is invaluable so that the city is dug up once only, if possible.

4. *Implement a "pay once" and "dig once" policy:* Following on from last point, countries like Nigeria and others are pioneering this innovative "pay once" and "dig once" approach to expediting fixed network rollout and investment. Nigeria clearly

---

4 Acronym for public private partnerships.

recognized the issue of the sprawling telecommunications sector cutting across many Nigerian states and the many regulatory agencies and bureaucracies adversely affecting the ease of doing business. This compelled the government to adopt a "pay once" policy which allows for just one agency to streamline all the bureaucratic processes, levies, and taxes. The private sector player, in theory, just pays once. Secondly, Nigeria is now committed to a "dig once" philosophy where infrastructure providers create permanent ducts for fibre, thereby minimizing redigging and destroying roads. These are all important because the private sector monies go into infrastructure rather than into bureaucratic costs.

5. *Design and implement spine fibre access backbones*: Once fibre capacity is "landed" into a country, city, state, or province, this "capacity" has to be distributed (via spine fibre access backbone) to yield access networks into homes and offices. This must be a strong recommendation, or else why bother bring in the fibre into the state or city anyway?

FIXED ACCESS NETWORK VIA CORE NETWORK
TO A RANGE OF OTHER NETWORKS

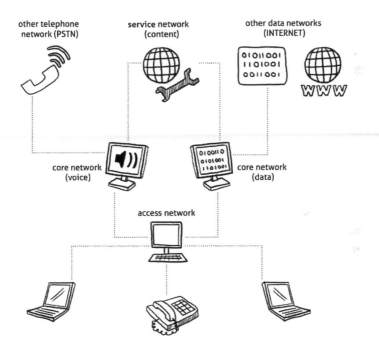

Figure 11: Fixed Access Network via Core Network to a Range of Other Networks

Clearly, the regulator should be vigilant of such access networks evolving *across* the African continent and elsewhere—literally like a rash—ensuring the rules for both access and ongoing costs for their use by other players are set up early (and up front) to encourage competition.

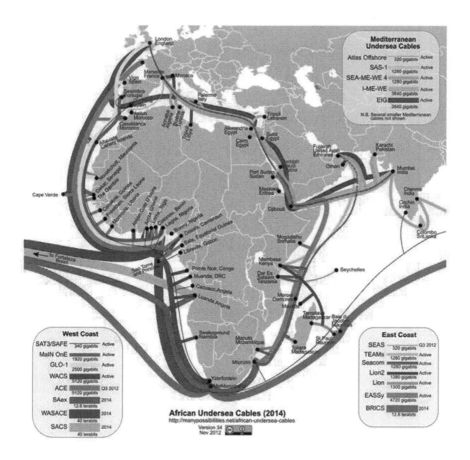

Figure 12: Africa Undersea Cables (2014)

(Source: Steve Song, http://manypossibilities.net/african-undersea-cables;
reproduced with permission of the copyright owner.)

The Core Fixed Data/Voice Network and other Networks

From the access network, the voice or data from the home flows into the national core network, sometimes via a local exchange, sometimes not. Core networks are typically for voice or for data, though some modern networks do both seamlessly. They basically consist of voice switches and data routers.[5] Core networks aggregate voice and data traffic from several access networks, ensure they are from genuine customers, and charge for the service and routes or switch the data in both directions onto international networks (e.g., the Internet) or from other parts of the world back onto the access networks. Most core networks tend to be national, e.g., Safaricom's core network is in Kenya. The core network also links to a range of other networks, as shown in figure 11, like the Internet, service network (e.g., MTN's service network), or other fixed line public telephone networks.

The International Network, International Gateways, and IXPs (Peering Points)

From the core network, the voice call from Lagos or the server request for a page in California from Lagos (see figure 9) gets sent on via an international gateway, like the Internet Exchange Point of Nigeria/Nigerian Internet Exchange (IXPN)[6] onto an international network, like the Internet via submarine (or deep sea) fibre all the way to America. International gateway equivalents for the Internet are called Internet exchange points (IXPs), also called a *peering point* (PP).

IXPs are a vital part of the Internet ecosystem as they enable two networks to exchange information efficiently. This could be the Cameroon network and the Chad networks in western Africa exchanging information efficiently without having to go all the way via LINX[7] in London or to Paris. Up until relatively recently (2012), much of the international connectivity from Africa was via satellite, which was very expensive. Many submarine cables now provide competition to satellite, and costs have dropped significantly in many countries on the continent, as discussed below.

---

5   A router receives the electronic information message, notes the traffic condition on the network, and determines the best possible path for that message to get to its destination.

6   Source: http://www.ixp.net.ng (accessed October 2013).

7   Acronym for London Internet Exchange. Much of the Internet traffic going in and out of the United Kingdom is via this IXP called LINX.

Submarine Fibre to and from Africa and Intra-African Fibre Backbone

As noted above, Africa no longer relies mainly on its Internet connectivity via satellite for its main regional and international communications. So much major investments have been made on submarine and terrestrial fibre that by July 2012, Africa's total submarine cable fibre *design* capacity[8] had grown to 25.5 TBps[9] (terabytes per second), and according to some this number will triple by 2014,[10] though I believe this tripling of design capacity is more likely to happen in 2015/16 or later. The submarine cables carry terabytes of data to international destinations. The submarine cable map is looking more impressive by the year (see figure 12), depicting some serious design capacity at least being added to the continent. The dark dots on the map depict the primary "landing points" and cities for the various submarine cables on the east, west, and south of the continent. The new cable fibre capacity has alleviated some of the problems of slow and very expensive Internet access on the continent.

The next and arguably more important problem to solve right now is the issue of building out the terrestrial fibre national backbones on the continent as well as the international fibre spines, i.e., intra-African fibre backbone. The most informed data in 2013/14 suggests that less than 10 percent of this landed capacity is being utilised on the continent today, thanks to the paucity of national backbone fibre networks.

This is gradually happening. Looking at figure 12, the 17,000km ACE cable system on the West Coast of Africa went live in December 2012 and links thirteen countries; it will eventually link twenty-three countries, ranging from France to South Africa. Similarly, the

---

8 As opposed to actual "lit" capacity, which tends to be commercially sensitive information. Much fibre is still "dark," i.e., it is not "lit" or being used.

9 1 Tbps = 1 trillion bytes per second = 10^{12} bytes = 1,000 gigabytes

10 Mwangi, Michuki (2013), Developing Internet Exchange Points in Africa, in *Africa Infrastructure Investment Report 2013*, Commonwealth Business Council, March 2013, p. 161; http://www.cbcglobal.org, p. 169.

16,000-km West African Cable System (WACS) came online in May 2012, linking ten African countries to the United Kingdom with a design capacity of 5.12 TB/s funded by eleven African telecoms operators led by the MTN Group. This is much changed from 2008 when just one cable, SAT-3, served the entire African continent, to fifteen in 2013/14!

Terrestrial National and Regional Fibre IXPs in Africa Is the Real Challenge: The Kigali to Nairobi-Type Problem

Having all these terabytes per second of capacity provided by these deep sea cables is not of much use unless we have a terrestrial national fibre backbone as well as a regional backbone network to make use of all this capacity. Again Mwangi[11] of the Internet Society notes that by July 2012, terrestrial fibre had reached 732,662 km of inventory with 40 percent of the African population being within a range of 25 km to a fibre node. For decision makers and entrepreneurs, the following are key points of information and/or recommendations:

1. *Expensive and suboptimal routing of cross-border Internet and data traffic:* Mwangi raises the real problem when he notes that

   > despite the significant growth in regional infrastructure, and an increase in direct physical interconnection between African cities, most African Internet traffic (local-to-local exchange of traffic) travels through Europe and North America. (Mwangi, 2013)

   The reason, he explains, is the insufficient Internet exchange points (IXPs) on the continent of Africa. There were only twenty-four IXPs on the African continent as of February

---

11 Mwangi, Michuki (2013), Developing Internet Exchange Points in Africa, Source:, in *Africa Infrastructure Investment Report 2013*, Commonwealth Business Council, March 2013, p. 161; http://www.cbcglobal.org, p. 169.

2013, with only six on the western half of the continent, including Nigeria. This is—without putting too fine a point on it—crazily small.

Mwangi provides a real example which illustrates the lack of IXPs or peering points by reporting on tracing the path followed by an Internet data packet from Kigali (Rwanda) to Nairobi (Kenya). The data packet from Kigali goes through the terrestrial fibre optic cables that *traverse past* Nairobi. Due to lack of the required IXP between Rwanda and Kenya, this packet unbelievably uses one of the three submarine landing cables landing in Mombasa in Kenya to go to Europe. Looking at the map in figure 12, this is one of TEAMs, Seacom, or Lion2. Then this packet returns to Nairobi using the same cables.

He also provides additional evidence by noting that satellite routing policies are still predominant in submarine cable and terrestrial fibre settings, which clearly should not be so.

Even if this specific Kigali-Nairobi problem is solved by a new IXP between Rwanda and Kenya in the next couple of years, there will be many, many other Kigali-Nairobi–type problems elsewhere on the continent. Having few IXPs in Africa is a clear brake on the development of Internet in Africa, and regional regulators, governments, and policy makers must prioritise this. This suboptimal routing of cross-border traffic within Africa has significant negative financial implications. Mwangi notes that independent analysis has suggested Africa pays over US$600 million to countries with more developed infrastructure for *intra-country and inter-African traffic* exchange that is routed outside the continent. This is, frankly, crazy. Sending traffic outside the continent is extremely expensive, and this can be reduced with little human ingenuity and effort.

2. *Regional Economic Communities like ECCAS, EAC, ECOWAS, SADC[12], etc., governments, policy makers and regulators should prioritise Internet exchange points (IXPs—Africa really should aim for at least one IXP/peering point per country in the short term):* There really should be a goal of countries hosting an IXP/peering point or two in the next three to five years, i.e., heading up to one hundred peering points by 2020 and two hundred into the 2020s. Regional economic bodies, decision makers, and regulators must intervene to enable entrepreneurs to finance and build local IXP infrastructure and keep "local exchange to local exchange" African traffic truly local to Africa. This will not only improve quality of service by not routing traffic through Europe and North America, but it is more efficient—and hence takes costs out of African interconnection costs.

Keeping Africa traffic local will lead to better interconnectivity within Africa, improve regional integration, and lay good bases for setting up e-businesses across the continent. Regional regulators bodies[13] and regional ICT ministerial councils must also prioritise this area too. There is neither an IXP in Cameroon, for example, nor is there one in Brazzaville, Congo, or Senegal either, as of late 2013. Less than 50 percent of African countries currently host IXPs on the African continent. Some of this, surprisingly and arguably, has colonial

---

12 SADC is the Southern African Development Community (SADC), which consists of fifteen member states, including Angola, Botswana, DRC, Lesotho, Malawi, Mauritius, Mozambique, Namibia, Seychelles, South Africa, Swaziland, Tanzania, Zambia, and Zimbabwe. The East African Community (EAC) consists of Kenya, Uganda, Tanzania, Rwanda, and Burundi. The Economic Community of West African States (ECOWAS) consists of fifteen West African states, including Benin, Burkina Faso, Cape Verde, Ivory Coast, Gambia, Ghana, Guinea, Guinea Bissau, Liberia, Mali, Niger, Nigeria, Senegal, Sierra Leone, and Togo. The Economic Community of Central African States (ECCAS) consists of Angola, Burundi, Cameroon, Central African Republic, Chad, Congo Brazzaville, DRC, Equatorial Guinea, Gabaon, Rwanda, and Sao Tome et Principe.

13 EACO, the East African Communications Organisation, is a good example here, www.eaco.int.

and/or parent company bases: some Francophone countries preferring to use IXPs (peering points) in France and/or operators owned/controlled by foreign multinationals preferring to use IXPs in the home countries of their parent companies. This makes little sense when seen continent-wide. There is obviously a clear commercial side to IXPs. The issue is a critical mass of telecoms operators must agree to make IXPs self-sustainable.

I am aware of efforts to establish thirty national IXPs and five super IXPs (or regional IXPs) on the continent, e.g., in The Gambia with the support of the African Union Commission, but these efforts must be speeded up. It is also heartening to see some "competition" for IXPs on the east side of the continent, where small Burundi is likely to realise an IXP in early 2014 under the AXIS[14] programme funded by the EU-ITF. This is partly because most other countries in the EAC, including Kenya, Tanzania, Uganda, and Rwanda, host IXPs, and so Burundi wants to host one too. Having a situation today where 90 percent of African traffic is routed[15] through Europe or North America is just untenable. The problem is so big at state level that it is recommended that regional economic communities and governments should own this problem and address it forthwith. I am in no doubt that Africa in the 2020s needs to have two hundred or so IXPs at a minimum—Africa is a wireless continent, and intra-African traffic needs to remain local within Africa.

3. *Subscale "Clearing Houses" may want to consider merging and evolving into full-scale country and regional IXPs/peering points:* There are the makings of new IXPs within countries on the continent. I have seen the emergence of many subscale "clearing houses," like in Nigeria where, as of 2013/14, there

---

14 http://pages.au.int/axis (accessed October 2013)

15 "Bond Africa via fibre networking," editorial, *Africa Telecom & IT*, vol. 4, no. 10, October 2013, p. 4.

are about six of them. These are small, private companies who "peer" traffic between communications service providers whilst taking a cut of termination revenues. Anecdotal evidence suggests that these subscale companies are probably not making any profits as they depend on their revenues from the big mobile operators who do not currently guarantee traffic flow through these clearing houses. These operations may want to consider merging in order to reach scale, and the merged entity could evolve into *de facto* country IXPs who not only peer traffic within the country but peer traffic between countries.

4. *Regional economic communities like ECOWAS, SADC, etc., policy makers and regulators should also prioritise national and regional backbones across the continent, and this backbone distribution must be relatively even:* National and regional backbones must happen. If this backhaul and distribution infrastructure is not developed, this submarine cable capacity being landed on the continent will go underutilised. Evidence suggests that less than 5–10 percent of the submarine capacity is being used today. If this continues into the medium term, many of the private companies landing all this capacity will go bust. Then there is the issue of evenness of the distribution of the landed submarine capacity. There is so much fibre capacity laid between Lagos and Abuja[16], say, in Nigeria, or Lagos to Port Harcourt, but hardly any fibre between Abuja and Sokoto (in northern Nigeria). Whilst this is driven by economics, there is a clear role here for government to pre-empt and address some of the coordination failure (or, in the extremes, market failure, or more bluntly, refusals to grant access to competitors) which results in some routes having no distribution at all. Government and regulators can and should encourage backbone operators to buy into

---

16 Every fibre pair between these two cities has a capacity of circa 400GB/s, and many such fibre pairs exist on this route – yet all the data in Nigeria going between Lagos and Abuja can be carried in a small fraction of just a single pair.

infrastructure-sharing models by putting in place an open access model. And where there is only one or two backbone operators on some key routes, there may a strong case here for regulated pricing. Similarly where there are no takers on many routes to other parts of the country, there is a clear role here for government to be the backbone provider of last resort (if there is clear market failure), or perhaps a regulated PPP is encouraged to emerge via regulation.

Regional backbones, or intracountry backbones, are also extremely important. Liquid Telecom Group, for example, has constructed one of Africa's largest single fibre networks spanning from north of Uganda, down east Africa to Cape Town. It is the first fibre network to cross country borders covering some of Africa's fastest-growing economies capable of providing wholesale bandwidth to connect Nairobi (Kenya), Dar es Salaam (Tanzania), Kampala (Uganda), and Kigali (Rwanda). Liquid's pan-African fibre totalled 15,000 km as of 2013. If the market, as in this case, can deliver such regional infrastructure, that is good news. However, other countries may need to collectively pool their efforts in other cases.

5. *Regulators should be ready to regulate wholesale and retail fibre prices:* In the previous recommendation, the case is made for wholesale regulation, particularly for routes where there is not enough fibre competition, as in the case of Abuja-Yola. However, there is a good case for looking at wholesale prices already. This is because as each company builds out their own broadband infrastructure backbone, they are literally pricing at will, particularly in the absence of competition. What this means is Company A may be trying to recover all its costs (including profits) in five years, say, whilst Company B may choose ten years, say. In most cases, prices would be quite high. The regulator may want to provide some pricing guidelines

based on costs orientation.[17] Nevertheless, regulation should not just be for wholesale access by businesses from the cable/fibre operators who wholesale their landed submarine capacity. Arguably more important are retail competition and regulation of the retail market. That is, these companies that buy wholesale capacity must pass on the benefits of competition at the wholesale level to retail consumers and not make supernormal profits. There is already emerging evidence[18] that consumers are still paying high broadband costs even though their suppliers are getting competitive pricing from their wholesalers. Overall, it is highly likely the regulator may need to step in to set regulatory policy which both encourages innovation and backbone rollout but also which bounds pricing. Pricing is crucial to help stimulate wholesale and retail demand.

6. *International gateways (IGWs) should be liberalised from many current IGW monopolies across the continent:* I am fully conversant with the arguments for IGW monopolies across emerging markets, with particular sympathies to the argument that IGW monopolies maintain higher international outbound call prices. These high prices would discourage outbound calls—and the pricing is more to the price points and purchasing power parity (PPP) of developing nations. Therefore, inbound calls effectively generate profits since outbound calls are minimal, so inbound revenues far outweigh outbound costs.

This delta (profits) can be used—and has been used in the past—to fund networks in developing countries. The force of this argument has been progressively weakened by technology (e.g., voice over IP via Skype, Viber, Google+, etc.) and satellites

---

17 Cost orientation refers to the requirement (typically imposed by a regulator) that specific services be sold at a price that is derived from some measure of the cost to provide that service.

18 For example, "Nigeria failing to make most of undersea cable," *Africa Telecom & IT*, vol. 4, no. 10, October 2013, pp. 26–27.

(e.g., VSATs)[19] which are more plentiful now in emerging markets than a generation ago. This is now a question of the balance of risks and timing. The idea that these IGW monopolies in most countries are still true monopolies is false considering the serious competition from VSATs, VoIP, and indeed illegal bypass operators who provide poor quality but cheaper IGW services. Illegal bypass traffic sometimes accounts for more than 50 percent of incoming and outgoing international traffic in some countries like Bangladesh, 45 percent for Egypt, and 30 percent for Chad and Democratic Republic of Congo (DRC).[20] Even government officials and government ministries in some countries use competitive services for their IGW monopolies (who typically offer poor quality services), which demonstrate amply the mockery of the current situation. More than on balance, the benefits of liberalising IGWs to competition far outweigh the benefits of maintaining monopolies, as liberalisation increases competition, lowers prices, improves reliability/quality, and drives up volumes and investment, which in turn leads to higher tax receipts and higher GDP. One significant plausible explanation to the paucity of IXPs on the continent resulting in Kigali-Nairobi–type problems (along with the $600 million outflow from Africa) is because of the culture of monopoly IGWs on the continent who are not subject to competition. On the timing question, I believe it must be now. Monopoly IGWs force competitors today to also charge higher prices for poor services. Policy makers and regulators must face up to this lost cause of monopoly IGWs. I recommend the commission of a business case over five years, and I believe the answer will be unequivocal.

7. *Chief information officers, ICT directors, and state/provincial authorities should lobby their ministers, national policy*

---

19 Acronym for very small aperture satellite dishes technologies (VSATs).

20 As quoted in "Gateway Liberalisation: Stimulating Economic Growth," GSM Association, http://www.gsma.com/publicpolicy/wp-content/uploads/2012/03/gatewayliberalisation.pdf (accessed September 2013).

makers, and regulators: More pressure from local authorities on national policy makers and regulators is recommended here to ensure more IXPs evolve on the continent even faster and that the national fibre backbones within countries are hastened. They should see these IXPs and national fibre spine backbones as critical national infrastructure.

8. *Emerging unregulated monopolies or duopolies of intracountry fibre backbone providers must be preempted*: Once fibre is landed into a country, this "capacity" has to be distributed via national backbones within the country as mentioned above. In several countries, the governments take responsibility for this. In others, there is a creeping and emerging risk where one or two operators take the lead to build the intracountry national backbone (or parts of it) with the acquiescence of government authorities whilst bypassing the relevant regulators. The operators make the usual arguments that they are taking risks and that these "backbones" would benefit the countries concerned. Whilst this may be true, without very clearly agreed upon rules up front on access to these backbones, this amounts in effect to the emergence of monopolies or duopolies that would be nightmares to regulate. Regulating fixed behemoths is very hard and sucks so much regulator resources who could be gainfully employed on other important projects. Catch these behemoths on their way up is the simple advice here.

Investing in Fixed or Wired Broadband Infrastructure

"Broadband is the oxygen of the digital revolution."
—Microsoft

9. *Government policy makers, regulators, and ministers must be clear what their plans and policies for wired broadband are. Given broadband is the undisputed oxygen of the digital economy, no country or significant state can live without one. And the answer is surely not a complete reliance on mobile*

broadband. The following are some key recommended con-siderations relating to investing in fixed: Though fibre to the home (FTTH) is a nonstarter in most parts of Africa for economic and a host of other reasons,[21] a fibre-to-the-curb (FTTC) strategy emphasising areas like business parks, shopping centres, universities, government offices, major TMT hubs, etc., must be sensible. I see very little evidence of clear plans which are being implemented for fixed broadband on the continent. Africa has the lowest fixed-line penetration rates in the world. Beyond Tunisia, South Africa, Egypt, Morocco, Botswana, and Namibia, fixed-line teledensity (i.e., the number of fixed lines as a percentage of the population) is mostly below a woeful 3 percent! Whilst some of this can be explained by higher GDP per capita levels in the above countries, the rest of Africa can be explained by the appalling way in which fixed line incumbents were run on the continent—and if decision makers want to see the outcomes which accrue from monopolies, no competition, unliberalised sectors, etc., they should look no further than many of these original fixed line incumbents on the continent, including Onatel (Burkina Faso), CamTel (Cameroon), TDM (Mozambique), Telecom Namibia, Nitel (Nigeria), Telkom (South Africa), TelOne (Zimbabwe), and so on. When compared to what is happening with mobile, it is truly a salutary lesson for policy makers on the African continent.

As the next section highlights, mobile broadband can only carry so much "bits" thanks to the limitations of radio channels and Shannon's law.[22] Fixed broadband penetration rates on the

---

21 Unplanned streets and roads, lack of developed sewage systems which can provide ducts infrastructure, lack of duck and pole infrastructure, etc.

22 Claude Shannon, a mathematical genius, demonstrated conclusively in the 1940s that there is a theoretical maximum amount of information carried by a communications system based upon the physical laws of physics, specifically of thermodynamics. In plain English, radio airwaves have a finite capacity.

continent needed for SMEs are just appalling. Addressing this woeful broadband deficit is a long-term issue.

This "investing in broadband infrastructure" is one Dr. Hamadoun Toure, the Malian current secretary-general of the International Telecommunications Union (ITU), also shares.[23] Agreeing that it should be a long-term focus for governments, Toure, however, notes the complex challenge in investing in broadband which governments, entrepreneurs, and regulators on the continent should be aware of.

	Order of Costs	Payback period	Examples
Passive layer	70–80% of network costs	15 years	Trenches, ducts, and dark fibre
Active infra-structure layer	20–30% of network costs	7-year rate of return	Electronic equipment, OSS, and BSS
Service layer	N/A	A few months to 3 years	Content, services, and applications

Figure 13—Investing In Different Network Layers for
Broadband Infrastructure (Toure, 2013)[24]

Toure rightly notes, as shown in figure 13, that a broadband network consists of three distinct layers with very different characteristics from a cost and return on investment perspective. The passive layer can account for up to 80 percent of the

23 Toure, Hamadoun (2013), Investing in Broadband Infrastructure, in *Africa Infrastructure Investment Report 2013*, Commonwealth Business Council, March 2013, p. 164; http://www.cbcglobal.org, p. 169.
24 Ibid.

costs, but has a very long payback period of approximately fifteen years. The active layer, where the intelligence resides, has a five- to seven-year payback period, whilst the service layer's payback period is even shorter at a maximum of three years.

Governments and policy makers should therefore note the different investment requirements and hence different types of investors required of all three layers. Governments or states co-financing with long-term private investors on a PPP basis of the passive layer would make much sense, market conditions permitting. However, as noted earlier, regulation for competition and open access of this passive layer is absolutely essential. The active infrastructure layer, where much of this equipment here is shared, will require different investment thinking. For example, one "dominant" player may invest in all this equipment but get regulated returns and access fees set by the regulator for its competitors to use these assets. Such a model is in operation in the United Kingdom with BT Openreach.[25] The service layer is clearly in the gift of all the competitors at the layer.

Toure also correctly notes that a fixed broadband strategy for a country may need to segment the country into Tier 1, Tier 2, and Tier 3, etc., regions. Tier 1, in urban areas with high population densities, may be invested in by private companies and may be largely optical fibre-based deployments. Tier 2 may be a combination of some microwave and some fibre. Tier 3 "no broadband" areas may be TV white spaces or satellite areas. Either way, each country needs a clearly articulated, investable, and executable broadband plan.

---

25 BT Openreach is a fully regulated part of former state telecommunications operator BT plc in the United Kingdom. Ofcom regulates an equality of access regime as well as wholesale access pricing regime such that its retail BT plc's retail arm, BT Retail, is charged the same prices as charged to BT Retail's broadband competitors.

2.1.2 Wireless and Satellite Communications Activities

Whereas wired/fixed activities refer to services provided over communications networks which serve *fixed* locations, *wireless and satellite services* can be used whilst on the move.

Using the joint themes of geography and anatomy, wireless networks similarly consist of a wireless access network, also called the radio access network (RAN), a fixed core network also connected to other networks (e.g., as in figure 14, below), the Internet, other operators' networks, international gateways, etc. The core network for wireless has some technical differences to that described earlier for wired networks. It is called the mobile switching centre (MSC), that core of the network that sets up and handles calls made over the network, but we can leave such details out.

The real difference between wireless networks and wired networks really resides in the RAN. And the RAN specifically allows a scenario where, instead of an individual being tied to a fixed location, the RAN is able to facilitate *anyone* to access *anything* (i.e., any network service) using a mobile handset/device from *anywhere*, at *any time*.

Wireless Cellular Radio Access Network (RAN)

A cellular or mobile network typically has land- and radio-based parts. It consists of the following, as figure 14 illustrates:

- mobile device (MDs): e.g., mobile phones, smartphones, or other devices, such as cars
- base station equipment (BST), specifically a transceiver or a transmitter/receiver for transmitting/receiving radio signals over various radio interfaces technologies called 2G, 2.5G, 3G, and 4G. We can also ignore the technical details here, but suffice to say 4G can carry more data than 3G, and 3G can carry more voice and data than 2G, etc. There are also typically thousands of base station sites on a single operator's

network across a country. Each base station roughly looks like figure 15.

- core network: this is as already described above
- public switch telephone network (PSTN), not shown in figure 14—the land-based part of the network. Unlike in African countries where there are few PSTN, Western countries have them, and many calls originated on wireless networks get terminated on a fixed PSTN network.[26]

RADIO ACCESS NETWORKS

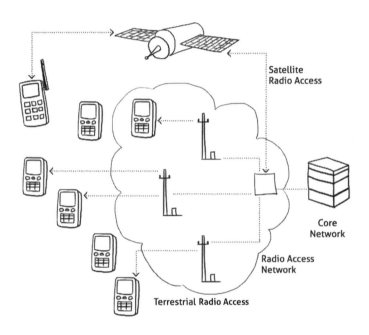

Figure 14: Wireless and Satellite Radio Access Networks

A specific region is divided up into cells, with each cell having a BST that transmits and receives data via radio links to/from mobile

---

26 This is a classic case of using a mobile phone to call a fixed home phone line in the wired network described earlier on page XX.

devices within that cell. Several BSTs are linked to a base station controller (BSC), whilst a group of BSCs are linked into a core MSC network via *microwave* or fibre lines. The MSC is connected to the PSTN, which does the switching of the voice calls to other mobile devices or to land-based telephones. To make the most use of the scarcest mobile resource—frequency spectrum—nonadjacent cells reuse the same frequencies.

Do not worry if you do not fully understand the above. The reason for covering some of these is to draw out some key differences between wired and wireless networks which have implications to decision makers, entrepreneurs, and others. They include:

- Wireless involves a very challenging access medium— intangible radio channels as opposed to tangible and fixed optical fibre, copper, or coaxial on wired.
- This radio channel is shared between many users, so interference is a big issue to contend with. More so, the radio channels are also shared amongst different radio technologies such as 2G, 3G, or 4G. Radio waves are also subject to obstruction from objects in the environment, such as trees, buildings, and rain, leading to effects like fading, shadowing, and multipath effects.[27] Radio channels are indeed challenging.
- Even harder, users roam or move about—sometimes at low speeds (i.e., walking) and sometimes at high speeds (as in cars, trains, or planes). The wireless network must be able to find the users and deliver their calls, texts and e-mails., and whilst users are moving, calls must be maintained.

---

27 Multipath refers to receiving the same message from different directions or paths because the signals have bounced off walls of buildings, etc.

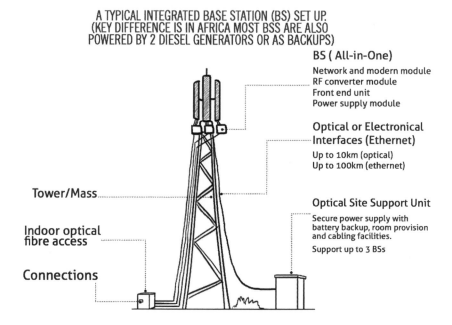

Figure 15: A Typical Integrated Base Station (BS) Setup
(the key difference is that in Africa most BSs are also powered by
two diesel generators or as backups)

Key lessons here for decision makers, entrepreneurs, industry players, etc., include the following:

10. *Spectrum is scarce and crucial and hence must be licensed from a state authority, typically the regulator*: Without *clean* access to the radio channels or radio airwaves (or spectrum), there is no wireless business—it's as simple as that. If that spectrum is being used by someone else at that location, then you cannot use it there too, certainly not at the same time. Spectrum is also scarce: there is not much of it or of the right type to go around. This is a core reason why spectrum is licensed and is usually awarded competitively through auctions. Spectrum is fought over keenly.

11. *RAN networks are expensive to set up and run, therefore networks can only go as far as they make monies*: In Africa, a typical average costs for setting up every RAN base station is US$130,000 as of June 2013, with a monthly operational expenditure on the continent of roughly US$4,000. If you consider the average revenue per user (ARPU) on the continent is between five and ten dollars a month, you need more than four hundred to eight hundred users *just* to cover the operating costs of each base station, yet alone covering the costs of the head office, core network (MSC), international interconnections, marketing, etc. With such costs, you can understand why operators do not venture into covering rural areas where the revenues are nonexistent, and they tread with care into semirural areas. This is the reason why you may not have coverage where you think you should—and even where you do, the capacity may not be enough, and you suffer dropped calls. For this reason as well, despite competition worries, regulators are increasingly allowing cellular operators to share passive base station infrastructure to share costs and reduce their individual costs burdens. Indeed, active sharing of antenna and other active elements should be considered too subject to regulatory oversight.

12. *Wireless networks cannot fully exist without wired networks, and indeed, they have to interconnect with so many other networks*: Even though they are frequently called "mobile networks," there is nothing mobile about them. Wireless networks are *fixed* at the sites of the base stations. It is the users that are *mobile*. That is why wireless networks is a more apt term. They also have to interconnect on national fibre backbones (at gateways or at IXPs) and with PSTN networks; with international gateways; with other wireless operators; and with content/services networks. To interconnect is therefore one of the biggest headaches in networks businesses and fraught with much legal

and technical haggling. Just one look at an interconnect agreement should confirm this. However, decision makers must be aware of the importance of interconnect issues.

13. *As networks' capacities get eaten up by more subscribers and their increasing usage levels, more spectrum will need to be brought onto mobile markets in the future to cope with the capacity growth*: Since radio channels are shared, at some stage there will be no more capacity. As their capacity gets eaten up, the operator has a few options:

   a. The operator may cell split, i.e., redesign their networks to make their cells smaller and reuse their frequencies in more places, thereby increasing capacity.
   b. They may try and off-load data traffic from their networks onto Wi-Fi.
   c. They may use smaller cell technologies like femtocells.
   d. They may use better and improved technology radio channel air interfaces like 3G, 3.5G, and 4G, and, in the future, 5G.
   e. And if they have done these all and still have problems meeting their demand growth, they will just have to acquire more spectrum, typically via competitive auctions. This is why there is likely to be a new round of spectrum releases or auctions on the continent in the 2015–2017 timescales, if not earlier in some countries.

14. *Mobile Internet and/or mobile data is coming. The risks to creating a world of haves and have-nots are very high across the continent; it feels almost inevitable:* The question is, what are the policy makers, regulators, and industry players proposing to do to preempt this suboptimal looming outcome?

15. *Drawing from the latter, regulators and government policy makers must make clear plans to release more spectrums as early as 2015, particularly 4G spectrum for mobile Internet. They must clarify their plans generally for UHF spectrum on*

the continent (470–862 MHz): Releasing spectrum goes beyond the release process—I know this firsthand. The regulator must first conduct an in-depth set of analyses of the competitive structure to the market they would like to see post the release (or auction) and use this in the design of the rules of the spectrum release or spectrum auction. They would need to start thinking about the coverage versus capacity question and decide whether they want to consider coverage obligations for 4G in at least one of the licenses to be issued at a forthcoming release or auction. The UK regulator Ofcom did such a competitive market analysis before in its auction. The regulator and/or government may want to consider new entrants. How proportionate would be the different proposals within the different contexts of different African and emerging economies? These are difficult questions for even the best regulators and policy makers in the world, yet alone resources-constrained African ones. It takes about one to two good years to prepare for such complex auctions. For 2015/16 auctions, the work should start now or should have started already.

16. *Profitability in telecommunications is declining/will decline due to competition, expanding coverage to underserved areas, and the increasing dominance of data over the next decade. Policy makers should look to design and implement policies (taxes, custom tariffs on telecommunications good and services, etc.) which continue to encourage continued growth of this subsector, along with technology and media subsectors too:* This to some degree goes with a maturing subsector, but given this industry needs to invest even more in networks, spectrum, and data, there is a strong case for policy makers and decision makers *not* to inadvertently kill the goose that lays the golden egg. Policies to drive continued growth and investment in this sector across the continent are absolutely needed.

17. *Improve on what are important "hygiene issues" to the industry:* Other hygiene (logistical) factors also need to be looked at.

For example, governments should realise that it is not proportionate to expect private companies to be able to make investments and deploy base stations in parts of the country where the government itself has not built any roads, though there may be major population centres there. How do they expect these companies to transport equipment to set up mobile base stations in these places? Given that there is presumably no electricity in these areas, how do companies regularly transport diesel to base stations powered by diesel generators? I noted such "hygiene" issues to an African minister once and received a shrug-of-the-shoulder, noncommittal response.

Satellite Wireless Access Network

Now that we have described cellular networks, satellite access networks may sound complicated because there are expensive satellites orbiting in the skies.

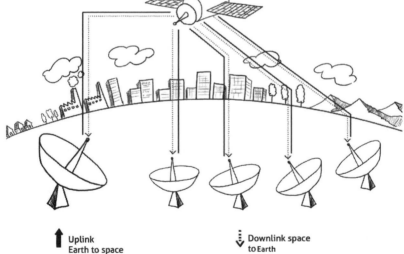

A TYPICAL FIXED SATELLITE SERVICE SETUP

Uplink
Earth to space

Downlink space
to Earth

Figure 16: A Typical Fixed Satellite Service Setup

However, one view of satellite network is essentially a wireless network whose RAN consists of radio base stations orbiting the earth instead of being fixed on the ground like the base station in figure 14. Some satellite phones, for example, use satellites in geostationary orbit, which are meant to stay in the same position. Three of four of such satellites sitting at altitudes of 35,000 km and weighing five tons each are spatially positioned to provide global coverage all over the earth. Satellites have been relied upon in Africa for too long now, and the new submarine capacity is providing far more capacity, more cheaply.

A fixed satellite service (FSS) is a satellite system where the earth station is at a specified fixed point, e.g., the Eurobird 2 satellite is located at coordinates of 25.5 east, providing ninety-six TV, twenty-four radio, and one data channel. It could also be at any fixed point within a specified area. For traditional point-to-point intercontinental data, the two Earth stations would be at known fixed locations.

Fixed satellite systems are used to deliver one-way and two-way services, including providing international data connectivity from Africa and elsewhere into the Internet.

Mobile satellite service (MSS) is provided between *mobile* Earth stations on the ground and one or more space stations. An example of an MSS application is communication to ships or handheld satellite telephones. It is defined by the ITU as a radio communication service between

- mobile Earth stations and one or more space stations,
- between space stations used by this service, or
- between mobile Earth stations by means of one or more space stations.

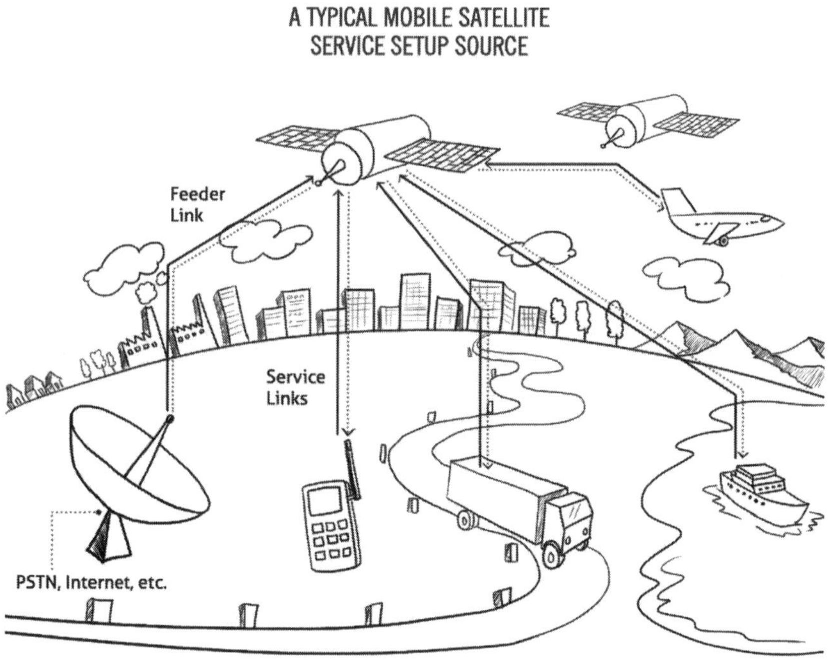

Figure 17: A Typical Mobile Satellite Service Setup

Typical MSS applications are very diverse and include low data rate applications (e.g., asset tracking, like for ships, particularly to remote locations).

There are other types of satellite services, like earth exploration satellite service (EESS), used for meteorological services, and global navigation satellite services (GNSS), used for vehicle satellite navigation, etc.

Key messages here for decisions makers on satellite communications include the following:

- *Satellite spectrum is scarce, extremely competitive, and needs an international regulator*: Playing the satellite game is not for the fainthearted; it is an extremely expensive and risky business. Launching a satellite costs dozens to hundreds of millions of dollars. The ITU is the holder and final arbiter of all orbital slot quarrels between all the world's satellite operators.

- *Satellite communications is very expensive*: It costs almost one hundred million dollars to successfully launch one or a couple of satellites. It is no wonder they are so expensive.
- *Even with the migration of capacity from expensive FSS satellites to submarine fibre across Africa, it is still important for satellites to be considered as full-coverage fillers or as backup for disaster recovery purposes*: As our communications systems move to become *de facto* critical national infrastructure, satellite still has a role to play in the communications ecosystem. Terrestrial networks will never cover 100 percent of the *population* in most countries, yet alone 100 percent of the *geographies*. FSS satellite networks are much better placed to go where terrestrial networks cannot plausibly commercially go. MSS's role in tracking valuable assets (e.g., trucks carrying expensive goods or ships navigating close to the pirate-infested Somalian waters) are quite clear to see.

2.1.3 Other Telecommunications Activities

There are numerous other telecommunication activities beyond wired, wireless, and satellite telecommunication activities on the African continent which are only just mentioned. They employ and will be employing thousands of people and even more in the future. This is not meant to be exhaustive, rather to show the diversity of the telecoms subsector.

Most of the below activities do not need the extensive descriptions given above for the activities for wired and wireless telecommunications—so brief descriptions only will do for some of them. For others, their relevance in the African economies is more limited or not at all. For some, they are most relevant for emerging economies. Several are described in some more detail. It must be re-emphasised up front that these activities are by no means exhaustive.

- *Regulatory activities*: There is a chapter of this volume dedicated to regulation (Chapter 11), but hopefully you are beginning to concur with the observations in this chapter that regulation is a constant presence in any well-functioning telecommunications sector. Hopefully, as we expound on this later, some (students) reading this volume may choose careers in telecommunications regulation; policy makers on the continent should understand more why they should let regulation loose to professionals by creating true independent regulators, and the industrialists get to see regulators are there for the countries' consumers and citizens. Suffice to say for now that TMT in Africa and *some* emerging market countries need very strong regulatory skills and activities, many of which are not on the continent or in these countries. Ministers, policy makers, and decision makers should prioritise strengthening of their regulators. The multiplier effect of good and predictable regulation is incalculable. I have seen this firsthand. Africa arguably needs two or three true centres of excellence to train their regulators, and not necessarily only TMT-specific ones, as many of the skills are transferable across regulators. This is something ministers and policy makers should consider.

- *Device and equipment manufacturing activities*: Device manufacturing in the main does not happen and is unlikely to happen on the African continent. This is frankly not only because the skills required are very complex and the costs of setting up manufacturing plants are extremely high. It's more because manufacturing is linked ownership of patent rights, and the latter are linked to first-class primary research and development activities which do not happen on the African continent. Furthermore, the world needs hubs where manufacturing happens, and these hubs have now mostly emerged in the Far East, in China (Huawei, ZTE, etc.), Korea (Samsung, LG, etc.), Japan (Sony, Panasonic, etc.), Singapore, etc. Even American-owned Apple iPhones are manufactured in China.

So, most manufacturing already happens in some emerging markets, like India and China. It is arguable in this specific context of TMT whether these two countries, for example, should be classified as emerging market countries. However, it does not mean such large-scale manufacturing will never happen in Africa in the medium to long term. Small-scale manufacturing will happen on the continent, particularly in areas where Africa has those specific needs and where we can best specify the requirements. Money-transfer terminals for money transfers may best be specified and manufactured on the continent, or *not*. Entrepreneurs should look out for such opportunities to start building manufacturing bases on the African continent, and policy makers should ensure such manufacturing activities are given tax breaks and other "leg ups."

- *Silicon chip design activities*: As per device and equipment manufacturing, not much of this activity will happen on the African continent in the short to medium term, frankly for the next fifteen years, say. I know several Africans who hold essential patents working with key Chinese and Japanese companies, and they will tell you the critical mass of unique skills that need to be assembled to carry out silicon chip design activities on the African continent are considerable.

- *Telecommunications trade associations*: Trade associations play an important role in the TMT sector. They are typically founded and funded by industry, and they engage in public relations activities, such as advertising, lobbying, publishing, and education. Their real main foci are in collaboration between companies and often in standardisation. They also run conferences and networking events and offer classes. Many of them are nonprofit. Trade associations should and will emerge on the African continent. Some already exist today, but they could be more professionally run.

- *Tower company activities*: There are already several tower companies operating on the continent, including Eaton

Towers,[28] Helios Towers,[29] and IHS.[30] These companies have a comparative advantage in that they concentrate solely on managing the passive sites' assets wherein they find and build the base station sites which are occupied by operators such as MTN, Vodacom, Orange, Bharti, and others. They are currently (as in 2013/14) small scale in the sense that most of them own far fewer sites than the mobile operators at the moment. For example, Helios Towers Nigeria today owns owns or operates circa 1,300 base station sites compared to MTN's 8,000+ sites in Nigeria.[31] This sector is bound to grow.

- *Repair of telecommunications equipment activities*: This is an important, albeit specialised, area of activity. At the moment many wired and wireless telecommunication organisations on the continent rely on other electronic repairers outside the country, which is a disadvantage to them in the following: turnaround time, fluctuating exchange rate, and high costs of repairs. I have advised one organization (in the past) on the continent on a strategy to set up a fully-fledged electronic repair centre for the organisation. Once set up, the established entity will be responsible for all the repairs for all transmission, switching, access systems, and customer premises equipment as well as repairs for other fixed telecommunications equipment. To take costs out as well as improve turnaround times, most of the repairs of telecommunications should occur on the continent.

- *Telecommunications accounting activities*: Telecommunications is already a big sector on the continent, and the emergence of accountants on the continent with sector knowledge of telecommunications is important. Telecommunications education institutions and business schools on the continent must introduce and train more telecoms-savvy accountants.

---

28 www.eatontowers.com

29 www.heliostowersafrica.com

30 www.ihstowers.com

31 As of July 2013. Source: personal communication.

- *Telecoms gaming activities*: As operators seek further ways to drive up their ARPUs, there will be opportunities for entrepreneurs to write African-oriented games, apps, etc., for these operators.
- *Mobile advertising activities*: Mobile advertising is emerging as a key activity in the telecommunications sector. A mobile device is a *personal* device and offers opportunities for bulk, targeted SMS (i.e., texts) and value-added services to the owner. Entrepreneurs will work with operators for mutual benefits in this area of mobile advertising activities.
- *Telecommunications consultancy activities*: This is already a relatively big sector on the continent, which should and will become so much bigger. You can possibly already attest to the value *good* consultants can add, as this is quite a complicated sector. TMT is hardly that established in Africa and some emerging market countries. Therefore, *ipso facto*, it needs advice from outside the continent on a whole host of areas.
- *Mobile money activities*: This is covered later in chapter 12 but suffice to note here that only 20–25 percent of Africans had bank accounts as of June 2013, and telecommunications operators have been filling the gap in providing some modicum of banking type services to the 75 percent unbanked on the continent. This is a true area of African innovation. Nowhere in the TMT sector on the continent is the aphorism "necessity is the mother of invention" more true than with mobile money. Africa must truly capitalise on this and continue world leadership in this area.
- *Telecommunication processes activities*: Telecommunications has dozens of unique processes in addition to other generic ones, and process consultants can add much value here too. Figure 18 depicts the processes in summary. In these processes there are opportunities for entrepreneurs to improve on their efficiency with many of the operators on the continent via automation, process redesign, outsourcing, etc.

TELECOMMUNICATIONS BUSINESS
PROCESSES SOURCE

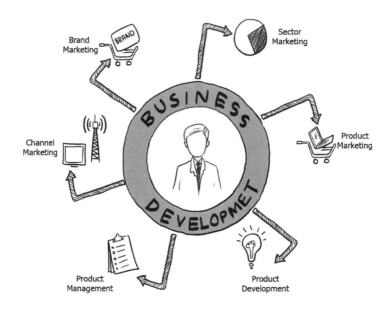

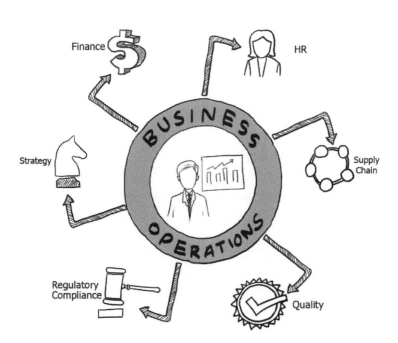

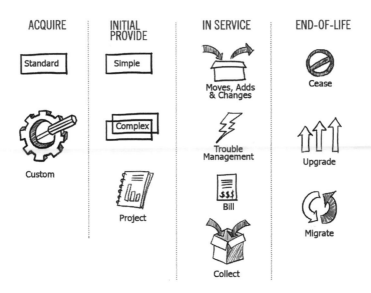

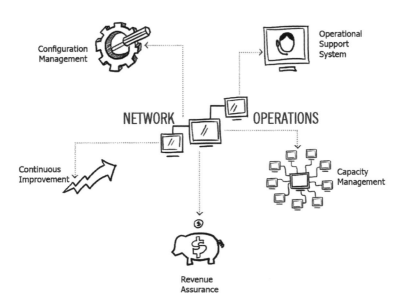

Figure 18—Telecommunications Business Processes
(Source: adapted from Telecoms Academy, Informa Telecoms & Media)

2.2 The Geography, Anatomy, and Lessons for the Technology Subsector

Remember (after many pages of exploring the telecommunications subsector) that the key goals of this geography/anatomy chapter (and hence this technology subsector too) are

- to be clear what these subsectors *entail*,
- to explore if they are developed to their potential in Africa and other emerging markets,
- draw from the developed markets, and
- to elicit key lessons to consider as the African and emerging market TMT sectors are designed or redesigned, in some cases from close to nought.

We have just completed the tour of the telecommunications sector—and we delved into its geography and anatomy (as necessary) to highlight some key lessons towards getting the foundations right for African TMT. We now turn to the technology and media subsectors.

The technology and media subsectors on the African continent, as we highlighted in chapter 1, are much less mature in comparison to the telecommunications subsector. Indeed, anecdotal ratios of current revenue earned from the Big 4 consulting firms on the continent suggest a 70: 20:10 percent revenue ratio for telecommunications, technology, and media, respectively.[32]

However, as chapter 1 demonstrated in terms of the comparison with the London TMT sector, 47 percent of the jobs in the London TMT are classified as media jobs, 42 percent as technology, and only 9 percent being for telecommunications. Relating the 70:20:10 ratios with the London TMT jobs ratio clearly demonstrates the "upside" there still is in terms of maturity of the technology and media subsectors on the African continent. Even more promising

---

32 Personal communications with partners with three of the four African Big 4 firms: Deloitte, PwC, EY, and KPMG.

is the fact that this is *not* a zero-sum game. The size of the three subsectors on the African continent are bound to grow—although it is to be expected that the rate of growth of the technology and media subsectors should be higher, as they are starting from a very low base.

Before we return to figure 9 at the beginning of this chapter, it is worth making the obvious point that technology and ICT primarily improve productivity and increase efficiency, not only in TMT but across most other sectors. You just have to see and admire how Amazon and eBay have used technology to reduce costs, improve choice, and increase efficiency and productivity in the retailing sector for books and a whole range of other commodities. Those who fly these days typically have to print their own e-tickets or just use their smartphones for access. This is all enabled by technology.

Technology at its best reduces transaction costs, bypasses the unnecessary middlemen, encourages innovation, and fosters creativity. One of the biggest frustrations I see (by a mile) on the African continent are ministers and decision makers who truly have little or no idea about how much technology is able to change the face of our economies. For this reason, it is important and illustrative to include figure 19, which shows London's ICT contributions to just the top twenty sectors. Overall, Deloitte (quoting an EU consortium) notes that ICT Technology contributes around 5 percent of UK economic output by making sectors more productive and efficient, or the equivalent of £65 billion. Decision makers on the continent looking at figure 19 must see for themselves the opportunity cost to the economy they inflict when not setting the technology sector up for success. Practically all of the sectors and more in figure 19 are ripe for a true revolution if technology is developed and left free to reign on them. This should reinforce all the work needed to improve on the wired and wireless infrastructure on the continent which has been described earlier on in this chapter. Technology contributing to all these sectors means jobs for a significant number of the tens of thousands of students graduating from African universities every year.

Figure 19—Total Broad London Gross Value Add (GVA)

from London ICT, 2010 (£m)

(Source: adapted from Deloitte)[33]

Technology typically comes in the form of hardware and software. It must also be pointed out that much technology hardware and software platforms needed on the continent have been developed elsewhere. However, there will be lots of customisation activities of these technology platforms back on the continent of Africa or in other emerging market countries. For example, there are many technology platforms that cover most of the telecommunication processes shown

---

33 *London—Enabling a World Leading Digital Hub*, Deloitte, July 2013, www. deloitte.com, p. 28.

in figure 18, but they typically must be customised to the realities of the local operators on the ground on the African continent. In some cases, local entrepreneurs do develop successful but much cheaper competing solutions—and this must be encouraged.

Returning to figure 9 at the beginning of this chapter, we note the many activities for the technology subsector which should in due course evolve *at scale* on the continent, namely:

- *Web portals*: A portal is a website that collates diverse information in a uniform way. There is so much information on the African continent waiting to be collated and presented uniformly. Therefore, with the right broadband Internet infrastructure within various countries on the continent, literally tens of thousands of web portals will emerge for retailers, SMEs, SOHOs,[34] newspapers, personal portals, state portals, cultural portals, alumni portals, entertainment portals—the list is endless. These all creates jobs.

- *Data processing and hosting activities*: All the tens of thousands of portals and other assorted websites of the next decade will all have to be hosted. Like elsewhere, the data traffic from digitising movies, songs, etc., all need to be processed, indexed, catalogued, and monetised.

- *Cloud and big data computing activities*: There is a strong case to make that—on a continent which so far relies so much on mobile operators mainly for its data needs—most Africans may have to hold most of their data in the cloud. Cloud computing, in essence, lets you run your applications (e.g., spreadsheets, word processing packages, drawing packages, etc.) off the web, i.e., somewhere in the "cloud" of other computers and servers on web, without having to hold them locally on a local computer, which Africans may not be able to afford. Cloud computing could, and many fellow computer scientists say "would," change the face of computing as we know it over the

---

34 Small offices and home offices are one- or two-person organisations or sole proprietorships.

next couple of decades, and if it does, Africa is likely to be at the vanguard of it due to cloud computing's promised cheaper economic business model. We discuss cloud and big data computing in the last chapter.

- *Computer consulting activities*: Like with telecommunications consultancy activities, this is also a relatively sizeable sector on the continent which should see double digit growth rates for many years over—decades if we get the ICT infrastructure and electricity/power issues right.

- *Computer programming activities*: African computer programmers would emerge, along with significant African software firms. Some of the most exciting and promising apps I have seen recently are being programmed in Africa.

- *Technology wholesale*: As noted earlier, most hardware and software technology platforms have been developed outside Africa already and can therefore be wholesaled on the continent, along with some customisations as necessary by local professionals.

- *Technology manufacturing and research activities*: It is important Africa does *not* see primary technology manufacturing and research as something they must always import. There are many areas where the problem at hand is so "African" that Africans are best placed to research it and follow up with the necessary manufacturing and productization if necessary. The whole area of mobile money transfers was literally invented in Africa. The technology applications which will be developed to provide financial and banking services to the 75percent of the African unbanked will be preferably researched, specified, and developed on the African continent. The hardware terminals and the software technologies to guarantee authentication of clients to ensure they are who they say they are in order to retrieve monies—it may be through biometric technology—will have to be designed and manufactured locally.

- *Repair of computers, peripherals, and computer equipment activities*: Some of these are already happening on the continent, but there is much skilling up (or training) (training) to do, and it needs to be more professional.
- *Home working (telecommuting):* This is a unique category included here. One just has to see the traffic issues we have on all the major cities on the continent, with no mass transit transportation systems in sight, to wonder whether technology would not play a part sooner than later in order to let employees work from home on the continent. This would drive up so much productivity. The traffic jams you see in many of our capital cities in Africa should be seen for what they truly are—inefficiency and poor productivity which home working would alleviate.
- *Other IT and computer activities*: This is just a catch-all category of activities, including geographical information systems and technology contributions to a range of other sectors, as shown in figure 19.

2.3 The Geography, Anatomy, and Lessons for the Media Subsector

The media sector in much of the African continent is moribund, arguably in the Dark Ages relative to the developed media sectors. You will see why I make such a strong assertion in a page or two. However, it could—and would—be so much different in a short space of time, like a decade.

The basic anatomy of the media sector in Africa today consists of radio broadcasting, TV broadcasting, and newspapers. I do not describe these subsectors individually here, as I cover them in some detail (along with their history) in chapter 8. Rather, this old traditional broadcasting-led media in Africa is described in the context of what is going on around it, which will forever change both it and the shape of media in Africa and elsewhere over the next decade or two.

UNILEVER, ESPN, MINDSHARE MEDIA 2015 SCENARIO MATRIX
SOURCE: UNILEVER

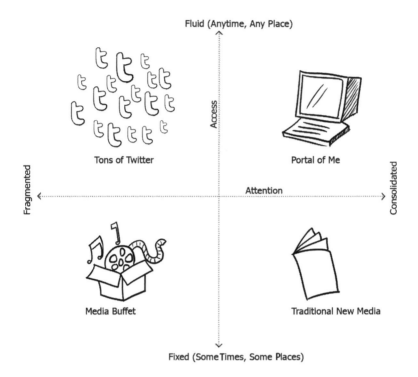

Figure 20—Unilever, ESPN, Mindshare Media 2015 Scenario Matrix
(Source: adapted from Unilever)[35]

The geography (and anatomy too) of the media sector in developed economies is in a period of evolutionary-to-revolutionary change. Google is arguably the biggest and most well-known part of the world media geography today, yet this company did not exist twenty years ago. Google UK—from nowhere ten years ago—overtook (in terms of advertising income) the biggest independent TV broadcaster in the United Kingdom back in 2007/08. This is a revolution. Much of the media sector is built on advertising revenues, and so any description

---

35 "Media 2015—The Future of Media, A Report from The Futures Company," www.unileverusa.com/Images/FOM_Final_09_tcm23-206938.pdf   (accessed September 2013).

of this sector must major on advertising. Another case in point is *social media*, which is still less than ten years old. However, it is clearly a key part of the geography *today* in Western markets (and even in pockets in some African markets too), as it has a major impact on the media scene. Clearly, the impact is much less in Africa, due to access problems and more.

Social media is essentially a form of communication amongst people who create, share, and exchange information in virtual communities. They do it in many guises: blogs, wiki, social networks, podcasts, photographs, videos, etc. The impact that social media is having on the media sector has still to fully "play out," and established advertisers and broadcasters are very concerned. Why? Simply, this is because social media fragments consumers' attention away from other traditional media. Fragmentation means it is harder for advertisers reach who they want, both efficiently and cost effectively. If most teenagers spend most of their "media" time on Twitter, Facebook, and YouTube, advertisers would be wasting their valuable advertising dollars placing expensive adverts on television, which is not that widespread on the African continent anyway. To put this point in context, the chief financial officer of Facebook announced that Facebook users spend 20 billion minutes a day on Facebook as of June 2013,[36] and Facebook is likely to make more than US$2 billion in mobile advertising in 2013 alone. Given he also announced that there were 819 million active monthly users, this suggests that users spend on average twenty-five minutes *per day* on Facebook. The real addicts are no doubt spending much more than this. Your son or daughter, niece or nephew, brother or sister may likely be one of these Facebook addicts (subject to Internet access) if not you yourself! And if that is where they are, that is where the advertisers will go to seek them out! Another case in point—if Wayne Rooney[37] has six million Twitter followers, as he does, this makes for an extremely valuable following from an advertiser's perspective. "Followers" are by definition more keen (or likely) to read

---

36 "Facebook shares up 18% on ads boost," BBC News, www.bbc.co.uk, July 25, 2013 (accessed August 2013).

37 Wayne Rooney is an English international footballer with Manchester United, as of October 2013.

more avidly the tweets from those they are following. An advertiser can get to six million followers more easily by getting Mr. Rooney to tweet to his followers!

In short, much of the user generated content (UGC) in vogue today—on YouTube, Facebook, Twitter, Google+, Skype, etc., mostly did not exist a decade to fifteen years ago. Fifteen years ago, consumers consumed content that the traditional media and big studios or TV/radio producers generated. Not anymore—people consume content today, even in Africa, in so many different ways today. Some consume more radio content, some TV, some mainly Internet, some mainly music, whilst others play games. In the African context, some watch mainly locally produced video content, e.g., Nollywood video content is quite popular in west Africa.

So describing the geography of the media sector—beyond the traditional colonial media in Africa of radio, TV, and newspapers described in chapter 8—is arguably best done by describing the base scenarios which capture how best people within the continent consume content at the current or some future time. One of the best such scenario matrices which feels quite relevant to the African and emerging markets scene is the Unilever-ESPN-Mindshare matrix adapted from the original and shown in figure 20. It was developed as part of a scenario planning for the future of media in 2015, but the broad categories feel very relevant and illustrative of what is happening today and, with some minor modifications of the descriptions of these categories, can fit most markets.

Starting from the bottom right of figure 20, we begin with *Traditional New Media*, or in the case of Africa, Colonial Old Media. "Colonial" because not much has changed in much of Africa with "official" media since the colonial days, as described in chapter 8. This is the most passive scenario, where consumers' media interaction is quite habitual, almost formulaic, and always consuming content generated by others—almost always linear content like broadcast radio or TV, or newspapers. In much of Africa, it must be acknowledged that this is very much for a small, elite minority too. The "public" in "Public Service Broadcasting" only truly relates to a tiny minority in most African counties as we know it. In any case, with traditional media in the West (and for the lucky few in Africa), one may get wo-ken up in the morning to the news on radio, read the papers on public transportation on the way to work, dip in and out of preferred and *trusted* websites during the day like Google, BBC, their trusted sports website, or Facebook (if they have Internet access). On returning home from work, they are slaves to the TV schedules, where they watch TV soaps during evening dinner, the nightly news later, sports, and some entertainment programmes before they go to bed.

The advertisers love this group. They live their media lives by a well-known formula, so the advertisers can get at them easily. In the original version of this traditional world, the geography of the play-ers was easy to chart. The big broadcasters like BBC generate lots of content on radio and TV—the BBC has circa ten radio channels in the United Kingdom and circa five to ten TV channels on air at any one time. They produce drama, soaps, news, children's TV, documenta-ries, food programmes, educational programmes, etc., on both radio and TV—and they schedule them predictably. The big movie studios, mostly in the United States (Hollywood), make blockbuster produc-tions which are first distributed to movie theatres (the first window), next as video-on-demand (the second window, e.g., on airplanes), and later on DVD/Blu-ray or on premium cable or satellite networks (the third window). Sometimes, depending on how big the satellite/cable companies are, they get the movies in the second window. All of these "windows" are optimised to maximise monetising this content. As this is described, one can see that Africa on the whole never quite achieved even this traditional media, as their discretionary spend (as reflected in the GDP per capita in most African countries) just could not afford it.

The Media Buffet Category reflects a more (highly) fragmented media consumption. This category of consumers dips in and out of media as they do not trust just one media to satisfy them. They may wake up not to news on radio or TV but just for the headlines and do the same with the morning newspapers. They have multiple devices, perhaps a smartphone and tablet. They are listening to music on their commute or watching something they downloaded earlier but had not watched. Lunchtime, they dip in and out of several websites, perhaps hunting for angles on stories that caught their fancy, but they are not loyal to any one site. In the evening, they may watch a video. So in a day, they probably consume ten media genres: radio, TV, newspapers, blogs, YouTube, video CD, news websites, Twitter, Facebook, and Google. This group is a bit of a nightmare to advertisers.

The Portal of Me Scenario is truly quite a futuristic scenario, but one can see ingredients of this with many people one knows already today, even in Africa and other emerging economies, particularly people who have very punctuated days. Their media access is always on, but their attention has been somewhat captured by some trusted third parties. Perhaps they depend on some specific source, or portal, for traffic news, weather news, and recommendations for children's activities, for what is "hot,: gossip they are interested in, recommendations for books or movies they should watch, etc. They will punctuate their days with phone chats, looking at recommended news links, keeping up with their social networks. One can see this scenario is about the "me"—or the person.

The Tons of Twitter Category—another futuristic title—but which is illustrative of what is happening with some people around us who are lucky to be connected. Their attention is highly fragmented. They wake up to blogs, e-mails, and tweets. They constantly communicate and access information and entertainment, but they also express themselves across a wide range of media. This happens all day long. Wayne Rooney, the UK footballer, has an incredible six million followers. Members of this category do a lot of creating, receiving, searching, and sharing. They want their blogs or tweets to be consumed by others. They live on iPhones, BlackBerries, smart tablets, etc. This group is certainly an even greater nightmare to advertisers.

The matrix of figure 20 and the descriptions above start to paint a picture of a media sector that does *not* exist on the African continent today, nor in many emerging economies—hence the term "moribund"—but which is no doubt on its way as discretionary expenditure rises with improving GDP per capita in these countries. The proportions of how consumers in countries in Africa and emerging markets today fall on such a matrix—if applicable—is a function of the discretionary expenditure profiles in that country.

In any case, it is fair to conclude that Africa has a reasonably unsophisticated media sector in 2013. The reasons are clearer by returning to figure 9 (adapted to include more geography headings) which lists some of media's constituent geographical parts. Only general observations are made here as it is difficult to get real data to them based on:

- *TV programming and broadcasting activities:* Beyond a few diversified economies like South Africa, Egypt, and a couple or so more, including Nigeria (with ninety-four TV stations), there are so few terrestrial channels on the continent since they were still mostly analogue in 2013/14, and the population coverage of these networks is so limited (note the earlier reference to 24 percent analogue coverage in Tanzania or 40 percent population coverage in Cameroon). Clearly with only one or a couple of channels on air on average—and not great content at that—there is very little take-up or viewership from those lucky ones who happen to live in a TV coverage area. If most of these channels were subject to true market forces—rather than government subsidies—almost all of them will be bankrupt. However, the digital revolution is nigh: with the switchover from analogue terrestrial TV to digital imminent in many countries, this is a golden opportunity to revolutionise the TMT subsector in most of Africa in general, and the media sector in particular. Take-up should certainly be higher if there are twenty to thirty channels rather than one! One worries about the quality of content that will go on some of these new digital channels. However, this is the opportunity for a significant increase in the TV and broadcasting activities on the continent. I have already made a (hopefully) cogent case in chapter 1 to use digital switch over (DSO) to revolutionise the TV and broadcasting sector. Chapter 9 covers this in some more detail.
- *Radio programming and broadcasting activities:* Across Africa there are no doubt lots of radio stations (the dominant media), some good but most truly mediocre to terrible. You just have to tune through the FM space in most cities

on the continent to confirm this. Anecdotal evidence suggests that a significant proportion of radio stations across the continent do not even hold broadcasting licenses from state authorities and are run on shoestring budgets, as the advertising revenues are miniscule in most countries. The concept of national commercial radio stations really does not exist across most countries, yet alone across international borders. Beyond South Africa and a few other countries (Namibia, Uganda, Kenya, and a couple more), community stations are also not easily identifiable across the continent beyond labelling themselves as such. There is much room for a better and a more financially sustainable industry structure for radio and TV in most countries. As TV goes digital, perhaps private broadcasters will emerge with both TV and radio assets and more across the continent.

- *Film activities:* I have already described emerging movie production outlets across the continent. Clearly more sophisticated markets (like diversified African economies, such as Egypt, Morocco, Tunisia, and South Africa) are producing more movies every year. Nigeria is the runaway largest producer of movies/films every year, thanks to Nollywood.

- *Sound recording and music publishing activities*: Some state-of-the-art sound recording studios already exist in many African countries, though they are few and far between. Apple with its iTunes platform has already revolutionised music purchasing for good. Like elsewhere, a lot of music is pirated, but this problem is arguably worse in Africa, to the detriment of African music and African artists. How much better it would be if African artists could mostly be online and could meet and transact with their fans online too.

- *News and information service activities:* More digital channels will mean more news and information services, particularly local ones. More news and information on radio and other media channels, e.g., SMS, websites, etc., will emerge.

- *Advertising and media representation activities:* The previous description of the matrix provides a general overview of a relatively unsophisticated advertising African sector in general, particularly outside South Africa.

- *Animation activities:* Animation is very expensive to produce, and I am not aware of any major animation production centres on the African continent. However, I am aware some countries like Nigeria are planning on such having such animation activities in the medium term.
- *Documentary filmmaking:* This is quite a multiskilled activity, including directing, shooting, editing, and producing. Given the sophistication required here, and no clear business model to recoup the costs, it is no surprise that hardly any private players on the continent do this genre seriously.
- *Commercials and advertisements activities*: The quality of the commercials on the continent is very variable. Some are very good, from the big brands like Unilever, Orange, MTN, etc., and others much less so. It is not obvious that many countries have decent advertising agencies for producing commercials. Given the sectors are not economically viable, why should they?
- *Corporate production activities*: This describes SMEs who help corporations to do films, CD-ROMs, and DVD formats for training, public relations (PR), or sales.
- *Interactive media activities:* This describes SMEs, typically, that can do web, offline multimedia, interactive TV, games, premium rate calls, etc. This is clearly a sophisticated area.
- *Publishing of books, newspapers, and periodicals:* Major publishing houses are beginning to emerge on the continent, and they will get more sophisticated.
- *Game design:* Publishing of computer games and software will evolve over the next decade.

What you should note most from the above list is the range of activities that happen in the media sector. Wonder no more why it employs so much more than the technology and telecommunications sectors combined in Western economies. Most of these jobs tend to require freelance people who compete furiously for contracts. The following from AGCAS[38] summarise some of key roles that will emerge in the African media sector as the sector matures:

- animator
- broadcast engineer
- broadcast journalist
- film/video editor
- games developer
- graphics designer
- lighting technician, broadcasting/film/video
- location manager
- production designer, theatre/television/film
- programme researcher, broadcasting/film/video
- radio broadcast assistant
- radio producer
- runner, broadcasting/film/video
- sound technician, broadcasting/film/video
- television camera operator
- television/broadcasting/film/video producer
- television floor manage
- television production assistant
- website (interactive) developers

This concludes the geography and anatomy of TMT, along with some reflections and lessons to consider for Africa.

---

38 *Association of Graduate Careers Advisory Services,* http://www.agcas.org.uk.

SECTION II

A BLUEPRINT FOR TMT

CHAPTER 3

A BLUEPRINT FOR TMT IN AFRICA AND SOME EMERGING MARKETS

"By failing to prepare, you are preparing to fail."
—Benjamin Franklin

"Nigerians do not like solutions—they prefer options."

—Anonymous joke

Benjamin Franklin could not have uttered a truer set of only nine words. This quote of his is about planning and clearly depicts a statesman who knew how to make things happen. This chapter draws from the following in order to derive a blueprint for TMT in Africa and some emerging market countries: from understanding the key drivers of the TMT sector; from chapter 1, which makes the case for TMT in Africa and emerging markets as well as the necessity of business plans; and from chapter 2, which draws some clear lessons after the overview of the anatomy and geography of TMT.

These yield a TMT blueprint for Africa and for some other emerging market countries. It must be emphasized that it is *a* blueprint, not *the* blueprint. I would not dare be that arrogant anyway. In any case, the context on the ground in all countries varies significantly. Other competing blueprints would also be equally as valid, which may or may not include some of the views expounded in this chapter.

Importantly, the blueprint provides for a base "set of recommendations: for TMT in Africa—i.e., one view of *what* needs to happen for the TMT vision that this volume advocates for Africa and some emerging markets to emerge in the 2020s. It also ventures on the *how* to get there, or perhaps more accurately on how to sequence a set of activities. To this extent, it provides the beginnings of a plan. No matter its merits and demerits, if it helps drive a debate amongst policy makers and other key stakeholders in all these countries (a debate I would be happy to join or engage), the effort would have been fully worthwhile.

The joke above about Nigerians not liking solutions but rather preferring options is interesting and has done the rounds online. How else, as the joke implicitly refers, do you explain so many upper- and middleclass Nigerians

- being their own one-family-utility companies in their homes (pumping water from boreholes for general use and buying drinking water rather than having a functional water grid; generating power from diesel generators rather than relying on their dysfunctional national grid; supplying their own gas for cooking rather than having a gas grid),
- having several cars for different road conditions rather having the roads graded for all,
- having multiple SIMs from different networks rather than having one and being able to switch easily,
- suffering crippling traffic rather than having a functional mass transit system of buses and trains, etc.

Yes, these are options, but I hope you agree that they are very suboptimal and inefficient options for all. The unapologetic view of this chapter is to aim at long-term solutions with good long-term outcomes for consumers and citizens. This will always be better than proliferating and extending other short-term, suboptimal "options."

3.1 Key Drivers of the TMT Sector

It is important before any blueprint is posited to be clear about the drivers of the TMT sector. Indeed, the blueprint recommendations later are categorized under these drivers—yet another important reason why we cover them. There are five main ones of note, and they are shown in figure 21: technological changes, consumer behaviour, industry, the macroeconomy, and regulation. Together, they truly shape the TMG sector. We look at them in turn.

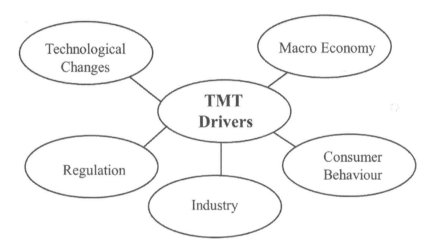

Figure 21—Key Factors that Drive the TMT Sector

3.1.1 Technological Changes

Arguably, no other sector of the economy is as subject to its own forces of technological changes as the TMT sector (i.e., technology is changing its own sector markedly all the time). Indeed, no sector of the economy is immune to the influence of technology. The one thing that is constant about technology is change itself—and this is a blessing, but is sometimes seen as a curse. A blessing because technology ushers in efficiency, reduces costs, and introduces innovation and new ways of working. It changes industry value chains too. A curse because humans instinctively resist change, and if the rate of change is too fast, where you continually have to keep up with new technologies, it becomes costly, at least in the short term.

Imagine the headache (i.e., costs) that the mobile operators have of maintaining three generations of networks at the same time: 2G networks for voice, and 2.5G networks and 3G networks for data. And now in African and emerging markets, they have to contend with rolling out 4G networks shortly. It is akin to having the vinyl record disks, cassette tapes, CDs, DVDs, Blu-ray disks,[1] and MP3[2] formats of your music all existing at the same time. We typically try and retire some of these formats and move on—and so will the operators have to retire certain technologies at some time and at significant costs to themselves.

Below is a short, nonexhaustive list of some of the technological changes:

- mobile: 1G[3] to 2G[4] to 2.5G EDGE networks[5] to 3G[6] to 4G[7] to 5G

---

1 Blue-ray disk is a new storage disc format which supersedes the DVD and CD formats.

2 MP3 is an abbreviation for "MPEG Layer 3"—a compressed digital sound format that is ideal for downloading music from the Internet.

3 1G is first-generation mobile. Now obsolete, it was analogue and offered only 9.6kb/s.

4 Second generation (2G) systems, in contrast, are digital and enable cross-border "roaming." Standardization of frequency use was absolutely vital. Otherwise, we all would be using different phones/devices operating on different frequencies in different countries—a recipe for unmitigated chaos. Europe agreed on a system called the Global System for Mobile communications (GSM), whilst the United States adopted two 2G standards: CDMA and Digital AMPs (D-AMPS). Japan's 2G system was called Personal Digital Cellular (PDC). However, GSM is by far the largest 2G system, with most operators across the African continent and other emerging markets having GSM. CDMA lost out.

5 Like GSM but with speeds from circa 56 to 115 kb/s.

6 3G is third generation. It is really a "catchall" term to describe faster access, which includes digital video, and it is also called UMTS. Speeds start from at least 200 kb/s and go up to 42 Mbps and higher.

7 4G is fourth generation. It is an all Internet protocol (IP) network with speeds from 100 Mbps up to 1 GB/s. Africa and emerging markets still have to deploy these networks.

- broadband: DSL to cable to FTTC to FTTH[8]
- digital storage: CD to DVD to PVR (personal video recorders) to home servers to cloud services
- digital broadcast: standard TV (SDTV) to high definition TV (HDTV) to 3DTV (three-dimensional TV) to on demand TV
- navigation: analogue maps to digital satellite navigation (SatNav) systems
- books: analogue paper books to digital e-books and e-readers like the Amazon Kindle) (you may be reading this book as an e-book)
- bookshops: brick-and-mortar bookshops in towns/cities to digital online stores like Amazon
- TVs: from CRT (analogue cathode ray tubes) to plasma and LCD (liquid crystal display) TVs to 3DTVs to ultra-high definition TV to flexible and stretchable screens, etc.
- Devices: more powerful by the year in terms of speed of processing, storage capacity, able to deal with more technologies (e.g., Wi-Fi, 2G, 3G, 4G, Bluetooth, etc.) and able to deliver multiple services

What the list begins to illustrate is the juggernaut of technology evolution driven largely by packets of data, addressed according to the Internet protocol TCP/IP[9] that are sent to the destination in any order, along multiple network routes. Upon arrival, the recipient computer recompiles the data into the intended order. Networks are designed in such a manner that there are multiple routes available to the data, thereby ensuring there is no single point of weakness. The increasing use of IP is a major driver of change in the TMT sector. Internet protocol fundamentally changes the economics of many a value chain,

---

8 DSL is digital subscriber line. Cable is usually two or more metal wires running side by side. Optical fibre uses glass and transmits light between the two ends of the fibre carrying vast amounts of data. FTTC is fibre to the curb, whilst FTTP is fibre to the premises or to the home (FTTH).

9 Transmission control protocol/Internet protocol—the communications protocol developed to enable computers of all kinds to share services and communicate directly as if part of a seamless network.

resulting in significant innovations, as has happened in the books and music retailing sectors. I acquire most of my music and books now digitally, by purchasing and downloading them online.

Why worry about technology changes in the design or redesign of the TMT sector in Africa and emerging markets? There are three good reasons. Firstly, technology change is a *constant* in our sector. Learning to manage a sector undergoing so much change is vital, and the skills required to manage such a sector of the economy are unique. Putting the economy in the hands of modern day Luddites[10] and nay-sayers to change is a positively suboptimal thing to do. Those who run the TMT policy and sectors of our economies must be comfortable with change, and not many are. Secondly, Africa and emerging markets have the benefit of learning from the mistakes of the Western nations. Hardly any of these countries implemented 1G analogue mobile technology—and most rightly went straight into 2G. They now have to make similar choices on TV and radio broadcast technologies, on ICT infrastructure, on types of regulation, etc. More informed choices can and should be made in these markets which drive efficiency, economic growth, innovation, and value for money for its citizens. The policy makers need to be well advised on such choices. Thirdly, convergence is truly real today in TMT, and it drives the sector to having ever larger and larger operators; e.g., Safaricom in Kenya is not only into mobile but arguably the biggest banking operator in the country. Big is sometimes good, but in the main is not. Monopolies in the long term are not in the best interests of consumers and citizens, and they must therefore be regulated firmly but fairly.

3.1.2 Consumer Behaviour

Consumers want value-for-money services; they demand new, better, and "shinier: technology—particularly the young who want "cool" devices and services. They want interactivity with their peer groups via Twitter and Facebook. They want the "portal of me," i.e., services

---

10 Luddites were nineteenth-century English textile workers who refused to embrace and protested against more efficient time- and labour-saving machinery being introduced then into the textiles sector between 1810 and 1820. They failed.

to their tastes or more personalised services, and to be always on if possible. They seek entertainment via YouTube, movies, and music, and they care less about the intricacies of technology. Your grandmother just wants her phone to work and not some convoluted explanation of how great the technology is. They want to be public (on Facebook) but also, paradoxically, want privacy. They want their service-agnostic devices to be able to be TV devices, phone devices, Facebook devices, video phone devices, Twitter devices, etc., simultaneously.

However, and this is the killer for our TMT sector, they want all of these for less, i.e., "more for less." Justifiably so, too, as they do not have that that much disposable income to spend on such communication services. The current ARPU[11] on the African continent is in the range of four to ten US dollars. Consumers do not want to double or triple this to get all these shiny new services. Consumer spending will indeed plateau. Remember the naked mobile data problem.

Why worry about consumers in the design or redesign of the TMT sector in Africa and emerging markets? Firstly, they pay all the wages, and they pay for the entire TMT sector. Gone are the days when fixed-term operators on the continent like NiTEL, CamTel, etc., ran roughshod over their customers. Secondly, consumer behaviour forces a continuous set of changes to service providers' offerings to meet evolving consumer needs. Consumer groups fragment into different segments who have different needs: the young, the over fifty-fives, women, business users, teenagers, etc. These groups all require different offerings which TMT service providers must offer, or else they do not get paid. Thirdly, policy makers must be able to specify and enable these consumer needs to emerge, and other government and industry stakeholders must be able to "size" this demand on network and infrastructure and supply accordingly. If all schools in the state are going to be linked on the same backbone infrastructure, you must anticipate what students and pupils will be doing at school to size the network infrastructure accordingly.

---

11 Average revenue per user (ARPU) is the monthly average takings per user earned from telecommunications customers.

3.1.3 Industry

Thanks to changes in technology and consumer behaviour above, industry operators have to respond to meet demand as required. Given the naked mobile data problem is real (see figure 3), and consumers have to deal with the real-world share of wallet economics, industry has to build networks and provision services for consumers within the constraints of what consumers are prepared to pay.

The TMT sector will have to contend with more and more data at marginal revenues (the naked mobile data challenge) and strive to retain customers. The instinct for players to merge (both vertically and horizontally) into larger monoliths therefore grows by the day, rather than these companies innovating to continue competing. Over the top (OTT) players are also creating problems for the industry. Take Skype for example as an "over the top: service. If one uses a handset connected to a Wi-Fi hot spot to Skype-call someone else, one is using the operators' and others' infrastructure but not fully paying for it. Worse, by them using such an OTT service, they are not using the operator's (e.g., Vodacom's or Orange's) service. Google Search is another OTT service in which Google does not pay operators to host on *their* networks.

So similarly, why worry about industry in the design or redesign of the TMT sector in Africa and emerging markets? Firstly, they provide the services to consumers in the industry and so provide significant consumer surplus to the TMT sector. Secondly, regulators and policy makers want a TMT sector thriving with competition and innovation in the face of pressures from industry operators to merge into ever larger companies and innovate less—but emerging monopolies are no good in the long term. Thirdly, policy makers and regulators must realise that data and analytics become the key differentiators to gaining invaluable insight to compete and achieving the returns that investors expect. This means that knowing much more about their customers, i.e., gathering more and more personal data and customers' preferences, is vital to monetizing them better. Fourthly, industry value chains change due to the Internet protocol, and it is important for regulators and the government to be on top of such changes.

3.1.4 Macroeconomy

The macroeconomy clearly is a key driver of the TMT sector, as is the case with many other sectors of the economy. If there is low economic growth or even a recession or high inflation, people are less prone to wanting to spend on anything but essential services. Telecommunications is evolving to be an "essential" service, but less so media services and arguably many technology services. Nations with very young populations (60 percent of Africans are below thirty years old according to the World Bank) present different macroeconomic challenges. Such a demographic profile is very different from that in Europe and the Western world, necessitating different types of services, e.g., much more pay-as-you-go services for the cash-poor who are under thirty compared to more monthly contract services required by more cash-rich middle classes in Europe.

For example, it must be pointed out that political and macroeconomic stability in addition to microeconomic reforms are the key reasons for the unleashed growth in the telecommunications sector in Africa and emerging economies over the last fifteen years.[12] McKinsey cites World Bank data which shows inflation dropped from circa 22 percent per annum to 8 percent in the 1990s to 2000s, government debt fell from 82 percent of GDP to 59 percent, and budget deficits shrunk from 4.6 percent of GDP to 1.8 percent in these periods. Other microeconomic reforms were enacted covering trade policy, credit regulation, labour market regulation, business regulation, strengthening our courts, etc.

It should therefore be clear why one worries about the macroeconomy in the design or redesign of the TMT sector in Africa and emerging markets. Firstly, governments should continue to do more of these macroeconomic reforms that have led to more than a hundred companies on the African continent with revenues greater than one billion dollars by the time McKinsey published their 2010 *Lions on the Move* report (McKinsey, 2010), and that has also led to more than

---

12 *Lions on the move: The progress and potential of African economies,* McKinsey & Company: McKinsey Global Institute, June 2010.

1,400 listed companies on African bourses. There is much to do on regional trade, protectionism, and commodity pricing on the continent still controlled by governments. Secondly, the growth of TMT relies on many of these macro- and microeconomic factors being managed in the right way in the economy. Thirdly, macroeconomic factors can and do have other drastic impacts on the TMT sector. Lack of access to bond markets would hold back investment in networks in the sector. Lack of financial incentives and access to credit would spell danger for any emerging production and media sector on the continents. Weak courts discourage investment in the event business disputes emerge, and they would aplenty in the TMT sector.

3.1.5 Regulation

All through the pages thus far, the role of regulation in the TMT sector has been gradually emerging. The reason is because regulators' primary raison d'être for their existence is for the benefits of consumers and citizens. This makes regulation—whether carried out by independent regulators or by arms of governments—a key driver of the TMT sector. This is covered more in chapter 11. However, these examples below illustrate the importance of regulation:

- *Liberalisation and Competition:* Telecommunications in Africa and emerging markets have changed incredibly and become very dynamic because telecoms markets were liberalised, i.e., many constraints, including majority foreign brands owning national licenses, were swept away. Imagine if those rules still existed ensuring that MTN, being a South African–headquartered company, could not enter Nigeria. Where would Nigeria telecoms sector be today? MTN's risk entering Nigeria has benefited its nearly fifty million subscribers in Nigeria by 2013.
- *Spectrum Management:* The efficient allocation of spectrum airwaves can only happen with good regulation. Markets

which have been liberalised, opened up to competition, and issued several spectrum licenses to mobile operators have seen competition thrive, leading to mobile prices plummeting in recent years. Ethiopia still operates a regime in 2013/14 where there is no true independent regulator, and the ministry has not established a spectrum policy. As a result, there is almost no competition as yet for spectrum in Ethiopia, and Ethiopian consumers and citizens are the losers. Not picking on Ethiopia, it is fair to see in an increasingly wireless world that access to spectrum licenses is a major gating factor to investment in a country.

- *Telecommunications Bottlenecks:* Telecommunications is mired with many bottlenecks, as we saw in chapters 1 and 2, be they at the last mile that get into premises, at interconnection points into international gateways, or at exchanges, at ducts, at poles, etc. Ducts and poles which connect fixed cables such as optical fibre or other communication wires to homes and offices clearly need access rights established, or else one company could dominate an entire market to the detriment of consumers. There must be an entity that regulates access to such bottleneck assets, and this is typically the regulator, though not always necessarily. Otherwise, new entrants will never be able to get into the market, and weaker incumbents may be crushed by the bigger ones who control access to such bottleneck assets.

- *Interconnection:* Terminating calls is a natural monopoly element of a network. Call origination may be competitive, i.e., you may dial from a fixed line or from one of several mobile operators' networks (or lines) or maybe even a Skype call. However, if that individual is calling your number, only your network can terminate that call on your phone device. This gives it immense monopoly power, and this operator can charge as it likes unless it is regulated. Regulators have to regulate such mobile termination rates to be as close as possible to that of a virtual equally efficient operator (EEO)—a synthetic virtual operator which a regulator creates and models to work out and arrive at what the efficient true costs should be.

Regulation is a mainstay of the TMT sector and one of its key drivers. A market which is not regulated properly will not attract investments and will lead to higher prices, poor quality of service, poor innovation, poor competition, few new entrants, and fewer jobs. Why would you want to guarantee such outcomes? A rhetorical question, but an important one nonetheless.

3.2 Towards a Blueprint for the TMT Sector

One of the *Chambers Twentieth Century Dictionary* (new edition 1983) definitions of "blueprint" is a
> preliminary sketch or plan of work to be done, or a
> guide or model provided by agreed principles or rules
> or by conclusions from earlier experiment.

This definition is perfect for the context of this chapter, as it notes the following: it is a *preliminary sketch/plan*—and that is all it is. It is a *guide/model* based on some agreed *principles/rules*.

The rules are also *conclusions from earlier experiments*—in our case, in what has happened elsewhere in the developed world. This is why this section draws from both chapters 1 and 2. Both chapters started sketching out some plans and as introduced key *in situ* principles/rules like competition, coverage, universal access, broader social value, new entrants, and access right of ways to bottleneck assets like ducts and poles, regulation of access charges, etc. These prior chapters emphasised that these are what decision makers, policy makers, and entrepreneurs should worry about, and less so the details of the technology. Both chapters alluded to some "experiments," e.g., the Kigali-Nairobi problem where intra-Africa traffic gets routed via Europe or the brave experiment of "comparing" the London TMT sector to what African TMT media hubs may aspire. Of course, no Africa media hub will rival London anytime soon, but there is a gold standard. So both prior chapters point to conclusions from elsewhere in Europe and North America, but they also point out that some of these conclusions need to be adapted for the idiosyncrasies of the African and other emerging economies' contexts.

Any blueprint here is just *one* blueprint or sketch plan. It is not *the* blueprint—that will be arrogant. It is preliminary, and it must acknowledge that the starting positions in all countries are different. Believing all African and emerging market countries as homogenous entities will be naïve to the extreme. However, the hypothesis or assumption here is that the similarities in the TMT contexts in these countries are greater than their differences. Furthermore, that the paths that they are all likely to travel to achieve TMT excellence are likely to be similar if they choose to do that. Otherwise, a blueprint is nonsensical.

With this preamble, let us proceed to be even more explicit about some further caveats on any such blueprint.

- Countries are not homogenous, and so they all have different starting positions. Arguably one of the best frameworks to characterise the countries on the African continent is that in McKinsey's *Lions on the Move* 2010 report (McKinsey, 2010).

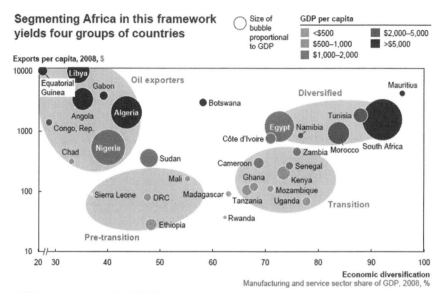

Figure 22—McKinsey Segmentation of African Countries
(Source: McKinsey *Lions on the Move* Report 2010,[13] page 4.)

As figure 22 depicts, the McKinsey framework segments each country and typically characterises it as either one of oil exporter, diversified economy, pre-transition country, or a transition country. Though three years old, it is a remarkably resilient characterisation and would still apply for several years more. The GDP per capita for the African countries are clearly different, and hence their capacity and speed to engage the TMT projects in this volume will be different. However, engage they must!

- The core principles, rules, and conclusions we derive from chapters 1 and 2 which underpin the blueprint are captured in the following nonexhaustive and simplistic list which

13 *Lions on the move: The progress and potential of African economies,* McKinsey & Company: McKinsey Global Institute, June 2010, http://www.mckinsey.com/insights/africa/lions_on_the_move (accessed July 2013).

nevertheless deserves repetition over and over again. Most times, they are captured in dense prose in academic books, but frankly they are no more complex in essence than below.

- ○ Competition is good, and policies to encourage more competition must be fostered. In the medium to long term, it drives innovation, drives up quality, lowers costs, and fosters sustainable growth.
- ○ Liberalisation of the TMT sector is good. This is a clear conclusion from what has happened in the telecommunications sector in Africa and other emerging markets over the last fifteen years. It separates and clarifies the roles of government, industry, and the regulator, and it sweeps away unnecessary rules which stop markets growing, e.g., foreign ownership rules.
- ○ The emergence of monopolies is bad, and they must be checked.
- ○ Bottlenecks must be regulated in a FRND-ly way (i.e., fair, reasonable, and nondiscriminatory). There rules for access to bottleneck assets like ducts and poles must be agreed up front in FRND-ly manner.
- ○ Competition should also extend to *coverage*.
- ○ Universal access is good but must be pursued proportionately. It is always typically at odds with liberalisation. Companies cannot be compelled to do barmy uneconomic activities. However, having a nation of *haves* and complete *have-nots* is ultimately not good in the long term, both socially and economically too. Therefore, Internet policy, say, must be one of Internet for the masses too, not just Internet for the cities or rural areas.
- ○ Cooperation is good, particularly amongst regulators and governments. This will minimise much coordination failures on the continent.
- ○ Collusion amongst firms is obviously bad.

- Regulation is primarily for the benefit of consumers and citizens, not directly for industry's benefit. This is a good secondary side effect.
- Having business plans is good. It is not only best practice, but it forces decision makers to think clearly about the entire journey up front and its costs. With any luck, if it is a believable business plan, it would be invested in by third parties, which would both demonstrate validation of the government's plan and also gain a valuable partner(s) to keep the government honest on its way to implementing it.
- Doing nothing in TMT is not really an option. Doing nothing carries significant opportunity costs. By failing to plan for next spectrum releases now, countries are preparing to fail their 4G tests. By not planning for a media sector properly, countries will end up with terrible content on TV/radio and poor choice of digital channels and poorly funded sectors. By not planning for Internet for the masses now, the inevitable of Internet just for the cities or rural areas will happen as night follows day.
- Making the wrong decisions is even worse. Take good advice.
- When you get good advice, execute on the good even better. Better to execute properly on implementing only a subset of the good advice you can afford than trying to implement all of the good advice badly by spreading your resources too thinly. Also do not bother getting good advice if you have no intention of paying any attention to it. You are just wasting everyone's time—including yours.
- Decision makers, policy makers, governors, presidents, ministers, commissioners, senior civil servants, etc., must with *humility* realise this is a fast-moving sector and not constrain it by Luddite tendencies if they are wont to. They should get men and women of the right dynamic to direct it, but decision makers should fully sponsor and support it. Even the so-called TMT experts are continuously learning every day. This volume should be a salient lesson on how

complex and dynamic the sector is. African decision makers are well known for not wanting to do real training in new sectors and certainly wouldn't be seen dead in a training session with their subordinates. This is so passé, and those who pay the price are the disgruntled subordinates (whose good ideas get blocked as their bosses do not understand them) and the unsuspecting citizens and consumers of the country who suffer the bulk of the opportunity costs.

But how do you the decision maker make a start? The first two chapters have majored on the *what*—but what about the *how*?

Therefore, in a volume of this ilk, the blueprint also hopes to be a starting point which collates that first preliminary sketched plan—something that decision makers in all countries can use as a starting point to disagree from or to rework to suit their needs. The blueprint does not strive to be the *destination*; it is just the *start*. The real hard and beneficial work is in the *journey* to get to the individual destinations for all the different countries. This is a good area where the journey to the answer is more important than the answer itself.

A volume of this kind also hopes to engender collaboration amongst countries, particularly regional ones. It exposes the reality that many of these problems are shared and that TMT is a sector where the network effects rules, where economies of scale are king, and where networks between and within countries have to interconnect (network islands are no good to anyone), etc. It points out the obvious that if more countries choose to use the same combination of digital television broadcasting standards, e.g., DVB-T2/MPEG-4,[14] then their combined buying power will drive down set-top box costs and drive up affordability (and hence access) for African and emerging

---

14 DVB stands for digital video broadcasting, and MPEG stands for moving pictures expert group. DVB-T2 stands for DVB-second generation terrestrial and is a standard for digital transmission. DVB is already the dominant terrestrial digital terrestrial standard for ITU Region 1 that includes Africa and Europe. MPEG-4 is the most recent standard for compressing and encoding digital video and sound with minimum loss of quality.

markets' consumers and citizens. Frequency airwaves similarly do not respect international borders, so they must be coordinated. There is much coordination and collaboration that goes with TMT, without which coordination failures accrue. We already noted in chapter 2 that coordination failures lead to Africa having to pay up to six hundred million dollars to countries with more developed infrastructure for *intracountry and inter-African traffic* exchange that is routed outside the continent. Here is a concrete example of costs that accrue when we do not collaborate.

3.3 A Blueprint for African and Some Emerging Market TMT Sectors

The blueprint that this volume proposes follows, and as per the earlier Chambers definition, it is just a *preliminary sketch/plan*—and that is all it is. It is a *guide/model* based on some of the nonexhaustive list *principles/rules/conclusions* of section 3.2 and the contexts on the continent of Africa and other emerging markets as described in chapters 1 and 2.

It also makes sense to use the drivers of the TMT sector spelt out in section 3.1 in order to structure the preliminary sketch/plan. It is also in the form of a set of recommendations across all these key drivers of the TMT sector.

3.3.1 Overarching Blueprint Recommendations

The vital starting assumption here is that the government, state, or province (or whatever competent authority) believes in an overarching *growth* strategy, of which it considers the TMT sector to be a significant long-term growth engine it should invest in. It believes in not only the private value (i.e., profits and consumer surplus) that the sector will generate but also in the broader social value that a well-oiled broadcasting and media sector delivers. The broader social value refers to benefits like access and inclusion, a more educated and informed population, cultural understanding, belonging to a community, promoting democracy, and so on. Such broader social and citizen value cannot mostly be captured as profits, but they are most important nonetheless. It also assumes there is goodwill on behalf of the government or state to truly deliver for its electorate, a premise that does not necessarily hold true in many an African country know. I make no apologies for holding fervently to my view that public service is a vocation.

With the above assumptions, the following recommendations seem to follow naturally. Where the decision and policy makers need help, there are usually many good and competent, but oft ignored employees, to first seek out and listen to—and consultants of course beyond them. We will in these recommendations use "government" as a shorthand for government, state, province, council, etc. For the avoidance of doubt, most of the recommendations here are aimed and governments and states.

1. *Produce government's TMT vision and strategy, and agree on a very senior sponsor:* The government whilst conducting its overarching growth review identifies and agrees with the case for investing in the TMT sector for long-term growth. It starts by adopting a cost-is-not-a-problem approach. It should spell out the visions and strategy. Even more important, it should set out how to deliver the government's vision for TMT in the country and how it will deliver this and, most important, how it will demonstrate evidence of progress monthly, quarterly, twice yearly, or annually. The process should arguably start afresh or start from the ICT vision and strategy. Most important of all, a sponsor should be identified. For my monies in Africa, it should be the president himself/herself or his deputy; the governor himself/herself, etc. TMT is worth it! For example, the further down it is delegated, particularly to one ministry over the other, the larger the risk that the Ministry of Town Planning (who oversee ducts, poles, and city designs) will ignore all requests to meetings from the Ministry of TMT. Without sponsorship from the top, the Ministry of Power and Utilities may not be engaged either. One more thing—yes, you did read the "Ministry of TMT" with clear

ministerial briefs to drive all three subsectors. Having a Ministry of Communications, a Ministry of Broadcasting and Culture, and a Ministry of Post in an increasingly converged world is just frankly anachronistic.

It is also emphasised that this is the opportunity to consider a full (re)design of the TMT sector in your country. Revisit figure 8 and consider projects you are compelled to start, like the switchover from analogue TV to digital in order to release some frequencies, the future auction/release of these frequencies and more for 4G mobile broadband, existing national and regional fibre rollout projects, city fibre rollout projects using cities' ducts and poles, and potential TV whites paces–type projects. All of these projects are intertwined and interrelated and should be all revisited "in the round" as the new TMT sector is designed/redesigned.

In summary, such a vision and strategy document should cover the government's vision and strategy for
    a. passive layer ducts, poles and trenches infrastructure;
    b. fixed line infrastructure, including national and regional fibre backbones and their backup fibre and IXPs;
    c. the future growth of mobile infrastructure, particularly majoring on coverage;
    d. the future mobile 4G data market and future spectrum releases/auctions to deliver this;
    e. Internet and broadband infrastructure strategy, including Internet for the masses using TV white spaces technology or equivalent, in order to drive universal access of Internet;
    f. digital TV switchover strategy;
    g. media sector strategy which builds on the switchover strategy and more;
    h. digital devices, including computers, set-top boxes, handsets, strategy—principally to drive affordability;

     i.   policies and regulations strategies on how to create and develop the right policies and regulations to make the other work streams happen;;

     j.   training and skills development strategy; and, lastly,

     k.   funding strategy for all the above.

The funding strategy is truly important. Whilst diversified economies (like Egypt, Morocco, Tunisia, and South Africa) and oil Exporters (Nigeria, Angola, Gabon, etc.)—see figure 22—may be more easily be in a position to fund such projects, those pretransition and transition economies may have to be more proactive in how to secure funding for these projects.

This list is not exhaustive but covers the real invaluable ones.

2. *Produce a developed TMT business plan:* The TMT vision and strategy would arguably be best realised by a fully costed business plan. While it is best practice to have a business plan before one spends public funds, the greater benefit comes from the *process* of getting at one. It is recommended it is facilitated by an expert third party facilitator(s) who has/have carried out similar business cases before. It would bring together people across many government ministries and regulators and more. There are many important aspects to such business cases, hence why experts in facilitating the generation of these are recommended. They include:
   - enumerating the options to achieve the vision and strategy
   - appraising the pros and cons of these options
   - listing all key assumptions
   - identifying risks
   - defining how progress will be monitored
   - being clear on who will monitor the benefits
   - fully costing and evaluating the benefits and costs of the different options

As noted earlier in the case of the vision and strategy, the journey in producing such a business plan is perhaps more important than the final plan itself. Departments should see it as a way to ensure coordination across various government departments. And as a bonus, it would be an important set of documents for looking at opportunities for funding through PPPs, straight government funding, etc. During business planning, there would be a rigorous debate on prioritisations driven by funding constraints. The costs-are-not-a- problem approach falls away at this stage.

AN EXAMPLE UPCOMING FUTURE MILESTONES MONITORING DASHBOARD FOR A BUSY EXECUTIVE. SHOWS PROJECT 2 IS IN TROUBLE AND NEEDS IMMEDIATE ATTENTION WHILST PROJECT 4 NEEDS TO BE WATCHED CLOSELY.

PROJECT	DATE	DESCRIPTION	NOTES	STATUS
Project 1	23/03/13	Description 1	Note 1	Green
	30/03/13	Description 2	Note 2	Green
	29/02/13	Description 3	Note 3	Green
Project 2	21/03/13	Description 4	Note 4	Red
	22/02/13	Description 5	Note 5	Red
Project 3	28/02/13	Description 6	Note 6	Green
	15/03/13	Description 7	Note 7	Green
	30/03/13	Description 8	Note 8	Green
	31/03/13	Description 9	Note 9	Amber
Project 4	29/02/13	Description 10	Note 10	Amber
	30/03/13	Description 11	Note 11	Amber
	05/03/13	Description 12	Note 12	Green

Figure 23—An Example of Upcoming Future Milestones *Monitoring* Dashboard for a Busy Executive (shows Project 2 is in trouble and needs immediate attention, whilst Project 4 needs to be watched closely)

3. *Produce and agree upon the TMT programme governance and monitoring work stream:* Probably the most important of the recommendations—and it has nothing to do with TMT

substance *per se*—is to agree upon the TMT programme governance and all the work streams this early. This is a large programme, and the overall sponsor (governor, vice president, some really senior official who speaks with their authority) needs to set up the governance structure early. It may end up with a dozen sub work streams or even more and, more crucially, some simplified RAG[15] (red, amber, and green traffic lights) dashboards which give a basic summary of project progress. The sponsor should invest in professionals in setting up these dashboards, risks charts, and project plans, along with clearly defined and time-planned milestones which can be tracked weekly or bimonthly. Figure 23 shows one such dashboard, and there will be many others covering risks, costs, time, milestones, project plans, and interdependencies.

Africa must break its reputation of being poor implementers in the main or not managing our projects adequately. Some of the work streams would have their own subdashboards, milestone trackers, and risks charts. Indeed, the sponsor should probably be trained on using these tools to track his/her programme, asking tough questions as to why milestones are not being met, unblocking issues, minimising risks, etc. It is truly very rewarding, very productive—and indeed fun to all involved—when a complex programme is set up and run properly. I have had the pleasure of setting up and running some large programmes and can attest to these. The sponsor must appoint project managers for all these work-streams and, for some very large work streams, appoint subsponsors. However, the sponsor should be in charge of monitoring progress with energy and urgency. You were warned it had nothing to do with TMT substance, but this recommendation is the most important. The overall sponsor must put this is place. Lack of this just wastes public resources and time.

---

15 RAG stands for red, amber, and green traffic lights. Red issues need immediate attention, meetings to unblock as soon as possible. Greens are fine. Ambers needs careful watching in case they become reds. What mitigation actions do you need?

3.3.2 Macroeconomy Blueprint Recommendations

The macroeconomy clearly is the primary of all the key drivers of the TMT sector. All the other TMT sector drivers (i.e., technological changes, regulation, industry, and consumer behaviour) are arguably secondary to this one. It may be academic to talk about the rest if the economy is in the doldrums, for example. Nevertheless, from the lessons of chapters 1 and 2, there are some clear recommendations to draw.

4. *Hone and complete telecoms and ICT liberalisation and competition policies:* Most countries on the continent (apart from a few, including Ethiopia) have seen the benefits of liberalising and opening up their markets to competition. The drivers for increased revenues in ICT can be attributed to the liberalisation of the telecommunications sector which helped drive down prices and extend services available, particularly when supported by effective regulation. Nevertheless, despite the growth, Enrico Calandro, Alison Gillwald, Mpho Moyo, and Christoph Stork conclude—after their truly excellent and evidence-based comparative sector performance review of ICT Policy and regulation of seventeen African countries—that

> outcomes are sub-optimal in comparison to other regions of the world. While growth of the mobile market has been dramatic, sub-Saharan countries lag behind many other developing regions, including North Africa...several African countries have undergone a telecommunications reform process in order to meet international trade agreements, including the functional separation of government, the sectors' regulator and operators. However, the reform process has been uneven across the

continent. Almost most reform processes in Africa are *incomplete*.[16] (Calandro *et al.,* 2010[17])

I could not agree more, albeit from researching for this volume. However, the evidence from Calandro and his colleagues is incontrovertible and suggests most countries can still hone and complete liberalisation and competition policies. Their evidence clearly highlighted that some countries have only partially liberalised their telecommunications sectors and that access and affordability of services remain uneven and very paltry when compared to other regions of the world. Many fixed-line incumbent operators across the continent are still majority or 100 percent government owned. There is still much room to privatise these fixed-line players—though the true accounts of most of these businesses make them uninvestable.

The TMT strategy and vision as well as the business plan exercises and output will help inform the honing and completion of these policies across African countries. In countries like Ethiopia (whose prices are still politically determined in 2013/14), they only have to see the benefits that have accrued to other countries to fully liberalise their telecoms sector too.

5. *Liberalise the media sector too, and open for competition:* Governments should also seek to liberalise and open up their media sectors, as most have done this for telecoms except for the likes of Ethiopia as of 2013/14. The vision and strategy thinking would have had to contend with going from a one- or two- channel terrestrial analogue TV world to perhaps a twenty-channel digital TV world and the realities of the scenarios of figure 20 covering "Tons of Twitter," "Portal of me," etc. Surely, this process will not maintain the same moribund

---

16 Emphasis mine.

17 Enrico Calandro, Alison Gillwald, Mpho Moyo, and Christoph Stork (2010), *Comparative Sector Performance Review 2009/2010: Towards Evidence-based ICT Policy and Regulation,* Volume 2, Policy Paper 2, researchICTafrica.net, p. 44.

media policy stances in most African countries. Media policy at its best is about creating a vibrant public service and private sectors who are actively engaged in (i) *informing*, (ii) *educating*, and (iii) *entertaining* the nation's consumers and citizens. Further to these three core duties, these public and private sector institutions—if you look at the cases in the Western world, like the BBC and commercials broadcasters in the UK—provide an invaluable *watchdog* role which keeps many governments on their toes through thorough investigative journalism. Informing, educating, and entertaining not only create jobs and wealth but also create incredible broader social value not captured via profits. What price would you put on informed and educated citizens?

I emphasise this because some authors have, arguably, rightly drawn parallels by noting that African media policy reforms have in the main been quite superficial because of the superficial nature of democracy in most countries on the continent.[18] Decision and policy makers (i.e., ministers, governors, presidents, and/or their advisers) reading this should disavow themselves of this illusion of state control over the media sector in the second decade of the twenty-first century. The Arab Spring of 2011 happened despite state-controlled media in these countries. See where it got them in Egypt or Tunisia. In a social media world of Twitter, Facebook, YouTube, SMS, Skype, e-mails, and smartphones that can update to YouTube instantly—and with governments rolling out further ICT infrastructure to enhance access to these services—why do governments think they have a remote chance of controlling it? The so-called benefits that accrue from the illusion of some control of the media are far dwarfed by the benefits of having an informed, educated, and entertained citizenry.

---

18 See essays in Dumisani Moyo and Wallace Chuma (2010) (Editors), *Media Policy in a Changing southern Africa: Critical reflections on media reforms in the global age*, South Africa: Unisa Press. ISBN 978186888-569-5.

So the TMT vision and strategy must be both honest and bold on its TMT policy making, and even particularly challenging on media policy debates covering broadcasting, print, and other new media. As the TMT business plans will almost certainly be looking for more investments into the media sector, particularly stimulated by a massive addition to the media landscape in countries via analogue to digital switchover of TV, boldness and honesty in policy making are key. Moving to a multiple TV channel world requires investment in those channels and in professionalizing the content industry in most African countries. The vision and strategy of the TMT sector and the business plan should (and would) illuminate the amount of investment needed and the policies that would need enacting.

6. *Beware of the risks of "choking off" of benefits of liberalisation/competition:* Governments should beware of choking liberalisation policies that have worked so well with mobile investments on the continent over the last decade with largely none of these investments from governments. In the next decade, there is a vivid state involvement since governments are playing an increasing their role in the financing of fibre backbone infrastructure either through direct state capital or through PPPs. Combined with the global economic crisis of 2007/8, this has led to limited international/European investments. Three clear risks accrue. First, government and states become key players rather than final arbiters after the regulators, as they are providing funding themselves. This presents a set of risks in itself, including competition. Bringing in back the state is usually not good for liberalisation, and companies do not like competing against governments! Second, the continent has seen (and is seeing) a growing injection of soft financing from China and India. This is not all bad, but being "soft" suggests less transparency and accountability in the trade—and this is a suboptimal outcome for competition. There is growing evidence of short-term, cheaper up front pricing, but higher long-term total costs with some of these

soft loans. Third, risks of corruption are mounting. It was almost beautiful to watch the fully liberalised market at play in the roll out of the $150 billion of investment on the continent without governments' direct involvement—totally driven by capitalism and shareholder returns. States must be mindful of these clear risks and put in place governance to mitigate them. If not, the level of investments will drop markedly. Tanzania and Uganda have both implemented some of the best of liberalisation policies, which has ushered in much-needed competition of lots of licensed network operators, but sadly it has coupled with retrogressive and illiberal special taxes.

7. *Emphasise and address access and affordability concerns:* In their excellent comparative analysis across seventeen countries, Calandro *et al.* (2010) conclude that national objectives of achieving universal and affordable access to the full range of communication services have been largely undermined by a range of issues, including poor policies and even regressive taxes on usage. They rightly note that though "voice divide is decreasing, Internet divide is increasing and broadband is almost absent on the continent."[19]

As the previous two chapters emphasised, the Internet and broadband economics would worsen the divide, and up front or *ex ante* policy regulations should be designed to mitigate them. There is no excuse for not seeing this coming. Achieving a digital switchover but with set-top boxes costing two hundred dollars will guarantee little take up of digital television. They should be twenty-five. Tax exemptions (or even tax benefits) to drive up more personal computer take up in Africa makes sense rather than tax levies. Levying regressive "special" taxes (as Tanzania and Uganda have done in the past on communications and equipment going as high as 30 percent) provides for a

---

19 Enrico Calandro, Alison Gillwald, Mpho Moyo, and Christoph Stork (2010), *Comparative Sector Performance Review 2009/2010: Towards Evidence-based ICT Policy and Regulation*, Volume 2, Policy Paper 2, researchICTafrica.net.

different definition of liberalisation and is certainly not pro access and affordability. All TMT policy thinking going forward must emphasise access and affordability. African countries and emerging economies could downplay these with TMT's killer application of voice. Economic regulation regarding moving to Internet and broadband—where the broader social value trumps profits to be made—suggests bold policy making from governments and regulators. Fixed teledensity at less than 3 percent in most countries and with broadband rates in the same territory does point to different policy thinking.

8. *Strengthen converged and independent sector regulators, merge relevant regulators into converged ones, and encourage true intracontinent regulatory cooperation (the example of OHADA):* First and foremost, the continued clear-blue-waters functional separation of government, sector regulators, and industry should even be reinforced. Having existing senior civil servants (e.g., permanent secretaries) sitting on the boards of independent regulators does not bode well for true independent regulation. Similarly, independent regulators should not cultivate the culture of being *civil* servants, as many on the continent are wont to do, and condemn themselves to almost servitude to government. They are *public* servants who have the statutory honour to regulate confidently for citizen and consumer benefits. There is a clear difference here.

Next, the case for having converged regulators in a digital IP world should now be obvious. Trying to carry out a switchover project from analogue to digital terrestrial TV and auction the spectrum though a 4G auction with two regulators or more—typically a broadcasting regulator and a communications regulator as in Nigeria or Ghana[20]—is most suboptimal.

---

20 Nigeria Broadcasting Commission (NBC) for broadcasting and Nigeria Communications Commission (NCC) for telecommunications. In Ghana, National Media Commission (NMC) for Broadcasting and National Communications Authority (NCA) for Telecommunications.

The broadcasting regulator oversees broadcasting frequencies whilst the telecoms regulator oversees the telecommunications ones. This is nonsense in 2013/14. So countries like Cameroon, Mozambique, and Tunisia should enact converged communications acts sooner than later and move to converged regulation. Tunisia had begun this in 2013. They should take a leaf out of Uganda's book who legislated in early 2013 in the Uganda Communications Act (2013) and made the Ugandan Communications Commission (UCC) a converged regulator.

It is undoubtedly true that over 93 percent[21] of countries have established sectoral regulators. However, Calandro *et al.* (2010) also found much evidence of the lack of political autonomy to regulate independently and the capacity to regulate effectively to achieve FRND-ly regulation of their markets. So their study finds a largely negative perception of telecommunication regulatory environments in most African countries they researched. I can attest (having been a senior regulator in the UK) that good and evidenced-based regulation is incredibly hard work at the best of times, even with the best resources available and with a very clear and independent statutory mandate. Anything less is asking for trouble. Companies in this sector tend to be large multinationals with very well resourced lawyers and economists. Expecting underresourced and underqualified regulators to regulate this lot, coupled with political interference when the companies do not get their way, is no way to regulate such an important sector.

Another obvious consideration on the continent to address the above problem of many suboptimal regulators should be that of regional or African "superregulators." The lessons from Europe[22] and America[23] are clear. Regulation in Europe is

---

21 Some countries, unbelievably, have none, like Benin.

22 Though European countries all have their independent sectoral regulators, the EU provides for a "super-regulator" with real teeth.

23 The United States obviously has only the one key sector regulator in the FCC.

always a balance of international (EU) and national (e.g., UK) regulation. Such constraints mean national regulators have limited room for manoeuvre. For example, access and interconnect legislation in the United Kingdom almost completely emanates from the EU and is transposed into UK legislation. What this means is Europe operates a uniform access and interconnect legislation across EU-27. This allows for clarity and consistency. Having fifty-four separate interconnect legislations on the continent of Africa clearly makes less sense. Absent such a superregulator, the regional integration of regulatory frameworks should be seriously considered. Calandro and his colleagues report many of such commitments are "rhetorical" as national priorities take precedence over regional ones. This is indeed a shame.

A shame because there is precedence on the continent about having a group of countries harmonising their common laws, based on internationally accepted principle, in order to foster international investment in these countries on the continent. It is called OHADA. OHADA is the French acronym for "Organisation pour l'Harmonization en Afrique du Droit des Affaires," which translates into "the organisation for the harmonisation of business law in Africa." It is supported and financed by France and currently has seventeen[24] African countries who have decided to harmonise their commercial laws by executing the Port Louis (Mauritius) Treaty.[25] Fondufe and Mansuri (2013)[26] note that the World Bank and the International Finance Corporation concluded that OHADA

---

24 The countries are: Benin, Burkina Faso, Cameroon, Central Africa Republic, Chad, Comoros, Congo, Ivory Coast, Democratic Republic of Congo, Equatorial Guinea, Gabon, Guinea, Guinea-Bissau, Mali, Niger, Senegal, and Togo.

25 "The Harmonization of Business Law in Africa: Possibility or Fantasy?" *The African Counsel,* vol. I, issue 2, June 2009.

26 Clement N. Fondufe and Sara Mansuri (2013), "Doing Deals in Africa— Reflections on What is Different and What is Not," *Business Law International,* Vol. 14, No: 2, May 2013.

represents a serious effort from member states to harmonise their business laws in order to provide certainty and predictability for investors. Fondufe and Mansuri note that since 2005, thanks to OHADA, the number of procedures required to set up a business is down by 25 percent, delays down by 29 percent, and costs down by 67 percent. This is an incredible untold story of cooperation in Africa.

Why this digression then? This is because such regional harmonisation is already working on the continent. It makes sense. It creates efficiency for international investors. Broadband, Internet, and media investments would benefit from it. OHADA presents an excellent model. There is much in TMT regulation that will benefit from such OHADA-type harmonisation.

9. *Governments should encourage use of their powers to direct sector regulators to ensure their priorities mirror the TMT vision and strategy—spectrum auctions, digital switch over for terrestrial TV, universal access, etc.:* This is consistent with having a national TMT vision and strategy. There is a strong case as the digital switchover (DSO) is about to happen in many African countries for sectoral regulators to publish clear plans on areas like defining the strategy for UHF spectrum. Some of this valuable spectrum will be cleared via DSO. However, the key next steps are auctioning some of the spectrum for 4G and using some for digital TV, and I also propose license exempting[27] or light licensing some of it for TV white spaces in order to drive up options for access and affordability in the rural areas. Similarly, regulators should publish their 4G release or auction plans and commence the eighteen-month- to two-year process of preparation, including understanding and analysing the competitive market structure in the market today and

---

27 License exemption is an approach to licensing spectrum wherein operators are able to operate electromagnetic communications equipment using frequency airwaves without having to hold a license from the regulator. Without a license, they also operate on a best efforts basis with respect to interference issues.

the broadband market structure the regulator would like to see after the auction/release. All of these need to be consulted on and converted into auction/release rules, which are designed into auction software that will be used to run the auction. The important point here is one of clarity, urgency, and transparency about the regulator's priorities and their consistency with the national TMT Vision and Strategy.

3.3.3 Technological Blueprint Recommendation Process

Decision makers are many times prone to be scared off by technology issues. I hope you are so far concluding to yourself that TMT technology is different, but not quite rocket science. Chapter 2 majored on the basics, emphasising the areas that decision makers should worry about, whilst leaving the other details to the technology nerds. Indeed, these principles are further collated in section 3.2—in slightly unstructured but hopefully simple prose. This is deliberate because that level of description in chapter 2 along with the principles in section 3.2 are more than sufficient to truly direct technical staff along with economic, legal, and other senior civil servants to both formulate and implement good policy. So the recommendation here is one of a *process* you can adopt.

The technological blueprint recommendation here is an approach to interrogate things technical, without being that technical yourself. The recommendation here is presented for the benefit of the project sponsor or his appointed subsponsor. What should he or she do? It is assumed here that he/she has already set up a technology work stream as per recommendations 1 and 3.

10. *Firm up, produce, and interrogate the detailed technology/ ICT implementation plans which are derived from the TMT strategy and vision:* Remember the strategy and vision outputs described above include the following: (i) passive layer ducts, poles, and trenches infrastructure, (ii) fixed-line infrastructure, including national and regional fibre backbones and

their backup fibre and IXPs, (iii) for the future, the growth of mobile infrastructure, particularly majoring on coverage, and (v) Internet and broadband infrastructure strategy, including Internet for the masses strategy using TV white spaces technology to drive universal access. These are all elements of the technology/ICT implementation plan.

You may be rightly concerned that you are not technical. Do not worry. You may choose then to appoint a trusted subsponsor of this work stream who is more technical to assist you. In any case, do not be scared off that easily. Try using the vertical layers model and/or the onion model below to help you interrogate some of the details of this telecoms and technology work stream.

ILLUSTRATIVE LAYERS TO VISUALISE TO INTERROGATE TECHNOLOGY

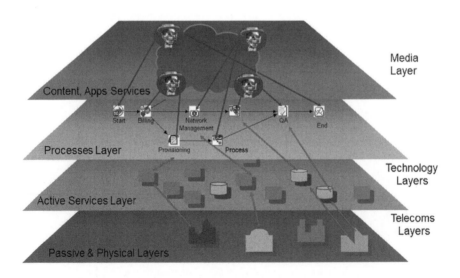

Figure 24—Illustrative Layers to Visualise to Interrogate Technology

ILLUSTRATIVE ONION MODEL TO VISUALISE TO
INTERROGATE TECHNOLOGY/TELECOMS LAYERS

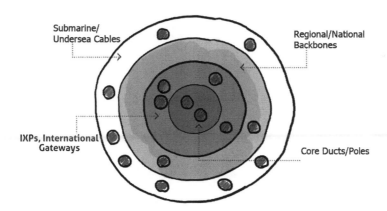

Figure 25—Illustrative Onion Model to Visualise to Interrogate
Technology/Telecoms Layers

First, visualise the different layers of the TMT stack as in figure 24: the passive layer of ducts, poles, dark fibre, and wireless
access; the active layer of electronic equipment; the processes
and systems layer and lastly the services layer.

Passive Layer Interrogation

Perhaps you want to start with the passive and physical layers. Perhaps you want to visualise an *onion model* which starts
with the submarine cables carrying dark fibre that run under
the oceans and that are "landed" in your country. So visualise starting from outside the country via the deep sea cables
coming into the cities'/towns' ducts and poles as shown in
figure 25.

Some questions to pose and interrogate follow (drawing from
chapter 2):

- How is competition working with all these submarine cables landed in your country or state or province?
- The next layer of the onion interrogates the distribution infrastructure both nationally and regionally. What does the national fibre spine look like, and what is its coverage? How are regulators and the TMT ministry ensuring interconnectivity?
- Have they coordinated with the town planning ministry to ensure that fibre breakout points have been adequately planned for shopping centres, business districts, major offices, mobile base-station sites, etc.?
- What is the coverage of the national backbone networks? Does it hit all the key Tier 1 and Tier 2 towns and cities?
- What are the plans for the Tier 3 regions where you may need a combination of satellite (FSS) and TV white spaces infrastructure or equivalent?
- Are all the regional, state, or provincial chief information officers (CIOs) or their equivalents clear on the regional distribution project plans?
- What percentage of the population is within 20 km, 15 km, 10 km, or 5 km from a fibre node?
- Are the wireless operators able to interconnect into the national and regional networks, in addition to their core and competitors networks?

Moving on to the next layer of the onion in figure 25, consider the following:

- Where are the IXPs located for regional interconnectivity?
- Where are the national international gateway points? How are they regulated for competition and interconnectivity? Are the costs FRND-ly? Can new entrants enter the market?
- How are the TMT ministry and the regulator working with other countries to ensure the emergence of regional IXPs to address the inter-Africa local traffic routing to minimise the Kigali-Nairobi problem?

Moving even deeper still into the innermost passive core and ducts layer, ask:

○ Are all Tier 1 and Tier 2 regions specifying and building out their duct and pole infrastructure?

○ Even if one company is the first to roll out its dark fibre in the city, has the CIO of the city or state or region ensured that the new ducts' infrastructure and rings (the city fibre spine) have been specified and signed off? Has he/she ensured the right city coverage with the right breakout points? Are there empty duct "pipes" to allow competitors to be able to thread through their own fibre (maybe up to four to five empty slots for competitors) without digging out the whole town/city again? If the fibre is running off poles, some of these access issues are easier.

○ Are the rules for access to these ducts and poles clear? What remedies have the regulator put in place if there is a dominant operator (e.g., an incumbent operator) who dominates access to duct and pole infrastructure?

○ Is all the funding for the city, national, and regional distribution in place? If not who are we talking to ensure the funding is in place, or do we prioritise for later?

You can see how a combination of two visual aids (the layers model and the onion rings)—along with some understanding of the anatomy and geography of TMT of chapter 2 and principles of section 3.2—have both helped in asking some really deep questions: some of them technical, some regulatory, some international, some financial, some common sense. Do you now believe you can do it? Ignore the 100 percent accuracy of the questions above and figures 24 and 25.

The same process can be done for the other layers of figure 24. Such a work stream and interrogation process would yield a really detailed city, national, and regional set of milestones, risks, project plans (some devolved), RAG charts, etc. The sponsor can see all of these quite readily. This is how you dissect, plan, and monitor such an important project whilst asking the questions that really matter.

3.3.4 Regulatory Blueprint Recommendations

I hope you are becoming more comfortable with the central role of regulation in TMT. Some recommendations (namely 8 and 9 above) are already concerned with strengthening/merging regulators and ensuring their priorities are aligned with government's TMT strategy and vision. These recommendations apply to government too.

11. *Regulators really need to be truly independent and confidently clarify priorities over three-to-five-year period windows and be hungry to up their games:* In order for Africa and emerging economies to have the TMT sectors they deserve for the 2020s as per the title of the book, much work needs to be done for the rest of this decade. The role of truly independent and confident regulators, as noted earlier, would be crucial. Many a time on the continent, industry and stakeholders are left in the dark by regulators about what their key priority projects are and why. This is just wrong. The answer I sometimes get from regulators that they do not have the resources to do all these projects is nothing but an excuse. Ruthless prioritisation is sometimes necessary for regulators. If there is a need to ensure digital switchover by June 17, 2015 or 2020, for thirty countries by ITU law/decision, every country should have a clear priority and a set of plans to make this happen. Industry should not be guessing as to what is happening. The point of the switchover is to reuse the frequencies for other services, including digital TV and mobile broadband/Internet. This will necessitate 3G liberalisation and/or a 4G auction, and the latter necessitates a fair amount of work in preparation covering competition, coverage, universal access to Internet, new entrants, and innovation. Given 2015 is around the corner, there should be clear programmes and plans to do all these which have fully been

consulted on so that industry and other interested stakeholders can provide their views.

Once you are clear on the multiyear programme, e.g., 2013–2018, it is important for the regulator to also be clear on the annual priorities. Figure 26 shows Ofcom's (the independent TMT regulator in the United Kingdom). If you look at the "Infrastructure & Spectrum" column, you see priorities around clearing 800 MHz spectrum and supporting digital switch over. All this was to ensure there was spectrum to auction for 4G. In the same column, you also see "prepare plans for release of spectrum for mobile broadband," which clearly demonstrates preparation for auctioning the 4G spectrum. DSO was completed in October 2012, and the auction was eventually completed later in February 2013. In parallel, looking at the "Competition" column, you see two projects relevant to mobile broadband: "promote effective competition in fixed and mobile telecoms" and "implement regulation to support effective competition and efficient investment in superfast broadband."

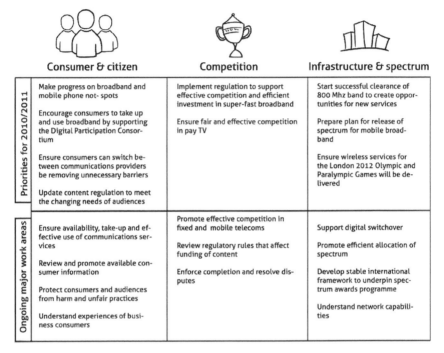

OFCOM (UK) ANNUAL PRIORITIES ACROSS THREE AREAS
FOR 2010-11 (SEVERAL OF THESE PRIORITIES WERE MULTI-YEAR PRIORITIES)
SOURCE: OFCOM UK WEBSITE

	Consumer & citizen	Competition	Infrastructure & spectrum
Priorities for 2010/2011	Make progress on broadband and mobile phone not-spots Encourage consumers to take up and use broadband by supporting the Digital Participation Consortium Ensure consumers can switch between communications providers be removing unnecessary barriers Update content regulation to meet the changing needs of audiences	Implement regulation to support effective competition and efficient investment in super-fast broadband Ensure fair and effective competition in pay TV	Start successful clearance of 800 Mhz band to create opportunities for new services Prepare plan for release of spectrum for mobile broadband Ensure wireless services for the London 2012 Olympic and Paralympic Games will be delivered
Ongoing major work areas	Ensure availability, take-up and effective use of communications services Review and promote available consumer information Protect consumers and audiences from harm and unfair practices Understand experiences of business consumers	Promote effective competition in fixed and mobile telecoms Review regulatory rules that affect funding of content Enforce completion and resolve disputes	Support digital switchover Promote efficient allocation of spectrum Develop stable international framework to underpin spectrum awards programme Understand network capabilities

Indentify opportunities for deregulation and simplification
Prepare to implement relevant European and UK legislative changes

Figure 26—Ofcom (UK) Annual Priorities across Three Areas for 2010–11
(several of these priorities were multiyear priorities)
(Source: Ofcom UK Website [Adapted])[28]

All these activities were priorities over several years, and some were still on going in 2013/14. The key point is industry, government, and all stakeholders were left in no doubt *what* Ofcom's priorities were and *why* and *when* Ofcom planned to realise them. They were also consulted. As the TMT thinking emerges across the continent, a similar clear set of internally

---

28   Source: http://www.ofcom.org.uk/files/2010/06/annplan1011.pdf (accessed August 2013).

consistent priorities across our regulators on the continent would be needed.

The role independent regulators have to play to prepare Africa TMT for the 2020s is so critical that governments should truly strengthen them, support them, and get out of their way. Regulators in return must be confident and learn assiduously over the next several years from experts and consultants how to regulate better and raise their games across the continent. Learning how some of the best independent converged regulators in the world work is highly recommended. Secondments from some of these best-in-class regulators should also be explored. The boards of these regulators should really be strengthened. The excellent comparative sector performance review of sectors by Colandro and his colleagues[29] should also be extended to cover more specifically the performance of regulators in the continent and across emerging markets, and their independent boards must act promptly and swiftly on any negative findings. Governments too must not meddle with independent regulators except via "directions" which force them to go back to their legislative bodies/parliaments. Every time I read on how some President or "Big Man" has intervened in the actions of an independent regulator, I am truly depressed as it sends such a bad signal to international (and even national) investors. President Mwai Kibaki of Kenya intervened in August 2012 (for the second time in as many years!) to prevent an independent regulator (CCK) from lowering the existing mobile termination rates (MTRs).[30] Critics noted Kibaki was protecting Safaricom, in which the government has a significant stake, as well as largely state-owned Telcom Kenya (Orange). Truly depressing!

---

29 Enrico Calandro, Alison Gillwald, Mpho Moyo, and Christoph Stork (2010), *Comparative Sector Performance Review 2009/2010: Towards Evidence-based ICT Policy and Regulation*, Volume 2, Policy Paper 2, researchICTafrica.net.

30 "Airtel Kenya has to sell 15% stake locally," *Africa Telecom & IT*, November 2012, p. 6.

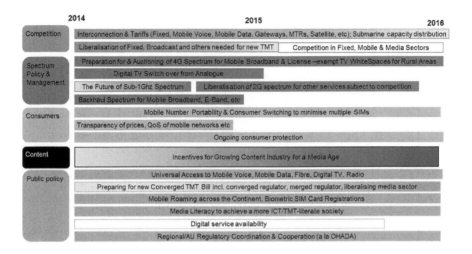

Figure 27—A Straw Man Set of Three-Year Strategic Priorities That May Apply to Many African Countries (note that this three-year agenda "window" could be moved to the right to span 2015 to 2017, 2016 to 2018, or 2017 to 2019)

12. *Some recommended areas which regulators must/could prioritise over the next three to five years in order to make the TMT vision happen in the 2020s:* Having pointed out that regulators must confidently spell out their priorities over the next several years to start sowing the seeds of the type of TMT sectors Africa deserves in the 2020s, it would be remiss not to suggest some on the basis of the analyses reported in the first three chapters so far. I do this in the spirit of providing a *this-is-one-I-prepared-earlier* in order to stimulate debate amongst policy makers and regulators. Some brief justifications follow.

Figure 27 is a brave attempt to provide a straw man three- to five-year key set of priorities for regulators and government policy makers to make the sort of TMT vision espoused in this volume happen in the 2020s. It will not be right in every country, but it provides a reasonable starting point. It is also sketched out as a blueprint to demonstrate to government policy makers why they need advice and why they need to strengthen regulators.

We look at the agenda groups of items in turn, and we draw from previous pages of this volume to help justify this straw man agenda.

- Competition: Interconnection and tariffs are priorities as they are still well-known issues on the continent. There is much international evidence that point to the fact that truly long-term cost-oriented mobile and fixed termination rates drive up competition and affordable pricing and tariffs. There are still some ridiculously high termination rates on the continent, e.g., in Cameroon, Benin, or South Africa (see Calandro *et al.*, 2010). They conclude that high tariffs have been a major barrier to access telecommunication services and a clear indicator to poor competition.

- Competition: Submarine international connectivity fibre distribution. Clearly all the seventy-five terabytes design capacity by 2014 of international capacity (see figure 12) being landed on the shores of Africa need to be distributed nationally and regionally. Otherwise, the business cases for these expensive landings will fail. There are significant competition issues to deal with in the national and regional distribution of this international connectivity, and regulation has a great role to play here. Some routes (e.g., Lagos to Abuja) will have excess capacity where the market will thrive, whilst many other routes would have no connectivity at all, necessitating a national backbone provider of last resort who would need to be regulated.

- Competition: Liberalisation of fixed, broadcast, etc., for TMT to happen. The gains from the liberalisation of the mobile sector are there for all to see across most of the continent in 2013/14 bar countries like Ethiopia. As we move into digital switch over and into the multichannel terrestrial TV world on the continent, the broadcast sector would need to be similarly liberalised. So do the fixed sectors where many fixed-line incumbents across the continent are still 100 percent or significantly government owned. Surely, this cannot be the case in 2020, and the work must start now.

- Competition: Continuous and improved competition in fixed, mobile voice, mobile data, and media must clearly be a priority. There are also pockets of suspected anticompetitive practices or dominant operators in most markets on the continent. Indeed, Calandro *et al.* (2010) conclude that an overwhelming majority of the seventeen countries they studied perceived authorities as ineffective in the regulation of anticompetitive practices.
- Spectrum: Liberalisation of 2G spectrum for 3G and other services. This is an important recommendation, as many countries already have been awarded 2G spectrum, and they are still meandering their way into providing 3G services. A policy of spectrum liberalisation is important wherein some of the spectrum is liberalised in the hands of the current incumbents so that they could use it not only for 2G services but also for other services they choose subject to some technical constraints. Liberalisation emphasises the technology and service neutrality principles. Some countries have already varied current licenses and made them technology and service neutral. Many others are still to do this. However, such liberalisations must always be mindful of competition checks, and this is explained further in chapter 5.
- Spectrum: Preparation for and releasing/auctioning of 4G spectrum for mobile broadband and license exemption or light licensing of TV white spaces. The case for this has been made several times already. There will have to be a spate of 4G auctions/releases in Africa in the 2015–2018 timescales for 4G covering 700 MHz or 800 MHz and 2.6 GHz. Universal access to broadband demands TV whites paces for rural broadband as another option.
- Spectrum: Digital TV switch over from analogue to digital. This needs to be completed by June 17, 2015, by ITU decision for the southern Africa states and 2020 for the remaining thirty of the African countries. Frankly though, most countries should aim for 2015.

- Spectrum: The Future of sub-1 GHz spectrum is an important initiative for the continent. Some countries are still hanging on to CDMA in 800 MHz, which is a very valuable spectrum, and in some countries like Nigeria it is doubtful if this constitutes optimal use of this valuable spectrum, particularly when the spectrum is effectively licensed regionally within the country, i.e., different operators have rights to the spectrum in different cities in the country. How much spectrum do African countries really need for TV? How much can be "reserved" for white spaces light licensing or license exemption, etc.?

- Spectrum: Backhaul spectrum—spectrum is being released for 4G broadband and TV white spaces; these networks also require backhaul spectrum which carry data from the access networks back into the core. Bands such as E-Band,[31] 28 GHz, 32 GHz, and 40 GHz, etc., could be considered for auctioning or licensing in some way on the continent.

- Consumers: Mobile number portability—there is an almost norm of multiple SIMs in many countries on the continent driven by perceived coverage and other issues. As some of these issues get alleviated over the next several years through coverage competition, consumer switching would (or should) become a key goal for making communications markets work well for consumers and citizens. It also would help minimise the "wastage" of numbers through increasingly needless multiple SIMs.

- Consumer: Transparency of prices, QoS of mobile networks: Another key initiative area for regulators to continuously fight for consumer interests on the continent today is in the area of complicated price tariffs, which truly need simplification in many countries. Similarly, many networks on the continent are beginning to creak under the weight of their bulging subscriber bases at the expense of many dropped calls and generally poor quality of service. These need to be continually monitored, and operators are required to improve their services to their

---

31 60–90 GHz microwave

customers. Further evidence to support this recommended priority comes from Calandro *et al.* (2010), who find a very poor quality of service perception across the seventeen countries they researched.

- Consumer: Ongoing consumer protection—this is not an area I perceive to be getting enough priority on the continent. Consumer protection is about preventing consumers from being directly impacted by unfair practices and scams, effectively preempting "consumer harm" being suffered by consumers.
- Content/Media: Incentives on growing content industry for a media age—as the TMT sector evolves, and the media sector is increasingly liberalised across the continent, regulatory and other government policy incentives and initiatives would be needed to facilitate the emergence and growth of a more professional content and media sector.
- Public Policy: Universal access to mobile voice, mobile data, fibre, digital TV and Radio—the evidence by Calandro *et al.* (2010) broadly suggests that many African countries are failing on their universal service obligations, concluding, "although several countries have established UAFs and often dedicated agencies to ensure their implementation, these have not yielded the intended results."

And this is in a world where voice is the dominant service. If this "culture of failure" is carried into mobile data/Internet, fibre and digital TV, consumers and citizens will really be short-changed.

- Public Policy: Preparing for a new converged TMT bill, including converged regulators, merged regulators, and liberalising the media sector—for TMT to emerge as this volume espouses in the 2020s, new enabling legislations must happen across all countries in the next three to five years, covering areas like creating converged regulators in some countries, enabling the liberalisation of media in most countries, strengthening regulators in most countries, etc.

- Public Policy: Mobile roaming across the continent—the roaming problem has been incredibly better addressed through competition in east Africa thanks largely to the actions of the then Zain (today called Bharti Airtel) who dropped all roaming charges between its networks in east Africa via their "One Network" policy across different markets in east Africa. Competitors had no choice but to respond. What an outcome! What a great example of competition working in the interests of east African consumers. Pity the same does not apply to west, southern, or North Africa as of 2013/14.

- Public Policy: Biometric SIM card registration—there is already a looming problem on the continent which concerns governments, regulators, and security agencies of poor on inexistent registration of SIM cards. Scrupulous criminals who use mobiles to scam foreign and/or national citizens must be traced, but today, in most countries on the continent, they cannot. With mobile payments growing on the continent so incredibly, authenticated SIMs are invaluable to the integrity of the transactions. Regulators may want to price for numbers sometime in the next decade, and biometrically registered SIMs will help authenticate the data to base such pricing.

- Public Policy: Cybersecurity—cybersecurity refers to the bevy of processes, systems, technologies, and best practices designed to protect computers, networks, data, and software from attack, snooping, outright damage, or fraud. Many African countries do not even have the requisite cybersecurity legislation, yet they have burgeoning mobile money systems. In Kenya alone, Deloitte estimates that the Kenyan economy loses US$35.7 million to cybercrime annually, and lost US$71.4 million to fraudsters between 2011 and 2012.[32] Ernst & Young (the Big 4 consultancy) also estimates the cost of cybercrimes to the Nigerian economy to be US$200 million but notes further that the international reputational damage is

---

32 "Kenya to force mobile money systems audit," *Africa Telecom & IT,* January 2013, p. 50.

much worse. Governments need advice to come up with fit-for-purpose cybersecurity legislation and possibly empower their independent communications regulators or another agent of government to provide cybersecurity services, disseminating cybersecurity information and acting as a national focal point on cybersecurity matters.

- Public Policy: Media literacy to achieve a more ICT/TMT-literate society—there will need to be a concerted effort through education primarily but also using other media such as broadcast TV to drive up ICT skills and media literacy on the continent as the TMT sector evolves.
- Public Policy: IPv4 to IPv6—every computer, device, or other equipment connected to the Internet needs a numerical number which constitutes its address so that it can be uniquely identified. This numerical address is called the Internet protocol (IP) address. Today we are using an IP addressing scheme called IP version 4 or IPv4, which is a thirty-two-bit number addressing system. This is an addressing scheme of thirty-two numbers consisting only of zeroes and ones.

To demystify this, the BBC website (i.e., the www.bbc.co.uk URL, which you and I will recognise) in computer-speak is actually and uniquely 194.33.160.25, which is what techies will reel out at you. The thirty-two-bit reality inside version which computers actually use is: 11000010 . 00100001 . 11000000 . 00011001 (without the dots and spaces). If you remember your base-2 arithmetic, you will (easily) work out at this four-set of eight numbers translates to 193.33.160.25, which computers will translate uniquely to the bbc.co.uk website.

The problem is that though this is a big number, the developed world (mostly) has already almost exhausted all these addresses, and the world needs a larger addressing pool. Thirty-two bits give us an addressing pool of about 4.3 billion unique BBC-type addresses. The expected explosion in broadband deployments in Africa, explosion in smartphones, and 'Internet of things'[33] all need unique IP addresses. Given there are already seven billion plus people on Earth, you can see we are already short. And in the future, a traffic light in Cairo would need its own unique IP address, as would your smart electric meter or gas meter in your home. So a new version called IP version 6 (IPv6), which uses 128-bit numbers, was developed in 1995, giving an addressing scheme of more than fifty-seven billion addresses. Africa and other emerging economies—by definition—are yet to "explode" in their demand of devices connected to the Internet. They are strongly recommended to promote IPv6 in their national ICT plans rather than IPv4. It is the case that IPv4 is quite entrenched today. However, this will be a future-proofing decision that future generations of Africans will thank our generation for. This is technical policy—but it must be done. Regulators and government should set up a local IPv6 taskforce with significant government and civil society to increase local awareness and encourage network operators to implement IPv6. They should engage AfriNIC,[34] who has been working with governments and the private sector to encourage IPv6 adoption.

- Public Policy: Regional/African union regulatory coordination and cooperation (a la OHADA)—I have already made the case for this earlier on in this chapter. One further look at this agenda also shows many areas where such cooperation may/would be invaluable, e.g., interconnection, roaming, universal access, spectrum, etc.

As noted earlier, whether you fully agree with this agenda is less the point. I obviously believe it is a defensible agenda to prepare

---

33   The "internet of things" is a concept that describes a future wherein everyday physical objects are or will be connected to the Internet to be able to identify themselves to other objects, e.g. milk bottles identifying themselves as "empty" to fridges.

34   AFRINIC defines itself as the regional registry for Internet number resources serving the African Internet Community (www.afrinic.net/).

Africa for the TMT sector it deserves for the 2020s. One thing is clear if you broadly agree with the above priorities: figure 27 is a challenging agenda which will stretch the best resourced regulators in the world, yet alone underresourced and underskilled ones on the continent. Furthermore, if they are not skilled or if regulators do not work together, then it is difficult to see how such a challenging agenda can be implemented for the sector. And working on such an agenda we must! African consumers and citizens deserve it. We will look at this issues some more in a subsequent chapter on regulation (see chapter 11).

3.3.5 Consumer and Industry Blueprint Recommendations

Consumers and industry also need to be looked after. These recommendations apply to Government, regulators, and the wider consumer and industry sectors.

13. *Consumers must advocate, and, more importantly, they must be helped to ensure their voices are heard in as many ways as possible:* It is the case that most TMT regulators have a primary statutory duty to further the interests of consumers and citizens in communications matters. It is also the case that the evidence, e.g., Calandro *et al.* (2010), is pointing to more African regulators than not failing in this primary duty. However, as the industry matures, there is also a strong case to be made that (i) consumers must also learn to help themselves, (ii) and as they should also be helped to help themselves. For the former, the emergence of consumer advocacy groups should and would emerge. Some of these groups on the continent could be organisations like Citizens Advice Bureaus (CABs), who advise consumers on miscellaneous issues or churches. For the latter, the regulator and government do have significant roles to play. Under the rubric "consumer empowerment," regulators can carry out initiatives that lead to consumers being able to act for themselves to secure benefits from the market. This

includes providing clear information to consumers, facilitating consumers being able to switch suppliers, and helping them understand fully their rights of redress. Regulators should also go out of their way to ensure representative "voices" of the customer are heard by setting up meaningful consumer panels, particularly for disadvantaged groups in our societies, like the old, in some cases women, and, of course, the disabled. On the part of the government, representatives of the people, including members of parliaments (MPs), senators, and councillors, should always see it as their responsibility to be the voice of the people on issues of telecommunications and raise issues with the TMT ministry and the regulator.

14. *Industry advocacy—via trade associations—must emphasise SMEs' and the third sector's voices:* It is a sad truism that regulators' attention and resources are disproportionately taken up by big industry operators and their issues. It is therefore invaluable that the voices of small and medium enterprises (SMEs) who employ the majority of people in societies are loudly heard. By definition, they are sprawling and fragmented, and this is always a problem. However, they are the ones who would and should be banging at the doors of national and state governments, demanding Internet and broadband yesterday. Such SME industry and third sector organisations like charities must really advocate over the next decade in a sustained manner, and some of you may choose to take up this mandate. Earlier on in this volume, we noted that trade associations play an important role in the TMT sector, how they are typically founded and funded by industry, and that they typically engage in public relations activities, such as advertising lobbying, publishing, and education. Organisations of this ilk must evolve across the continent of Africa. They would run conferences and networking events where government officials and regulators would be invited. Governments should also encourage the emergence of such advocacy groups to drive up standards in the TMT sector.

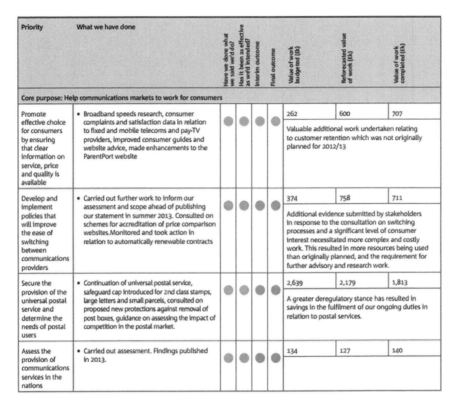

Priority	What we have done	Have we done what we said we'd do?	Has it been as effective as we'd intended?	Interim outcome	Final outcome	Value of work budgeted (£k)	Reforecasted value of work (£k)	Value of work completed (£k)
Core purpose: Help communications markets to work for consumers								
Promote effective choice for consumers by ensuring that clear information on service, price and quality is available	• Broadband speeds research, consumer complaints and satisfaction data in relation to fixed and mobile telecoms and pay-TV providers, improved consumer guides and website advice, made enhancements to the ParentPort website	◉	◉	◉	◉	262 Valuable additional work undertaken relating to customer retention which was not originally planned for 2012/13	600	707
Develop and implement policies that will improve the ease of switching between communications providers	• Carried out further work to inform our assessment and scope ahead of publishing our statement in summer 2013. Consulted on schemes for accreditation of price comparison websites.Monitored and took action in relation to automatically renewable contracts	◉	◉	◉	◉	374 Additional evidence submitted by stakeholders in response to the consultation on switching processes and a significant level of consumer interest necessitated more complex and costly work. This resulted in more resources being used than originally planned, and the requirement for further advisory and research work.	758	711
Secure the provision of the universal postal service and determine the needs of postal users	• Continuation of universal postal service, safeguard cap introduced for 2nd class stamps, large letters and small parcels, consulted on proposed new protections against removal of post boxes, guidance on assessing the impact of competition in the postal market.	◉	◉	◉	◉	2,639 A greater deregulatory stance has resulted in savings in the fulfilment of our ongoing duties in relation to postal services.	2,179	1,813
Assess the provision of communications services in the nations	• Carried out assessment. Findings published in 2013.	◉	◉	◉	◉	134	127	140

◉ We have done what we said we would do
◉ We continue to make progress towards achieving the priority

◉ We have not made as much progress as we thought we would do
◉ It is too early to assess our progress

Figure 28—Ofcom (UK) 2012–13 Annual Reporting against Its Annual Plan
Priorities (most of the priorities are multiyear priorities)
(Source: Ofcom UK Website[35])

15. *Ensure reporting on delivering against TMT priorities:* We return to the issue of reporting and monitoring. If one sets up an elaborate TMT sector plan, one must measure how well we are doing against them. The independent regulator is arguably best placed to provide an independent progress report not only on its own annual sector plan priorities but also on the government's annual and three-year plan (etc.) for the TMT sector.

---

35 http://www.ofcom.org.uk/files/2013/07/Ofcom_Annual-Report_AD600_ACC-2_English.pdf, (accessed August 2013).

I unashamedly borrow from my ex-colleagues at Ofcom on a sample model on how to report.

This sample report in figure 28 shows the following:

- The priority: name the priority clearly
- What we have done: what exactly has been done
- Have we done what we said we'd do
- Interim outcome: intended outcomes typically take several to many years to realise. A final coverage outcome for voice coverage may be to 95 percent36 population coverage (for voice in the country) is achieved. An interim outcome may be the government/regulator utilising the Universal Access Fund to carry out a successful pilot on how to get to some of the most rural areas in the country or the regulator imposing a license condition on one or more licensees to roll out to 95 percent of the population.
- Final outcome: as above.
- Value of work budgeted
- Value of work completed

Such a report is simple but comprehensive enough to provide a sample way of reporting on progress made in the TMT sector.

This concludes a blueprint for TMT in Africa and some emerging markets. It is *a* blueprint, not *the* blueprint. The rest of the volume delves into some of these areas. Each of these recommendations requires significant and different levels of work, which the stakeholders would mostly need external help to grapple with—help they are thoroughly advised to seek.

---

36 100 percent is typically too costly to achieve.

3.4 Example Outcomes from Three-Year Set of Strategic Priorities

The proposed agenda of figure 27 has a very clear set of intended interim and final outcomes which drive the rest of the book. You will have realized by now that the fervour and tone of this volume is nothing but outcomes oriented. Therefore, given the blueprint of this chapter, what are some of the key areas that need to be expounded upon in order to realise the rest of the goals the book set out to address? Some example intended outcomes from the proposed agenda of figure 27 may be the following:

- Competition: Ensure interconnection rates for fixed, mobile voice, mobile data, MTRs, wholesale charges for international bandwidth, etc., are cost oriented, i.e., determinations based on pure LRIC[37] costs. This will be an ideal outcome here. Otherwise it leads to high-end prices for consumers and stifled competition. Outcome areas concerned: lowest priced fixed, mobile voice, mobile data, and wholesale charges for international bandwidth.

- Competition: Ensure tariffs for fixed, mobile voice, and mobile data are subject to optimum competition. Pricing is always subject to so many factors, but arguably the number of competitors (e.g., above three) generally leads to fiercer competition and hence lower prices. In other countries, a disruptive and price-discounting new entrant is the answer. A good outcome here is one of the lowest benchmarked prices on the continent (or across emerging market countries) when benchmarked for country purchasing power parity too. Outcome areas concerned: lowest priced fixed, mobile voice, mobile data, and highest coverage.

---

37 Long-run incremental costs only, i.e., including no common costs, as in LRIC+.

- Competition: Ensure fixed, broadcast, and media sectors are liberalised for competition. A good outcome here would be these subsectors becoming far more dynamic than the moribund ones today on the continent, with more choice of providers (typically only one today), and much better quality and innovation. Outcome areas concerned: more competitively priced fixed supply and broadcast and media supply.

- Spectrum Policy and Management: All 2G spectrum liberalised for 3G and other services. This is theoretically the easiest first step to start addressing the mobile data tsunami problem, as it allows spectrum already out there in the market being made technology and service neutral.

- Spectrum Policy and Management: Digital TV switch over from analogue to digital terrestrial TV and Future of sub-1 GHz spectrum. A good outcome here will be all countries completing this process by June 17, 2015, or shortly thereafter, though many can do this later too. Another key outcome is by the end of 2015, all countries will have clear plans for their valuable spectrum below 1 GHz, including "spectrum re-pricing" of 900 MHz 2G spectrum to reflect true opportunity costs, plans for 800 MHz (e.g., clawing back some bands from CDMA operators), plans for 700 MHz, plans for 600 MHz (e.g., to TV whites paces), plans for Band III for TV, etc.

- Spectrum Policy and Management: 4G and backhaul spectrum for mobile broadband. A good interim outcome will be to ensure timely preparation and auction of 4G spectrum for both coverage (using sub-1 GHz spectrum above) and capacity by the end of 2015, including backhaul spectrums. A final medium-term (circa five to seven years) outcome is to have fierce competition for mobile data driving prices down to amongst the lowest on the continent, along with the highest percentage coverage of the population. Another good interim outcome will be the license exemption of TV whites paces for rural coverage as another option to achieve rural broadband. Outcome areas concerned: lowest priced fixed broadband, mobile data, and highest data and broadband coverage.

• Consumers: Mobile number portability (MNP) and switching. A good interim outcome will be the implementation and rolling out of MNP by 2015/16 and ensuring consumers and citizens can port their numbers from network to network (i.e., switch) in seventy-two hours. Another good outcome could be the reduction in the use of multiple SIMS from more than two per person to closer to one per person in five to seven years. This can be clearly tracked. Outcome areas concerned: mobile voice and mobile data.

• Consumers: Transparency of prices and QoS of mobile networks. A good interim outcome will be the implementation of a well-publicised price comparison accreditation scheme in order to help consumers choose the best tariffs for their level of usage. Over the long term, a final outcome would be an informed public (they can be polled) who are empowered and know how to get the best tariffs. Similar quality of mobile networks service data being published prominently will be a good interim outcome to drive up performance, with consumers being similarly empowered in the long term to know which networks provide the best service for them, and they can switch as they see fit. Outcome areas concerned: mobile voice and mobile data.

• Content: Incentives for growing the content industry for a media age. A good interim/final outcome here will be a more dynamic content sector (e.g., for TV channels) attracting significant and measurable cash investment; more choices and longer weekly measured TV/radio minutes of national and international news; more choices and longer weekly measured TV/radio minutes of national drama, children's, and comedy output, etc. Outcome areas concerned: TV, radio, Internet, etc.

- Public Policy: Universal access to mobile voice, mobile data, fibre, digital TV and radio, and digital service availability. A good interim outcome here would be annual increased measures of coverage as a percentage of population, particularly in rural areas for these services, and take up of these services. Another would be ensuring low-cost equipment is affordable even in less affluent rural areas, like set-top boxes, low-cost handsets, and low-cost data devices. Outcome areas concerned: TV, radio, Internet, mobile data, and mobile voice.

- Public Policy: Converged TMT legislations. A simple final outcome here would be fully independent converged (and merged) regulators across the continent and clearly implemented government acts liberalising the media and broadcast sectors. Outcome areas concerned: TV, radio, Internet, mobile data, and mobile voice.

- Public Policy: Mobile roaming across the continent. Parts of east Africa (Kenya, Tanzania, and Uganda) have addressed the mobile roaming problem through competition driven by Zain/ Bharti. A good final outcome will be other parts of Africa achieving the same outcome for roaming as these countries. Bharti operates in many more markets beyond these three east African countries. Outcome areas concerned: mobile data and mobile voice.

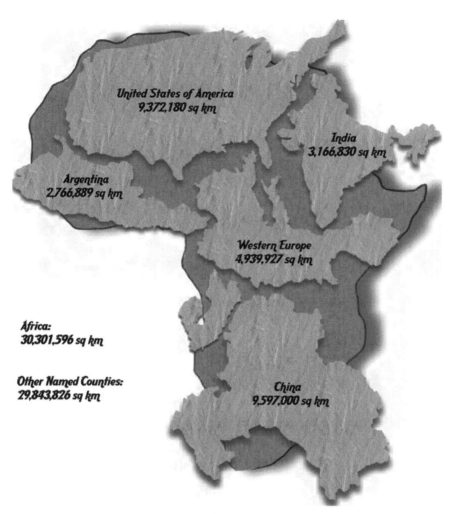

Africa Map: Africa Is a Massive Continent
(The USA, India, Western Europe, and China Can
Largely Fit into Africa's Land Mass)
(Source: Bill Hearmon)[38]

- Public Policy: Media literacy to achieve a more ICT/
  TMT-literate society. This will be starting from an extremely
  low base, and therefore interim outcomes will be consistent

---

38 William Hearmon, chairman at African Broadband Forum, presentation at
CTO Forum, Abuja, October 2012.

survey increases in media literacy over many years. Outcome areas concerned: TV, radio, Internet, mobile data, and mobile voice.

- Public Policy: Regional/AU regulatory coordination and cooperation (a la OHADA). For interim and final outcomes here, Africa should look no further than how European EU regulation operates through many harmonised areas of regulation of the TMT sector and, even closer to home, how OHADA operates.

You may disagree in places with some of the interim and final outcomes above—but at least we would be in a position to debate what the right outcomes should be rather than having none.

3.5 Summary of Desired Broad-Themed Outcomes from Blueprint

Finally, the outcomes and interim outcomes above point to some clear general-themed outcomes, which the rest of the volume expounds upon:

- widespread availability of affordable mobile voice (including roaming intracountry and across the continent) for the masses
- widespread availability of affordable mobile data and mobile Internet (3G/4G) and otherwise (e.g., TV white spaces) for rural parts, including mobile data roaming for the masses
- widespread availability of affordable radio (including community radio and temporary radio formats) and digital TV content (national and international news, comedy, drama, children's, documentary for the masses) and newspapers
- better availability of affordable fixed line and fixed Internet
- strong independent converged regulators (who work collectively and more formally too across the AU) and liberalised TMT sectors across the continent

We cover these and more in the rest of this volume.

No country which takes the blueprint recommendations in this chapter on board—or some other variants—to design its TMT sector would be accused of having failed to prepare its TMT sector, to quote Benjamin Franklin.

Lastly, but by no means least, as the you read the rest of the chapters of this volume, you should keep in mind these four significant further challenges about Africa, not much acknowledged in many other works.

- **Challenge 1—the incredible size of the African continent:** Africa is an incredibly big continent, as shown in the map above. Marvel at the fact that on the African continent you can fit the USA, India, Western Europe, China, and Argentina—and there is still some more land to spare. Africa is truly a vast continent. This means rolling out terrestrial networks of any kind is quite a costly exercise of humongous costs.

- **Challenge 2—Africa's one billion people are more evenly distributed across the continent compared to other continents:** following on from the first challenge is the challenge of the size of the African population at one billion people and growing. In comparison to Africa, the smaller populations of Canada, Australia, or the United States of America are not mostly concentrated around their coasts.
  - According to the Australian Bureau of Statistics (ABS) in 2001,[39] eight in ten Australians (85 percent) lived within 50 km of the coast, and there were only twenty-three million Australians, according to ABS in 2013.
  - Similarly, 80 percent of Canada's mere thirty-four million people live within 150 km of the US border, according to Wikipedia.[40]

---

39 Source: www.abs.gov.au

40 Source: http://en.wikipedia.org/wiki/Canada#Demographics (accessed October 2013)

○ Americans also largely live around their three major coasts. In 2000, almost two in three (64 percent) of Americans lived in states along these coasts: 38 percent along the Atlantic Ocean, 16 percent along the Pacific Ocean, and 12 percent along the Gulf of Mexico.

For these *developed* countries (which are all smaller than Africa) they can focus their terrestrial networks more easily and efficiently where the bulk of their populations live. Africa's fifty-four poorer *developing* countries distribute one billion peoples more thinly across the continent.

- **Challenge 3—seventy (70) percent of Africans reside in the rural parts of Africa:** this is an incredible challenge for inclusion and hence to achieving for adjectives like "widespread" and "affordable."

- **Challenge 4—low average revenue per user (ARPUs):** as we saw earlier in chapter 3, the current 2013 ARPU on the African continent is in the range of four to ten US dollars. This is only between 10 and 20 percent of developed countries' ARPUs, yet these revenues have to pay for more extensive networks on the African continent.

The first three triple whammy of challenges—along with the fourth, i.e., much smaller ARPUs on the continent—make rolling out financially sustainable and affordable networks for most Africans almost impossible. These overarching challenges must be borne in mind for the rest of the book, as they provide real and extremely costly hurdles to achieving the broad-themed outcomes of this blueprint. I do *not* want to give the impression that these outcomes are anything but nontrivial outcomes across the continent of Africa in particular.

SECTION III

TOWARDS WIDESPREAD AVAILABILITY OF AFFORDABLE HIGH-QUALITY MOBILE VOICE, MOBILE DATA, AND MOBILE INTERNET FOR THE MASSES

CHAPTER 4

SPECTRUM 101 AND TMT SPECTRUM RECOMMENDATIONS FOR AFRICA AND EMERGING MARKETS

"Spectrum is the oxygen of the wireless world."
—Julius Genachowski[1]

Radio spectrum is indeed the oxygen of all wireless communications and is so much more important in Africa and some emerging market countries like Myanmar, Bangladesh, etc., where there is a dearth of fixed line infrastructure. Wireless communications is *sine qua non* to African and emerging economies' TMT. Ergo radio spectrum is indispensable to African and emerging economies' TMT sectors, hence meriting a clear chapter in this volume.

---

1   Julius Genachowski was chairman of the US Federal Communications Commission (FCC) from June 2009 to April 2013.

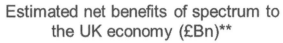

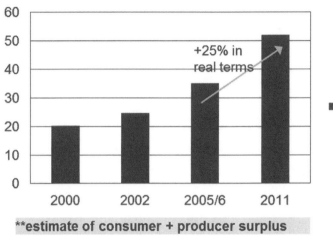

Source: *Europe Economics* (2006) & Analysys Mason (for 2011 number).

Figure 29—Radio Spectrum's Value to the UK Economy

(all African/emerging economies must carry out similar studies periodically)

The radio spectrum is the bevy of frequencies used for wireless applications, including broadcast TV, mobile voice, mobile data, satellite services, satellite navigation systems, satellite phones, Wi-Fi, police radio systems, emergency services, radio astronomy, store scanners, remote controls, car keys, home FM/AM radios, car radios, Bluetooth headsets, aeronautical radars to guide planes into airports, and so on.

Spectrum is indeed indispensable to this book. The previous chapter concluded with some of the desired broad-themed outcomes from the blueprint it proposed. The outcomes include:

(i) widespread and affordable mobile voice (including roaming across the continent) for the masses;

(ii) widespread and affordable mobile data (3G/4G), including rural parts of countries (e.g., using TV white spaces or equivalent) and mobile data roaming for the masses;

(iii) widespread digital TV content (including national and international news, comedy, drama, children's, documentary for the masses) and radio (including community radio and temporary radio formats); and

(iv) widespread and affordable Internet (mobile and fixed) for the businesses and consumers/citizens.

The first three can only be achieved using radio spectrum. Even parts of the last too need radio spectrum.

So we need to cover spectrum's relevance to this volume more and why we are singling out UHF spectrum. Indeed, what is UHF spectrum? Why single it out especially? The broad answer drives from the fact that spectrum is a finite and natural valuable resource, which is an absolute essential input to all sorts of wireless communications. There are literally thousands of applications that depend on radio spectrum, as the short list above attests.

In 2006, radio spectrum was worth £35 billion or $55 billion to the UK economy. By 2011, as figure 29 shows, a more recent study by Analysys Mason[2] on behalf on the UK government estimated that spectrum is now worth about £52 billion to UK GDP, i.e., more than 3.3 percent of the UK's GDP of circa 1.5 billion. Though admittedly, this is not an apple for apple study, it still does estimate a 25 percent growth in real terms. We can agree £52 billion (figure 33 later shows the breakdown) and 25 percent growth are incredible numbers, given the United Kingdom is clearly a more diversified economy than all African economies—it shows even how more important wireless spectrum in percentage terms would be to African and emerging market economies.

The 25 percent growth also did not happen by chance. It happened because of careful management of the United Kingdom's valuable airwaves as a national asset in order to drive as much optimal use of UK spectrum as possible—and optimal use here translates directly to economic benefits to the UK economy. So it is too that we must think of spectrum in all African countries and emerging markets. The fact that spectrum management today in 2013/4 on the continent is so lackadaisical is frankly very irksome, as it is shortchanging African

---

2 Source: https://www.gov.uk/government/publications/impact-of-radio-spectrum-on-the-uk-economy-and-factors-influencing-future-spectrum-demand (accessed August 2013).

consumers and citizens. All countries must be independently tracking (every five years, say) similar net benefits of spectrum use to their economies as depicted by figure 29 in order to give them (i.e., governments and regulators typically) an indication of how well they are doing managing this valuable asset on behalf of their citizens.

Now that we have covered a bit of why spectrum is important to our economies, the goals of the rest of the chapter are to cover the following:

- What indeed is spectrum? What is the "sweet spot" UHF of spectrum for TMT? What are some of the key services and benefits to consumer and citizens that depend or accrue from on radio spectrum?
- Why is sub-1 GHz UHF spectrum being singled out for Africa and emerging markets for TMT—and why now in 2013/14?
- Why does spectrum have to be managed?
- Why does spectrum have to be regulated? What are some of the key outcomes required from regulation? Why are spectrum policy and management invaluable to the TMT sector, and hence to an economy? What's the role of the independent regulator here?
- What is the future of UHF in Africa and emerging markets and why? What other spectrum does Africa and emerging markets need to prioritise and why?
- What other recommendations are relevant on spectrum matters going forward for Africa and emerging economies?

These feel enough for a largely spectrum 101 chapter, emphasising UHF and a bit more.

4.1 Understanding Spectrum, the Extended TMT Spectrum "Sweet Spot" and Its Benefits

Let us start with a dictionary definition of spectrum before we proceed to defining and illustrating the spectrum "sweet spot" and its benefits to consumers and citizens. The best relevant definition from any dictionary I have seen is from Oxford Dictionary Online, which defines electromagnetic spectrum as follows:

> the range of wavelengths or frequencies over which electromagnetic radiation extends. This is a kind of radiation including visible light, radio waves, gamma rays, and X-rays, in which electric and magnetic fields vary simultaneously.

This may still read as gobbledygook to you. Simplistically, spectrum is the range of frequencies/wavelengths, and each frequency/wavelength—if you cast your mind back to your secondary school physics classes—is nothing but a wave. The sound of your voice generated from the vocal cords in your throat is a wave. Playing your guitar creates vibrations that disturb the air sending out waves of varying air pressure—or sound waves shaped like in figure 30. Visible light is a wave too.

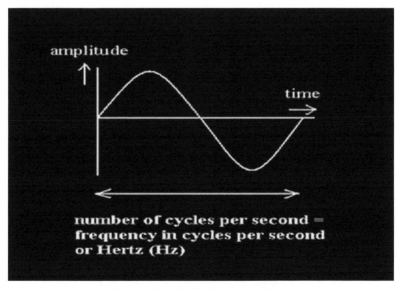

Figure 30—Radio Spectrum Wave

Frequency measured in Hertz refers to the number of cycles of this wave per second, as shown in figure 30, and the *wavelength* is the time in seconds of one complete cycle of the wave, as also shown in figure 30.

The higher the frequency, the lower the wavelength and the closer the spectrum waves are.

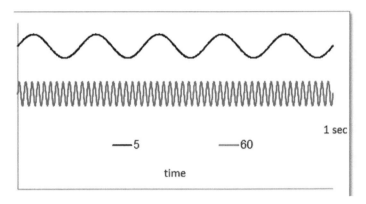

Figure 31—Radio Spectrum Waves Showing 5 Hz Wave (top)
and 60 Hz Wave (bottom)

Figure 31 shows a picture I produced from a spreadsheet visually depicting 5 Hz (i.e., five cycles per second for the black (top) wave; you can actually count the five complete troughs and peaks which make the five waves in one second. The red (bottom) wave in figure 31 is 60 Hz, and, as you can see, a higher frequency of sixty of such complete waves in one second. To put figure 31 into some further context, human voice is 4 to 20 KHz, i.e., between 4×10^3 and 20×10^3. This makes human voice a thousand times higher in frequency than figure 31.

Therefore, when earlier on in the book we talked about 2G spectrum in 900 MHz or 1,800 MHz, what we were really referring to was 900×10^6 and 1800×10^6 complete cycles in one second, respectively. These are much higher frequencies than those shown in figure 31, and you can visualize how close these higher frequencies are.

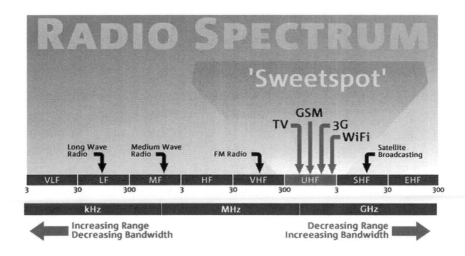

Figure 32—Radio Spectrum from 3 KHz to 300 GHz
(Source: Ofcom public spectrum consultations[3])

There are some important features to spectrum worth pulling out:

- As the frequency of the wave decreases, the farther the wave can travel. As the frequency increases, the less the wave can travel. Figure 32 depicts this. So long wave radio towards the far left of figure 32 travels much farther than the medium wave radio, which itself travels farther than FM radio. Low frequency (LF) radio waves are able to follow the curvature of the earth's surface and are therefore known as ground, or surface, waves. Given sufficient transmitter output power and large antenna arrays, long-range communications of up to three thousand kilometres is possible. You now know why BBC World Service can be broadcast all over the African continent on long wave radio whilst FM radio (e.g., a station can occupy 97.3 MHz or 97.3 × 10^6 Hz) will usually just range within a city and its outskirts.
- The lower the frequency as well (so the longer the wavelengths), the longer the aerials needed to receive this frequency. Aerials for long wave radio are generally longer than those required for

---

3 Source: www.ofcom.org.uk

medium waves, which in turn are longer than those required for FM radio in VHF. Indeed, one of the reasons mobile phones operate in the frequencies they do is because if they operated in much lower frequencies, say, VHF in figure 32, you the user would have to contend with pull-out aerials (antennas). Your phone rings, and you pull out the aerial to talk. How uncool would that be?

- The higher the frequency, the shorter the wavelength, and the higher the amount of information or data that the frequency can carry. To understand this, let us return to figure 31. Intuitively, you can see that the red (bottom) 60-Hz wave has sixty cycles in one second compared to the black (top) wave's only five cycles. Simplistically, in the sixty cycles, you can carry more information with every cycle you are transmitting than in only five cycles, even though the 60-Hz red (bottom) wave travels less range than the 5-Hz one. This is why figure 32 clearly depicts "decreasing range—increasing bandwidth" and "increasing range—decreasing bandwidth."

- Drawing from the exemplars of long wave radio, medium wave radio, and FM radio, it is evident that different parts of the spectrum bands lend themselves to different sorts of applications or services, as can be seen in figure 32 too. Long wave radio is in the low frequency (or LF) band, whilst FM radio is in the very high frequency (VHF) band. Alternatively, satellite broadcasting is in the super high frequency (SHF) band.

- The famous shortwave radio used for radio broadcasting in much of sub-Saharan Africa to reach widely scattered populations over large areas uses the upper MF and all of the HF frequencies in figure 32, i.e., from circa 1.8 MHz to 30 MHz. Where will a lot of Africans be without their shortwave radio sets through which they listened/listen to their venerable BBC World Service, Voice of America (VoA), or Radio France Internationale (RFI)?

- Figure 32 also shows "the bunching" of some really useful society services into one specific band. This is clearly the UHF band, which hosts TV, mobile voice phone services we use daily, 3G for mobile voice and data, and Wi-Fi. Now these are clearly some of the most valued services in use today, as is evidenced by the UK economic value of spectrum numbers in figure 33. In it you can see public mobile communications is worth about £30.2 billion to the UK economy in 2011, TV is worth £7.7 billion, etc. All these services are using ultra high frequency (UHF) spectrum, which makes this spectrum unquestionably very valuable in most TMT economies. This UHF spectrum is called the *sweet spot* spectrum because it hosts practically all the key wireless services to our economies today—and though figure 33 relates to the United Kingdom, Africa and emerging market economies are no different.

Spectrum use	2006 (£ billion)	2011 (£ billion)	Real % change 2006–2011	10-year NPV 2012–2021 (£ billion)
Public mobile communications	21.8	30.2	16%	273
Wi-Fi	–	1.8	–	25.6
TV broadcasting	3.6	7.7	79%	86.0
Radio broadcasting	1.9	3.1	35%	28.6
Microwave links	3.9	3.3	-29%	22.1
Satellite links	2.8	3.6	7%	31.3
Private mobile radio	1.2	2.3	55%	19.2
Total	35.2	52.0	25%	486

Figure 33—UK Net Economic Value of Spectrum by Subsectors
(Source: UK Government/Analysys Mason)[4]

- We note that the sweet spot in Africa and some emerging markets would almost certainly extend below the lower UHF boundary of 300 MHz to also include some of the top end VHF spectrum (reference figure 32). This is because many countries on the continent are planning to introduce their new digital TV services, not mainly in UHF but in Band III VHF spectrum, i.e., from 174 MHz to 230 MHz. For this reason this volume hereby coins the term "extended sweet spot," adding

4 Source: https://www.gov.uk/government/publications/impact-of-radio-spectrum-on-the-uk-economy-and-factors-influencing-future-spectrum-demand (accessed August 2013).

174–230 MHz to the UHF sweet spot depicted in figure 32. Together we call this the *extended sweet spot.*

• Therefore in order to manage and grow the TMT sector in any African or emerging market economy, government and regulators must be particularly attentive to managing all the frequencies in the extended sweet spot even more closely. As is evident later, all new 4G spectrum to be auctioned/released and the TV frequencies to be cleared by digital switchover and some used for TV whites paces broadband are all in the extended sweet spot.

To conclude this subsection, spectrum is a finite resource not too dissimilar to property or land. Like property or land, different types of spectrum have different values. Some spectrum frequencies are highly valuable, like property in the heart of Nairobi, Lagos, or Johannesburg, while others are like wasteland. Continued increases in demand for spectrum make it important to review where spectrum use can add the most value to the economy, with the aim of making it available to operators and innovators to drive growth and competitiveness.

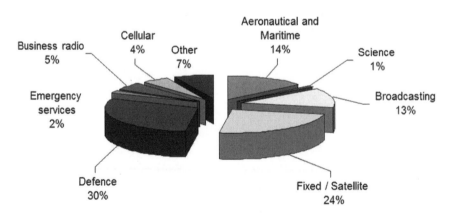

Figure 34—Distribution of Spectrum in the UK below 60 GHz as Per 2007 (weighted by frequency) (Source: Ofcom SFR-IP,[5] 2007)

---

5   Spectrum Framework Review: 2007, www.ofcom.org.uk; http://stakeholders. ofcom.org.uk/binaries/consultations/sfr/summary/sfr.pdf (accessed August 2013).

Thanks to such innovators, there are literally thousands of applications and services running on radio spectrum in existence today, and many sectors use this scarce natural resource. Figure 34 shows the distribution of spectrum across different sectors in the United Kingdom and illustrates how dependent a developed economy is on its radio spectrum. African countries should have similar pictures of their spectrum usage to this and should track changes over time. In addition to the previous shortlist of uses, all the following use radio spectrum: GPS, satellite TV, point of sale (POS) equipment, hospital scanners, traffic sensors, weather sensors, e-readers, cameras, music players, heart rate monitors, weighing scales, games consoles, and so on. The modern world will be lifeless without the use of radio spectrum today. As we move towards the era of the Internet of things, radio spectrum will become even so much more pervasive.

4.2 Why Sub-1 GHz UHF Spectrum Is Even More Key for TMT in the Next Several Years

Simply, sub-1 GHz UHF spectrum is the range of frequencies in the sweet spot which are below 1,000 MHz or 1 GHz, i.e., looking at figure 32, this refers to 300 MHz to just under 1 GHz.

There are several reasons why the sub-1 GHz spectrum would be so important on the continent, and why regulators and governments need to manage, regulate, and band-plan[6] it carefully over the next several years for the benefit of TMT. It is no exaggeration to point out that a significant part of the economic value to be created for TMT on the African continent and in other emerging markets will derive from sub-1 GHz spectrum. Let us review the reasons why and sequentially too.

- *Public mobile communications is already the biggest economic value radio spectrum driver with 900 MHz (2G)*

---

6 A band plan is a plan for using a particular set (or band) of radio frequencies, what range of frequencies and channels are included and what is carried on those channels.

spectrum perceived as even more valuable: As can be seen from the economic value numbers in figure 33 for the United Kingdom, public mobile communications is the most valuable subsector using radio spectrum, at £30.2 billion. This number does not include the February 2013 4G spectrum auction, which I had the distinct privilege of directing and leading. Today in Africa and other emerging markets, spectrum in the 800 MHz and 900 MHz (so sub-1 GHz spectrum) is being used for mobile voice communications, mostly using 2G technology. Other spectrum is also being used today for mobile voice and data, including 1,800 MHz and 2,100 GHz spectrum (i.e., not sub-1 GHz spectrum, as they are all higher than 1 GHz). However, for reasons explained next, 900 MHz spectrum is arguably a more valuable spectrum than 1,800 MHz and 2,100 MHz.

• *Recent 4G spectrum auctions in Europe and elsewhere demonstrate the clear preference for sub-1 GHz spectrum.* The 4G spectrum that has been auctioned in Europe are typically 800 MHz spectrum and 2,600 MHz. From the experience of recent 4G spectrum auctions (Europe in particular), sub-1 GHz public mobile communications spectrum would fetch more spectrum receipts on the continent than higher spectrum, as mobile operators have tended to compete more fiercely for it than for other spectrum.

	800 MHz	1800 MHz	2.6 GHz paired
Germany (5/2010)	33.0 (*)	N/A	1.0
Spain (7/2011)	17.6 (*)	N/A	1.0
Portugal (11/2011)	17.5 (*)	N/A	1.0
Italy (9/2011)	13.7 (*)	4.4	1.0
France (12/2011)	6.6 (*)	N/A.	1.0

UK[7] (2/2013)	4.7	N/A	1.0
Sweden (3/2011)	1.8	1.1	1.0
Average of 7 countries	13.5	N/A	1

(*) The benchmark figures used may include some offsetting of coverage obligations, but it is impossible to quantify

Table 1—Relative Value of Frequencies in Different Auctions/Proposals, Expressed as a Multiple of the Value of 2.6 GHz Paired Spectrum (Source: Ofcom and published data [month/year auction took place are shown in brackets])

The data in table 1 from various European auctions demonstrate unequivocal preference for sub-1 GHz spectrum over other spectrum in the sweet spot. The German operators were prepared to pay thirty-three times more for the same amount of sub-1 GHz spectrum compared to 2,600 MHz, whilst the French paid 6.6 times more. The average across all seven countries in the table is 13.5! So if and when African and emerging economies start to auction or release 4G spectrum (likely to be 700 MHz, 800 MHz, 1,800 MHz, or 2,600 MHz), they should expect much more vibrant interest and competition for the sub-1 GHz spectrum, like 700 MHz and 800 MHz.

- *There are two principal reasons for the clear preference shown in table 1: limited supply of sub-1 GHz spectrum (scarcity) and the importance of coverage.* The first reason is because there is not much of sub-1 GHz spectrum compared to 2,600 MHz, say. In Europe, there was only 2x30 MHz of 800 MHz spectrum,

---

7   The UK 4G auction was a complicated combinatorial clock auction, so it is impossible to disentangle similar ratios. However, the ratio of 4.7 is *illustrative* of *one* auction participant's preference: EE won and paid £589 million for one lot of 800 MHz and seven lots of 2,600 MHz. Given another operator (H3G paid £225 million reserve price for its own one lot of 800 MHz), we can infer EE paid £339 million for the seven lots of 2,600 MHz or £48.4 million per lot. Therefore £225 million/£48.2 million gives the ratio of 4.7.

compared to 190 MHz of 2,600 MHz spectrum. Hence, the classic demand-supply issue: if supply is plentiful, the price drops, and it rises otherwise. This is the scarcity issue.

The other principal reason is back to what we covered as one of the key features of different frequencies: as the frequency of the wave decreases, the farther the wave can travel. Sub-1 GHz spectrum, by the laws of physics, then travels much farther than higher frequency spectrum, like 1,800 MHz or 2,600 MHz in the tables above. As operators are also effectively competing on *coverage* too, it is important they also have low frequency spectrum, which reduces the amount of capital expenditure on base station equipment they will need to deploy. Figure 35 illustrates more clearly this coverage effect with different frequencies.

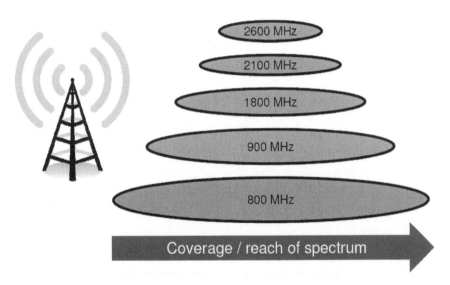

Figure 35—Coverage Effect with Different Frequencies

Figure 35 shows the relative coverage of 800 MHz and 900 MHz sub-1 GHz spectrum for the same power compared to other frequencies. It is clear to see why 2,600 MHz will need to deploy more base station sites to achieve the same coverage as 800 MHz. More base station sites translate to higher capital expenditure (Capex) and higher operational expenditure (Opex). A lower number of base station sites translates to the opposite. Therefore the operator with 800 MHz not only achieves lower Capex and Opex but also a quicker rollout to achieve national coverage. This is a significant reason why the sub-1 GHz spectrum is much at a premium for TMT.

- *Sub-1 GHz spectrum is where all digital TV/HDTV will reside too:* If we return to figure 33, we note that TV broadcasting had a net economic value of £7.7 billion in 2011, having grown an incredible 79 percent since 2006. This growth is significantly attributed to the United Kingdom going to digital TV from analogue. However, unlike with public mobile communications, the equivalent net economic number in most African and some emerging market economies will be practically zero, as there is hardly a digital terrestrial TV sector, and satellite TV is immature in most of these countries. Therefore this sub-1 GHz spectrum offers an incredible opportunity to create some significant and new net economic value over the next decade in these economies using band III VHF spectrum and/or UHF spectrum. Standard definition (SD) TV and high definition TV (HDTV) services would also be launched in these bands.

- *Other important services too will demand sub-1 GHz spectrum—three key ones include local TV, PMSE, and white spaces:* So far we have extolled the virtues of public mobile communication and TV services for having access to sub-1 GHz spectrum. One slightly technical point of note: typically the way TV networks are designed and built in Europe (mostly in UHF) will leave what is usually referred to as *geographically interleaved spectrum* in most areas. The reason is explained next.

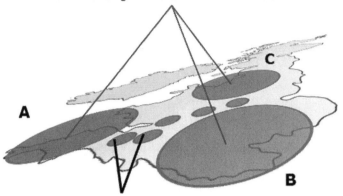

Example: High power TV broadcasts using the same frequency need to leave spaces between their coverage areas to avoid interference.

These frequencies can be used in the "white spaces" in between by lower-power devices.

Figure 36—Explaining Geographically Interleaved Spectrum
(Source: Ofcom public documents on white spaces)[8]

A good way to articulate geographically interleaved (shared) spectrum is via figure 36. TV networks tend to use very high power transmitters (compared to mobile networks, say), but even more importantly, they tend to use the same frequency (say, UHF Channel 40, i.e., 622–630 MHz) in different geographical parts of the country (say, Cities A, B, and C) using this same channel, leaving spaces between their coverage area to avoid interference as shown. This means this frequency (i.e., channel 40) is geographically interleaved "TV white space" in between these main cities A, B, and C areas, and they can be reused. Figure 36 shows how they can be reused (see smaller ovals or circles), particularly if lower power devices are employed, as they will not interfere into the main TV channels in areas A, B, and C.

---

8 www.ofcom.org.uk (accessed October 2013)

THE EXTENDED SWEET SPOT. WHAT WILL BECOME OF
THESE BANDS IN AFRICA AND SOME EMERGING ECONOMIES?

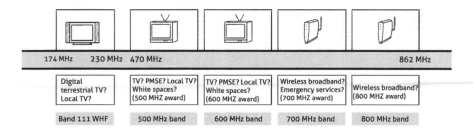

Band 111 WHF	500 MHz band	600 MHz band	700 MHz band	800 MHz band
Digital terrestrial TV? Local TV?	TV? PMSE? Local TV? White spaces? (500 MHZ award)	TV? PMSE? Local TV? White spaces? (600 MHZ award)	Wireless broadband? Emergency services? (700 MHZ award)	Wireless broadband? (800 MHZ award)

Figure 37—The Extended Spectrum Sweet Spot (What will become of
these bands in Africa and some emerging economies?)

Therefore interleaved spectrum is so called because it can be used at a local level or on a shared—or interleaved—basis with terrestrial television. In parts of Europe, this geographical interleaved and unused spectrum (or white spaces) is being used for local TV and PMSE, and a new proposal is for TV white spaces for mobile broadband. Imagine Channel 40 in figure 36 is not used in London. It could be licensed for low power local TV services, giving London an additional set of TV channels for London reporting on London local news, weather, theatre, businesses, politics, etc. In the new African TMT vision, the same local media should apply to large metropolitan African cities like Lagos, Cairo, Tunis, Cape Town, and so on. Another service of note that the African TMT sector should plan for is PMSE, which stands for programme making and special events. PMSE devices, such as wireless microphones, wireless cameras, and in-ear monitors, which are used for major events like African Nations Cups or live concerts, can also use interleaved spectrum. Interleaved spectrum can also be made available to PMSE equipment on a licensed basis. Lastly, these TV white spaces could also be used for rural broadband type applications and more. TV white spaces is the subject of chapter 6.

Even more interestingly for Africa and some emerging market countries—since many countries in Africa are using (or plan to use) band III VHF spectrum for TV, and since 800 MHz is not widely used across the continent, and 500 MHz, 600 MHz, and 700MHz are also largely clear—Africa and some emerging economies really have much valuable extended sweet spot spectrum which need to be properly band-planned in concert with other countries. TV white spaces in Africa may not need interleaved spectrum after all. Figure 37 demonstrates that there is still much thinking to do to decide on the future of UHF spectrum in Africa—a core reason there are many spectrum recommendations at the end of this chapter.

To conclude this section 4.2, the case for regulators and governments looking even more keenly at UHF in particular, and the extended spectrum sweet spot in general, is overwhelming. These bands needs to be redesigned once (and right too) and implemented for the economic benefit of our consumers and citizens.

It also needs to be now or very soon in 2013/14. Prevaricating on doing this on the basis of not having enough resources or whatever other reason carries a cost. The cost is principally borne by consumers and citizens through lost opportunities to have widespread mobile voice and data as soon as possible or widespread digital TV, which will usher in a genuinely new media sector on the African continent and in some other emerging economies. We have demonstrated and explained the benefits of the extended sweet spot spectrum; we have exemplified and illustrated the net economic value it brings, using the United Kingdom as an example. We have noted how Africa is blessed with enough UHF spectrums and more, and it offers opportunities to grow many bountiful businesses-based mobile voice, data, digital TV, radio, white space broadband, local TV, PMSE, and more.

4.3 Why Spectrum Needs to Be Managed and Regulated for TMT and How

I think you can answer this question to a good degree already. Let us summarise the reasons following:

- *Spectrum is a national and finite asset which needs to be actively managed*: Indeed, drawing from sections 4.1 and 4.2, you would agree not only what spectrum is but how important it is to a national economy. Spectrum is like extremely valuable property. You will want to grow your property portfolio, manage it better, ensure you maximize the rents you can extract from your current portfolio, and use these proceeds to buy more property and add to the portfolio. What more spectrum on which an entire new TMT sector can be built? This is why we illustrate its net economic benefits. The UK's net economic benefits from spectrum did not grow 25 percent as per figure 33 (from £37 billion in 2006 to £52 billion in 2011) by chance. It happened through active management of this valuable resource.

- *The extended spectrum sweet spot needs to be even more proactively and carefully managed to deliver the TMT sector Africa needs for the 2020s:* The case for managing the extended sweet spot even more closely has been made. This spectrum needs to be band-planned up front; like with property, if you design and carve out your land carefully, you can build more efficiently on it. However, you can only do this with the consent of your neighbours, so as to ensure what you do on your land is not to the detriment of them. Indeed you want to ensure that what you do enhances your neighbours' land too because it benefits the whole neighbourhood (resulting in it being sought after) and hence in return, appreciates the value of your property. So it is with spectrum and with spectrum bands. Part of the reason they have to be actively managed is because regulators and/or government need to plan spectrum along with other countries to ensure the spectrum commons is optimized for all countries.

- *Technological advances*: This is another reason that ensures spectrum needs to be actively managed. Engineers are continually finding ways of making efficient use of various spectrum bands. Some frequencies fall out of favour, whilst others come into vogue. It is akin to a city wherein some parts fall into disuse, whilst other parts suddenly begin to thrive. Thirty years ago the spectrum bands used today for mobile voice communications were moribund. See where they are today. With so many changes happening, spectrum needs to be actively managed.

- *Interference comes with spectrum as night follows day; it must be managed too:* There is this core externality called interference which comes along with spectrum. When you hear your long wave or FM radio "crackling" or "shhhing" (I know there is no such word) or what you consider noise, that is most likely interference. Interference—in layman's terms—is when two or more waves (a wanted signal and at least one unwanted signal) interfere or "superimpose," resulting is a poorer wave. It's the same effect you have in a room full of people all conversing, and you are trying to listen to one person (the wanted wave signal), but you have to contend with much interference from all the others speaking too. All the other people are generating sound waves (unwanted noise signals with respect to who/what you want to listen to) that are "interfering" with your wanted wave signal, i.e., that of the person you are speaking to. Interference is *de rigeur* with spectrum—and all bands suffer from interference. If your spectrum is being interfered into by others so you are not able to deliver your services to your customers, then this needs to be addressed. That interference needs to be cleared. This is a core reason why pirate radio stations have to be cleared down. They interfere into the spectrum of real licensed radio stations. As we try to use spectrum even more efficiently, the problem of managing interference increases in just the same way that if you build houses more closely, the problem of noisy (interfering) neighbours increases. Good management of spectrum ensures good outcomes for all concerned.

- *Ensuring the coexistence of different services in the same frequency band or adjacent bands:* Following on from the interference bullet above, managing spectrum helps ensure coexistence of different services in the same band or in adjacent bands. This maximizes the value of spectrum. For example, if four mobile voice operators are licensed spectrum in the 700-MHz band, we need to ensure all four of them are not interfering into one another in that band, or else all their customers will suffer. They all need to use their specified allocated licensed bands *only*, which has been specified in their license, just like people can only build on their own plot of land and not stray into their neighbours'. Similarly, those four mobile operators licensed in the 700-MHz band must also be able to coexist with their neighbouring services in 600 MHz, which may be TV services, and not mobile voice services.

- *Being lackadaisical in the management of such a scarce natural resource like spectrum is a sure way to ensure Africa and some emerging economies will not get the TMT sector they deserve for the 2020s:* The spectrum gestation period for managing spectrum is long. It is now clear how much spectrum will underpin the new African TMT sector. The fact that most African governments and/or regulators cannot tell you promptly the net economic benefit of spectrum to their economies proves the lackadaisical point firmly. I have asked many of them in my teachings and trainings to no avail. The band planning of spectrum takes years. The manufacturing of new devices takes years. Standardisation processes that needs to be happen with new technologies like TV white space technology for broadband takes years. Global harmonization processes are very slow as countries and regions of the world argue amongst themselves and express different preferences to start with. Some of the most painful meetings I have had the misfortune of attending earlier on in my career were harmonization and standardisation meetings. However, they are very necessary. Negotiation with neighbours on spectrum and interference issues takes years. These all add to long gestation periods for spectrum. After these, designing and running auctions and getting the spectrum into the right operators take time too. Building large networks takes years from the finances being secured to networks being built out.

• *Managing spectrum actively will yield widespread mobile voice and data for the masses, widespread digital TV and radio for the masses, some widespread Internet for the masses, etc.:* this is at the core of this book.

So now that we know why spectrum needs to be proactively managed, why does it also need to be regulated?

Spectrum regulation is hard. Indeed good sector regulation is hard. Chapter 3 noted that regulation is one of the key drivers of the TMT sector, and with spectrum being so invaluable to the sector, it must be firmly regulated. All the issues we noted in the last chapter pertaining to regulation, including liberalization, competition, efficient allocation of resources, managing bottlenecks, etc., all apply to spectrum. The proposed agenda in the last chapter captured in figure 27 is very spectrum heavy. To achieve the TMT sectors Africans deserve for the 2020s, spectrum needs to be heavily regulated too for the following reasons:

• *Every spectrum band is a scarce, finite, and monopoly band, so they need regulating:* You now understand enough about spectrum to realise that there is only one of each band. There is only one 97.3-MHz band across the country, and if one radio station is assigned (and licensed) this frequency at some city location, another radio station cannot be assigned/licensed the same frequency, or else interference reigns and chaos rules. Similarly there is only 800-MHz band, or one 700-MHz band. These are all scarce national and natural resources which are typically competed for, and fiercely so with some bands. We saw in table 1 how much more preferred sub-1 GHz spectrum is with respect to higher frequencies. Without some sort of a "referee" regulating access to these scarce monopoly frequencies, the spectrum bands are likely to fall in the "wrong" economic hands who generate little or no economic activity with the spectrum. This is a bad outcome for consumers and citizens. There is also an opportunity cost to any use. If some spectrum is being used for TV, it is not being used for mobile voice communications. Maybe it should be more productively use for the latter.

* *Spectrum regulation is about creating value and wealth with TMT, i.e., about delivering services that meet the needs of consumers and citizens:* Spectrum policies designed to maximize optimum spectrum efficiency (and therefore maximum net economic benefits to society) mean good regulation is necessary for TMT to grow—yes, it is about creating value and wealth. Again, like land, spectrum's value to society is to a significant part a function of the policies devised to manage it. If land is not liberalised and made tradable so that it can be bought and sold easily, if it is tied up in endless bureaucracy, if there are rules that forbid improving the land by building new buildings on them—then not much land will change hands, and little land economic activity will accrue. It is the same with spectrum. Even though spectrum is this special asset with side effects such as interference, the TMT sector will only grow if the policies that underpin spectrum regulation are progressive and, generally, market-oriented-type policies.

* *Spectrum needs to harmonised, coordinated, allocated, assigned, and licensed:* Without harmonization of spectrum bands, global and regional standards will not emerge. We take it for granted today that you can take your phone or handset from Europe to Africa and just roam on the networks in Africa. Alternatively, you can change the SIM in that handset, and it just works in Africa too. This can only happen because that spectrum has been harmonized across both the continents of Europe and Africa, i.e., the spectrum is being used for the same service. It can further also happen because the spectrum is harmonized across Europe and Africa (indeed most of the world), so handsets have been developed to the same standards by many manufacturers. Standardisation drives economies of

scale, which in turn drives down prices. To minimize interference, particular spectrum bands tend to be designated for a type of service, or *allocated*. So bands could be allocated to TV services or Wi-Fi services. Then specific blocks of spectrum within that allocated band are *assigned* in a coordinated fashion to specific licensed spectrum holders, like mobile operators or TV and radio stations. All of these processes—harmonization, coordination, allocation, assignment, and licensing—require active regulation and management of spectrum.

- *Spectrum regulation is also about competition, coverage, innovation, consumers, and public policy:* We return to this age-old good set of outcomes. All spectrum in some allocated band (e.g., a mobile band) cannot possibly all be assigned to one operator. This would be terrible for competition, as the monopoly player would in the long run drive up prices and deliver poor quality services, if at all. Can you now imagine if there were only one mobile operator in every country? Or just one across the continent of Africa, like MTN? This would be a bad outcome for African consumers and citizens. Spectrum regulation is also about coverage. As we have discussed many times already in previous chapters—but it is worth reiterating—competition only goes so far with respect to coverage. It would be a fantastic outcome if companies competed for 100 percent population coverage for all or most services, but that is not the real world. If they can only commercially go as far as 60 percent, say, that means 40 percent of the population will be out of coverage. Regulators do not like this and may have to regulate the spectrum in such a way that the coverage extends beyond 60 percent to benefit more consumers and citizens. They can do this by imposing certain coverage conditions on spectrum licenses. Spectrum regulation is also needed in order to achieve various public policy objectives, such as universal access to mobile voice services or universal access to digital TV and radio. Finally, spectrum regulation—like all good regulation—is ultimately about consumers and citizens, i.e., how you ensure that competition, coverage, innovation, and public policy objectives maximize consumer and citizen welfare.

4.4 The Role of the Independent Spectrum Regulator for TMT and How Spectrum Is Regulated

The role of managing and regulating spectrum in any TMT economy must fall into the hands of competent spectrum professionals within an independent regulator, and not to some faceless bureaucrats in government or incompetent/conflicted civil servants or ministers. This is not to denigrate civil servants and ministers. Ministers making spectrum decisions (as sometimes happen on the African continent) is fraught with horror stories of nepotism and unadulterated corruption. As can be seen from the previous section, managing and regulating spectrum is no mean feat. It is long and arduous process—and it must be carried out meticulously on a band-by-band basis in order to maximise the benefits to consumers and citizens, i.e., in order to grow the net economic benefits of that spectrum to the economy à la figure 29. This means that spectrum bands, particularly those in the extended sweet spot, have to be allocated to the highest value services and that the operators that are licensed to provide these services are those that value their licenses the most if the spectrum is in more demand. This combination of optimal allocation to services (as in mobile vs. broadcasting vs. PMSE, etc.) and optimal assignment to licensees maximises benefits for all. The fact that many spectrum regulators I meet on the African continent do not seem to understand this *prima facie* goal of managing spectrum optimally is deeply worrying, and it demonstrates that significant training needs to happen with the spectrum regulators in Africa and emerging economies.

Furthermore, the independent spectrum regulator is not only concerned with commercial uses of spectrum but also with public uses too. Emergency services like the police, ambulance services, fire services, security services, transport services, etc., all also need access to this natural and scarce resource. It is the job of the independent spectrum regulator to ensure all have access to spectrum in a FRND-ly (i.e., fair, reasonable, and nondiscriminatory) way.

Most competent independent spectrum regulators would have a statutory duty to secure "the optimal use for wireless telegraphy of the electromagnetic spectrum." How this typical statutory duty is interpreted is up to the independent regulator. In doing so, the regulator would have to consider the three main regulatory approaches to spectrum, namely command and control, market mechanisms, and licence exemption. We take each of them in turn.

- *Command and Control:* As the name states, the regulator decides what the best use of specific bands are (e.g., for mobile, for TV, for Wi-Fi, etc.) and which operators use the spectrum. The national regulator therefore decides on allocation and assignments. Spectrum is awarded by spectrum *grant* or by some sort of a *beauty contest*—i.e., who has the best paper business plan and "story" to achieve the outcomes that the government and regulator want. This is how much of the spectrum on the continent was awarded prior to telecommunication sectors becoming liberalized. And many of such awards ended up as unmitigated failures. Command and control is becoming passé as the key approach to managing spectrum because it assumes an all-knowing regulator who understands better than the market what the best *uses* and *users* of spectrum should be. In a new TMT world with thousands of services being innovated by radio, this is just not possible. However, command and control still does have its place in spectrum regulation and management. If you are organizing a major event like the Olympics, the spectrum organisers at such an event need to employ a complete command and control structure to ensure you are aware of every piece of radio equipment being used within an Olympic stadium, because the timing equipment to measure the time of a 9.8-second 100-metre final cannot be interfered with during that race!
- *Market Mechanisms:* The principle here is that, unlike with command and control, the market decides on the best use of

spectrum. The regulator defines initial access rights to the spectrum and then leaves it to the market to take over. Spectrum users in the market then decide on who uses the spectrum and for what, and this happens by them participating in an auction for the spectrum or by trading their spectrum rights in the market. The independent regulator also, in some cases, sets incentive prices to reflect opportunity costs if market prices do not exist. This is set to reflect the opportunity cost of spectrum denied to other users or uses. Pricing enables any asset like spectrum to be used more efficiently and not hoarded—if spectrum users have to pay for it.

- *License Exemption*: With license exemption, no one controls the spectrum. Anyone can use the spectrum provided they comply with certain technical rules. Because no one controls the spectrum, there is risk of interference. License exemption therefore is achieved by allocating parts of the spectrum to licence-free usage and ensuring regulations are made that ensure that certain types of equipment may be used without a license, provided the technical conditions set in the regulations are met. This is the case with Wi-Fi. As you use your Wi-Fi equipment or device to create a Skype session, you do not hold a license from the regulator like mobile operators hold licenses to use their assigned spectrum blocks. Similarly, the key fob for opening and locking your expensive car does not need any license from the regulator, though it is using radio spectrum. Indeed, any good independent spectrum regulator must ask itself this question first: Is it possible to operate the equipment without causing harmful interference? If the answer to this question is yes, then it should consider that spectrum involved as license exempt.

The spectrum regulator uses these three approaches. For TMT to thrive, there is a role for all three. Much innovation is driven by license exemption. Market mechanisms ensure market makes the best uses of spectrum too. The role of the regulator to drive up the net economic value of spectrum for TMT growth cannot be overstated.

4.5 TMT Key Spectrum Recommendations for Africa and Emerging Markets

You now know enough about spectrum and TMT to see how intertwined they both are in Africa in particular, and some emerging economies in general. As pointed out earlier, some spectrum is more valuable than others. The following recommendations naturally emerge from the sections above:

1. *Countries need competent spectrum professionals managing this key resource, and preferably they should all be homed in an independent converged regulator:* I hope the decision makers reading this volume are convinced of the importance of spectrum being actively managed, and given how important it is to the TMT economy, it must be left to real spectrum professionals. Skimping on not hiring and training these professionals properly costs us all in the long term—the opportunity costs themselves are too high. Where spectrum regulation still sits with government departments, the straw man three-year strategic priorities agenda proposed in chapter 3 (see figure 27) recommends the preparation of new converged TMT legislation/bills which would provide opportunities across countries to ensure spectrum regulation is properly homed in confident, converged regulators.

2. *Countries are recommended to start carrying out basic audits of their spectrum portfolios and categorise their balance of regulatory approaches to spectrum:* The lack of information on spectrum audits across the continent needs to be addressed. What has not been audited is *not* truly known about, and what is not known about (i.e., lack of information and transparency) is not prioritised. Spectrum audits lead to data such as that depicted in figure 34, which shows the pie chart breakdown of spectrum allocation to various sectors. Other data that should be audited include what percentage of spectrum is under command-and-control management, license exemption, and

market-based mechanisms. They would start of by showing much of the spectrum is under command-and-control management, but over the next decade into the 2020s, there should be a gradual move to market mechanisms.

3. *With the TMT vision and strategy and the TMT business plan both developed as part of the blueprint, it is recommended an umbrella national TMT spectrum policy framework is also developed by the spectrum regulator:* The new envisaged TMT sector with a liberalised media subsector and more need a revised national spectrum policy framework in most countries I know of on the African continent. Many countries still operate in command-and-control mode and possess little experience on license exemption and market-based mechanisms approaches to managing spectrum. Many are yet to fully appreciate that the full implications of the fact spectrum policy is about competition, coverage, innovation, consumers, and public policy. They fail to see the role of opportunity cost–based spectrum pricing or other market-based techniques, spectrum liberalisation[9] and trading, or the primacy of license exemption. I did some training in 2013 with some African spectrum regulators, and many of these concepts were alien to them. The emergence of a designed TMT sector provides a good opportunity to up-skill our spectrum professionals to understand and start implementing best practice spectrum policy across the continent. This will start with a revised spectrum policy framework for most African countries. A similar such framework

---

9 Spectrum liberalisation is a process wherein licence holders can request a variation to certain licence conditions. In this way, licensees can change how they use their spectrum assignments, subject to some constraints. A good example is where spectrum which was awarded just for 2G voice can post liberalisation be used for both 2G, 3G, and even 4G, subject to meeting similar technical interference constraints.

revolutionized spectrum management thinking in the United Kingdom from 2005 onwards.[10]

4. *It is recommended that coupled with the new spectrum policy framework, detailed spectrum plans are developed for the broad-themed outcomes that TMT sectors need*: I reiterate those outcomes here again. The outcomes include:

(i) widespread and affordable mobile voice (including roaming intercountry and across the continent) for the masses;
(ii) widespread and affordable mobile data (3G/4G) and otherwise in rural parts of countries (e.g., TV white spaces), including mobile data roaming for the masses;
(iii) widespread digital TV content (national and international news, comedy, drama, children's, documentary for the masses) and radio (including community radio and temporary radio formats); and
(iv) widespread and affordable Internet (mobile and fixed) for the businesses and consumers/citizens.

All four of these need detailed spectrum plans. All plans would be subject to statutory consultation processes.

○ For (i), a spectrum plan for widespread and affordable public mobile telecommunications services needs to be developed. Such a plan would naturally assume more liberalisation of the telecommunications sector. Indeed, it is encouraged that 2G spectrum is liberalised for 3G and other services. It must be cognisant of the development in new mobile technologies, such as long-term evolution and the identification of frequency bands for international mobile telecommunications (IMT) by the International Telecommunications Union. This detailed plan must

---

10 See *A Guide to the Spectrum Framework Review (SFR)*, September 2005, Office of Communications (Ofcom), http://stakeholders.ofcom.org.uk/binaries/consultations/sfr/annexes/sfr_guide.pdf (accessed August 2013).

identify the optimal frequency bands for public mobile voice. In Africa (being part of Region 1) it must include 700 MHz and/or 800 MHz (see figure 37), 900 MHz/1,800 MHz, 2,100 MHz, etc. There is an opportunity here to extend 3G networks across the continent. The idea here is to draw from optimal frequency bands and an analysis of the occupancy of those bands today (including coverage, capacity, and public policy objectives) across the countries and then move on to propose further frequency band plans if deemed necessary. It must also include plans to review some of the fees currently being paid by operators for their erstwhile 2G voice spectrum. Many countries just "gifted" their 900 MHz and 1,800 MHz spectrum to operators, and they now need, for spectrum efficiency reasons, to be subject to their full opportunity costs. CDMA has largely failed across Region 1,[11] and the regulators also have to seriously consider whether CDMA use continues to be the most optimal use of spectrum driving up significant net economic benefits relative to other uses and also if current CDMA spectrum is in the hands of the right users to drive most economic benefits to the countries concerned. This is an example of the sort of difficult decisions regulators make. It is the case in some countries like Nigeria and Cameroon that private operators are beginning to aggregate 800-MHz spectrum frequencies by buying them from other failed CDMA operators in order to use them for CDMA or for 4G. Prima facie, this is a good move. However, this may or may not be the most optimal for consumers and citizens of the country in question because the aggregators may not necessarily be the "best hands" who

---

11 CDMA is arguably a better technology than GSM, but nevertheless, the market has chosen/spoken: for example, CDMA has a meagre two hundred thousand subscribers in Ghana compared to twenty-four million GSM connections as of November 2012. Nigeria has less than five hundred thousand CDMA subscribers representing less than 0.5 percent of the Nigerian market. See pages 10–13 of *Africa Telecom & IT*, vol. 3, no. 11, November 2012.

would maximise the use of that spectrum for the country—
something a well-designed auction sets out to do.

○ For (ii), widespread and affordable mobile data (3G/4G),
including in rural parts of countries (e.g., TV white spaces)
and including mobile data roaming for the masses: This
needs a spectrum plan for accommodating such broadband wireless access (BWA) services. Such a plan must be
clear on the TMT BWA objectives (over a decade, say) and
would naturally assume too more liberalisation of the telecommunications sector. It must also be cognisant of the development in new mobile technologies, such as long-term
evolution (LTE or WiMAX, both 4G) and the identification of the relevant BWA frequency bands for IMT by the
ITU. The plan must review occupancy across the country
as well as the desired competitive BWA market structure.
Due consideration must be taken of coverage, capacity, innovation, and other public policy objectives. In Africa (being part of Region 1), the bands must include 450 MHz
(CDMA or LTE?), 700 MHz (LTE or 3G?), 800 MHz[12]
(CDMA or LTE?), 1,800 MHz (3G or 4G LTE?), 2,100
MHz, 2,300 MHz (WiMAX or LTE?), 2,400 MHz (Wi-Fi),
2,600 MHz (LTE?), 3,500 MHz (WiMAX?), and miscellaneous backhaul spectrum. You should worry less about
the acronyms here because the main point is that African
countries need to decide what BWA bands they need and
why. The TV bands (500 MHz and 600 MHz) should be
considered for license exemption for TV white spaces technology. The good news is that Arab and African countries

12 The 800-MHz (i.e., 790 MHz to 862 MHz) band has been auctioned across
many countries in Europe, also part of Region 1. However, when the 2007 World
Radio Conference allocated this band to mobile, many African countries (Ghana,
Nigeria, Cameroon, etc.) had already licensed 806 MHz to 86 2MHz partly to code
division multiple access (CDMA) operators. So Africa ended up with a 16-MHz
dividend (i.e., 790 MHz to 806 MHz), which they considered no dividend at all
in contrast to Europe's 72-MHz dividend. This was (and still is) the main driver
behind why Africa needs and led the movement to create another mobile dividend
in 694–790 MHz in Region 1 at the World Radio Conference of 2012.

are already demonstrating the political will to allocate TV frequency bands. The Arab Spectrum Management Group (ASMG) and the African Telecommunications Union (ATU) have already taken steps to facilitate the relocation of TV broadcasting below 694 MHz, freeing 168 MHz of valuable spectrum to mobile services. Furthermore the global harmonisation of the 700 MHz and 800 MHz bands for mobile service is progressing well.

∘ The first two points (i and ii) may also lead to a spectrum refarming plan. Refarming assesses current use of a band by existing users with respect to international harmonisation initiatives or with respect to other competing uses. Redesignating spectrum from one use to another is called refarming. There is a case for refarming some of the 2G bands of 900 MHz and 1,800 MHz, though it is easier to just liberalise these bands in current use. Either way, the question should be asked.

∘ For (iii) widespread digital TV content (national and international news, comedy, drama, children's, documentary for the masses) and radio (including community radio and temporary radio formats): This needs a spectrum plan for accommodating such digital TV and radio services. Much of this is already in place across the continent—or should be in place to achieve digital switch over by 2015 for southern African countries in particular or for all countries who have decided to switch to digital terrestrial TV early. However, Band III, 500 MHz, and 600 MHz must be included here.

∘ Backhaul spectrum plan: The proposed agenda of figure 27 has already proposed a backhaul spectrum plan for TMT mobile data and TV white spaces. Africa needs to make proposals and open up many bands that are used elsewhere for backhaul but which have hardly been licensed on the continent, including 28 GHz, 32 GHz, 40 GHz, E-Band (60–90 GHz), etc.

5. *African and other developing economy regulators are advised to find ways to ensure valuable spectrum gets into the hands of the "right users" and "right uses" for the economy (this is a key tenet of good spectrum policy):* In the previous recommendation, the question could be asked as to how valuable spectrum in the "wrong" hands or in "suboptimal" use could move to the "right" hands and in its most optimal use. Take the case of CDMA in the 800-MHz band. Any informed analysis of the 800-MHz band in 2013/14 would quickly lead to the conclusion that LTE/4G is arguably the more optimal use for the African/developing economy than for CDMA/2G/3G. So a change of use from CDMA to LTE/4G is a likely outcome of such a study. As a first approach (assuming the licenses are liberalised and tradable), this change of use can happen via the market wherein Company A who holds the spectrum rights today trades the spectrum (i.e., sells the rights to the spectrum) to Company B. The regulator is likely to subject any such trade to a competition check to ensure it does not distort competition adversely in the marketplace. Secondly, if the current operators just continue holding on to the spectrum, the regulator may consider a spectrum pricing approach. Or thirdly, it could enforce a regulatory "clearance" process (and compensation payments may or may not be paid). Alternatively and fourthly, some form of an incentive auction could be employed. An incentive auction is a voluntary, market-based approach which seeks to compensate existing spectrum licensees for returning their licenses to make spectrum available for more optimal or innovative new uses like mobile broadband/LTE. The regulator would auction the spectrum that licensees voluntarily return, with these *licensees* retaining a portion of the auction receipts. This is quite a complex auction and should be considered with care. In the United States, the Federal Communications Commission (FCC) is currently seeking to employ an incentive auction in the 700-MHz band in order to recover spectrum from broadcasters to enable a change of use (and user). There are, therefore, several ways to make this task happen.

6. *African and developing economy regulators and countries are recommended to work together to achieve the previous five recommendations*: In the blueprint of the previous chapter, this recommendation has already been argued for. There will be much commonality amongst countries on the work to achieve the above recommendations.

It is the case that some of these recommendations are hard to achieve as they require significant up-skilling of spectrum policy professionals across regulators across the continent. Without such awareness and understanding of some of the issues discussed in this chapter, such as a good understanding of spectrum policy regulation for competition, for coverage, for other public policy purposes, for innovation, etc., auctions or awards of spectrum for 4G across the continent would be ill-informed and poorly designed and would not maximise the benefits to consumers and citizens.

I am aware of regional regulatory training centres and initiatives across the African continent, but these have largely been ineffectual. Theses should be reinvigorated. This book is about making TMT improve economies in Africa and elsewhere for the 2020s, and it is in this context that these recommendations as well as others in this book should be seen.

CHAPTER 5

AUCTIONS AND OTHER SPECTRUM AWARDS

"It is not from the benevolence of the butcher, the brewer or the baker, that we expect our dinner, but from their regard to their own interest."
—*Adam Smith (1776)[1]*

Why—I ask you—is a chapter on auctions (and other spectrum awards) necessary in a book on making TMT improve developing economies in Africa and elsewhere for the 2020s? Being the smart reader you are who has just completed reading chapter 4, you answer quoting Genachowski that spectrum is the oxygen of the wireless world. You also emphasise that as Africans, Asians, Caribbeans, Indians, etc. are consuming more and more data on mobile networks, more spectrum needs to be released, likening that if the number of cars in a vehicle-crowded city doubles, then more road capacity would certainly need to be built in the absence of other mass transit systems, like trains. You would be right with this response.

This is the second chapter in the section titled "Towards Widespread Availability of High-Quality Mobile Voice, Mobile Data, and Mobile Internet." Yes, the African continent and elsewhere certainly need more spectrums to be released to achieve this aim—and this is an important goal of this chapter. However, this sole reason in itself of

---

1 Adam Smith, *The Wealth of Nations* (1776). Adam Smith is often referred to as the father of modern economics.

releasing more spectrums does not merit a chapter. What is more important is the *process* of releasing more spectrum and the many important *policy* considerations that must be taken on board this time round. "This time round" because the first and other rounds since of spectrum releases on the African continent and elsewhere to fuel the mobile telecommunications growth, circa 1999 onwards, did not consider properly some of the main takeaways of this chapter.

So what has the above preamble got to do with the quote from Adam Smith above? *Prima facie,* the quote has little to do with releasing spectrum. However, Adam Smith was a great economist—arguably the greatest ever—and the relevance here is *how* that release of spectrum happens efficiently. Or drawing from the last chapter, how does the release of spectrum maximize the net economic benefits to the nation's consumers and citizens?

Adam Smith's insight in the quote above is of important help because it suggests in free (competitive) markets—even of butchers, brewers, and bakers, or otherwise—each of these agents acts in his "own interest," and his (Smith's) dinner was not out of "benevolence."

Therefore, releasing spectrum to the market is *not* a "benevolent: act from the regulator or the government. The regulator has to act in the interest of the ultimate owners of that natural resource—its consumers and citizens—and ensure it acts in their interests. In economic terms, it must maximize the sum of consumer and produce surplus—do not worry, this is explained in chapter 11. In plain English, in competitive spectrum markets, buyers with the highest valuations get the spectrum. This is a simple but devastatingly important conclusion—and this is the simplest explanation there is as to why highly sought-after spectrum (or high-value spectrum—remember table 1's ratio of 13.5 in the last chapter) is awarded via auctions. Deviating from using auctions needs a high hurdle, and auctions should be the default for the spate of spectrum releases to fuel mobile data/Internet on the African continent and elsewhere.

This explains the need for this chapter on auctions. It is not that I am an auction hawk who just likes raising receipts via auctions as I did leading the United Kingdom's 4G auction of 2013. Indeed, and for the record, I also oversaw spectrum beauty contests too. It is more that well-defined auctions provide clear, efficient, and transparent ways of releasing a scarce and highly sought-after resource into the market. However, not all spectrum need to be released (or should be released) via auctions, hence we also look at other spectrum awards. As usual, as you would have noted so far in this book, it is the policy considerations, key desirable outcomes for the country, and other important key messages we amplify, rather than esoteric auction designs. (There are many esoteric issues in auction design which would interest the economics nerds, but they're not covered here.)

This chapter therefore aims to get the reader (particularly government policy or regulatory decision makers) to appreciate auctions and other spectrum release approaches. This is in order to able to enable them to ask the right questions of some very clever auction design experts, who when let loose can end up designing truly complicated auctions. Therefore questions this chapter seeks to address include the following:

- What are the typical desirable outcomes from releasing new spectrum into the market—whether by auction or otherwise? The answer to this fundamental question does not come from auction experts. It comes from the independent regulator and/ or relevant government department.
- What work underpins the desirable outcome, and who carries out this work?
- What are the other approaches to releasing spectrum into the market?
- When, why, and where do you use an auction as opposed to other spectrum release methods?
- Should the primary goal of auctions be to try and raise as much money for government treasury as possible?
- What are the different types of auction formats to choose from? What should decision makers care about with respect to the different formats?
- What do actual auction logistics entail?
- What are the important recommendations going forward to releasing spectrum into the market for Africa and other emerging economies?

5.1 Desirable Outcomes of Releasing Spectrum into the Market

What are the typical desirable outcomes of releasing new spectrum into the market—whether by auction or otherwise? This is the most important question that key government and regulatory professionals must ask up front. We just do not rock up and run an auction (or another type of spectrum release into the market) without a significant amount of up front work.

The desirable outcomes should *either* already be clear in

- the statutory duties, powers, and functions[2] of the independent regulator;
- or they may be prescribed in a direction[3] from government to the regulator or to the spectrum agency;
- or, failing both above in the case of no (independent) regulator or spectrum agency, it is also recommended the government still legislates for its desired outcomes and empowers whichever arm of government to run the auction or the spectrum release process. The ultimate result must be that spectrum gets released to the "right hands" to maximise benefits to the country's consumers and citizens.

Releasing spectrum is necessarily a very legal process—and so it must be as companies are making significant commitments of millions if not billions of dollars.

---

2 There are legal differences between these rather simple words: "duty," "power," and "function." With "duty," the regulatory agency has little discretion as to what/how to carry it out. Effectively, it has to do it. "Powers" are the instruments of implementing "duties." However, there is more discretion here: in *which* powers to use and *whether* and *how* to use it. "Functions" is the sum total of all powers and duties conferred on a regulatory agency via statute.

3 Within a typical act which creates an independent regulator are usually some legal clauses which allow governments to formally direct the independent regulator to achieve some particular policy goal. This is a very formal and legislative process, with a deliberately high hurdle in order to safeguard the regulator's independence and ensure governments do not use directions lightly.

In any case, the principal desirable outcomes include the following (we exemplify them for achieving mobile voice, mobile data, and mobile Internet for the masses in Africa):

- *Policy Goals:* Policy goals include economic goals, social goals, and other goal types. The policy goal typically must be to act in the best interest of its consumers and citizens, which means maximising the net economic benefits to the society from mobile voice, mobile data, and mobile Internet. Previous chapters have already focused on these. There are also social goals too, e.g., of being as inclusive as possible as is prescribed in universal access obligations and/or policies. Here again, we do not only want mobile Internet or mobile data in the cities— we also want to cover the rural areas. There may also be social objectives to be mindful of: minority groups in society, the disabled, women, religious denominations, or other disenfranchised groups. If spectrum is to be released, e.g., for broadcasting, special rules may have to be established to ensure that such groups can participate too on an equal footing in such release processes.

- *Liberalisation*: Most of the new spectrum releases on the continent should happen within a more liberalised context. Technology and service neutrality are now the *de facto* contexts of releasing high-value spectrum into the market. These come with market-based approaches to managing spectrum. *Technology neutrality* refers to the principle of the regulator or spectrum agency no longer prescribing (as part of the license) what technology the winning operator should use. If the operator chooses to deploy 3G technology in its spectrum block, that is up to the company. Similarly, if the company uses its so-called 3G voice spectrum (typically in 2,100 MHz) to offer data services, this is also a choice for the spectrum licensee to make. This is the *service neutrality* principle. Using the liberalisation principle, all 2G spectrum in 900 MHz and 1,800 MHz should be liberalised for 3G and other mobile data services. (R)

- *Competition*: A primary concern for all decision makers and regulators must be that of competition. How competitive is the mobile market today in the country? Has a *competitive market assessment* been carried out? Depending on the latter, how many licenses are desired to be released into the marketplace? If there are some dominant players in the market today as a result of the competitive market assessment, then spectrum caps may need to be proposed and implemented. *Spectrum caps* refer to the maximum amount of spectrum operators may be able to have of particular types. So spectrum caps preempt and prevent excessive acquisition of spectrum on the part of some players. For example, in the February 2013 UK auction, there were spectrum caps of no more than 27.5 MHz for sub-1 GHz spectrum, so players like Vodafone and Telefonica who already had 17.5 MHz of 900 MHz spectrum each could only bid for a maximum of 10 MHz of *more* of sub-1 GHz at the auction.

  Another competition remedy could be one of *market entry assistance*. In many countries in Africa and some emerging markets I can name, it would be necessary for competition reasons to reserve spectrum for new entrants into these markets. It cannot be axiomatic that all the current players in the market in all countries have to be the same players who would hold future licenses for 4G mobile broadband/data and mobile Internet. So to effect market entry, some assistance may be enabled by some spectrum being reserved for new entrants. Other market entry assistance may even extend to imposing national roaming arrangements on existing players for the new entrant. Otherwise, existing players may not offer commercial deals to new entrants, and since the new entrant's networks will almost certainly not be as extensive as the incumbents', such roaming deals will be invaluable to the new entrants for competition.

  Infrastructure sharing should be another big consideration on the continent since, as we covered in earlier chapters, the economics for mobile Internet coverage will be difficult in these markets.

Co-location of sites could be another important entry assistance tool to a new entrant, such that current players must provide access to their base station sites to the new entrant on FRND-ly terms. Another competition instrument in mobile markets is the emergence of mobile virtual network operators (MVNOs)[4]. There are hardly any MVNOs today on the African continent in 2013/14 outside South Africa for a variety of understandable reasons; even South Africa has only two. However, as new spectrum is being released, e.g., for 4G mobile data, it may be an opportunity for regulation to encourage the emergence of MVNOs. It is likely that many entrants on the African continent may be a full 4G (and *mobile data*) network players but only MVNOs for *mobile voice*. You can see there are many competition issues to consider before any auction or spectrum release. Countries should take good advice.

- *Coverage:* We have emphasised this many times so far in this book. Coverage obligations are a significant intervention in the functioning of a market, and particularly to any operator. This is because the operator is being constrained to roll out networks beyond what the operator may believe is commercially viable. If the regulator or government already believe from their research and consultations that operators will only roll out mobile Internet/data networks to 50 percent of the population (e.g., only the cities), what are they supposed to do about the other 50 percent? Universal access obligations suggest they do their best to maximise coverage. So African/emerging market authorities may decide, proportionately, on both a *population-based coverage obligation* of, say, 75 percent and/or a *geography-based obligation* of also covering

---

4   An MVNO is a company which has made an agreement with one of the existing "real" mobile operators, like MTN or Safaricom, to carry services and products on their behalf. An MVNO will brand the product and services (and handsets) as if it were they themselves that were operating a network. This may be a cost-effective way for supermarket chains, music stores, and youth-related industries to move into the mobile service arena. A real operator may also make use of MVNO branding to target niche segments of the market, such as youth culture, gaming, etc.

specific places like main arterial roads even in rural areas. These obligations may be coupled with a targeted *data rate obligation* too of, say, a minimum of 500 KB/s indoor with 90 percent probability. In the UK auction which I directed, my colleagues and I eventually imposed a 98-percent UK-wide population coverage obligation for one of the 800 MHz licensees with a minimum of 95 percent population coverage obligation in all of the United Kingdom's constituent nations.[5] For the 98 percent and 95 percent obligations, the order also added "and with a 90% probability that a user at Reference Indoor Locations anywhere within that area would be able to receive the service with a sustained downlink speed of not less than 2 Mbps in a lightly loaded cell."

In plain English, we imposed a stringent 2 Mbps indoor (i.e., inside the house) obligation, with UK users nine times out of ten being able to get 2 Mbps. We believe we were proportionate by only imposing this obligation on *only* one of the four 800-MHz licensees we auctioned. So the UK coverage obligation is population based (98 percent), geography based for nations (95 percent) and targeted and also had a clear data rate obligation. In any case, such a coverage obligation as this in the United Kingdom will be too onerous and disproportionate for almost all African countries I can think of apart from Rwanda and Burundi perhaps. One final piece of valuable advice: do not impose an obligation you cannot measure and hence cannot enforce. This would be meaningless.

You then can see that the desired outcomes are incredibly important, and they do not come from auction experts. These require the independent regulator and/or key competent government departments to commission key market studies to address and answer all the issues raised above. The choice of an auction or another spectrum release format actually depends on the answers to these desirable outcome questions.

---

5 The nations include England, Scotland, Wales, and Northern Ireland.

5.2 Work Underpinning Desirable Outcomes

Some of them have already been spelt out in the narrative above in section 5.1. However, here is a nonexhaustive list from my experience of the recommended work areas to proceed with some high-value spectrum releases, like 700 MHz, 800 MHz, and 2,600 MHz, and who should carry them out. As decision makers and policy makers, the following are what you request to be done. As entrepreneurs, industrialists, and other stakeholders, these are the reasons, too, why these work areas are important.

- *Competition Assessment and Consultation*: Each market, whether it is South African or Egyptian, Cameroonian, or Namibian, has a different set of dynamics, and no two markets will be the same. Assuming the agency has a clear statutory framework, this work should be carried our pursuant to the agency's statutory duties or some government direction to the agency. The aim of this is to release additional spectrum for next generation mobile broadband. However, the process must start with a complete understanding of the current spectrum holdings of the current operators in the country and their competitive positions, their strengths, and their weaknesses. Particular attention must be paid to the weaker players in the market to ensure that further release of spectrum into the market does not further weaken their position. Another aim could also be to liberalise some existing 2G spectrum already in the market. In order to do this, a competition market assessment must be commissioned and carried out—addressing the questions posed in the completion section above—which should inform appropriate and proportionate measures that should be put in place to promote competition in the spectrum release, most likely via an auction. Such an assessment is typically carried out by the independent spectrum agency who would commission various studies from economic consultants, technical consultants, and others. The final piece of work would be collated and cogently argued, beefed up by much evidence from all the commissioned studies. The competition assessment set of documents would typically conclude on the risks to the future competitiveness of the mobile market in the country if bidders could acquire any amount of spectrum during the spectrum release process or auction. The agency will then propose a series of measures and consult openly on them with all stakeholders before concluding in a statement on the measures it will put in place to promote competition in the market post the spectrum release into the market (i.e., spectrum floors, spectrum caps, number of licenses to be issued, new entrants, entry assistance measures, innovation measures, spectrum liberalisation, etc.). This is the key piece of work which draws many other pieces of work. The competition assessment should be both at the wholesale and retail levels. The failure of carrying out a good and transparent competition assessment is almost unforgivable in this day and age, as its importance cannot truly be overstated.

- *Technical studies (for competition, coverage, and various public policy goals):* Various technical studies also need to be commissioned from technical consultants. These technical studies are also important components of the overall competition assessment of the market and/or the measures the spectrum release/auction puts in place to promote completion, coverage, and innovation. Any measures that the regulatory agency puts in place must be proportionate. To be proportionate, prior studies must be carried out. For example, rollout or coverage obligations cannot be so onerous that they would bankrupt operators. A combination of technical and economic studies must inform the spectrum agency how far the market *would* go in terms of coverage and rollout obligations and how far it *could* go. The number could be 65/75 percent (would/could) in one country but only 55/65 percent in another. Other technical studies also help inform how the spectrum is packaged up. This means, should the spectrum be packed up in 2×5 MHz lots or 2×10 MHz lots, for example, and why? What sort of minimum spectrum portfolios should players have in the marketplace to be able to compete with each other properly? How much spectrum (and of which types, as in low-frequency spectrum and/or high-frequency spectrum) should be reserved for a new entrant to compete with established players? We could go on. There are clearly a lot of technical studies that would inform completion questions, coverage questions, and other public policy objectives.

- *Nontechnical licence conditions studies (length of licenses, spectrum fees, spectrum trading, scope of licenses, etc.):* Not all conditions that go into spectrum licenses are of a technical nature, like coverage obligations and target data rates. The agency needs to conclude on nontechnical conditions like the following:

  ○ How long should the licenses be for? An indefinite duration license but with an initial term of, say, fifteen or twenty years, but continuing until relinquished or revoked?

  ○ Should licences be country-wide? Preferably, they should also be technology and service neutral.

  ○ Should all types of spectrum trading be permitted subject to competition checks? This means licensees who gain spectrum may subsequently trade the spectrum off to other third parties who did not participate in the auction or spectrum release process.

  ○ What annual fees should be paid for some of the existing spectrum already in the market—particularly if the spectrum is being liberalised and being made tradable? By liberalising some spectrum—i.e., by reducing some of the constraints on the spectrum use—and making them tradable will implicitly appreciate its value. Should this value increase be captured to the benefit of the state?

These are important questions that studies must answer. These are typically led by the spectrum or regulatory agency supported by many consultant studies. Also, all these decisions should be transparently consulted upon and decided. Industry players will have their positions to preserve, and some of these processes are toughly argued, sometimes unfortunately ending up in the courts. If you are beginning to think releasing high-value spectrum for the benefit of consumers and citizens is not trivial, you are right.

5.3 Auctions

There are many approaches to releasing spectrum into the market. The most important in my view for the context of releasing spectrum towards widespread availability of quality mobile voice and mobile data/Internet must be auctions. Auctions are the main mechanisms to ensure spectrum released into the market is acquired by those who value it the most. This (as we now know from the beginning of this chapter) is the most optimal way to maximise the net economic benefits to society of that spectrum. We argued that in competitive markets, for scarce resources to be allocated efficiently, they should go to those who value them the most and are willing to pay the highest amounts.

This is not a textbook on auctions. Rather it tries to provide a broad overview of auctions, overviewing the different types and the issues to be mindful of towards the setup of the TMT sector. This includes the following important points of note on spectrum auctions, when and why they are used:

- If demand for spectrum is likely to exceed supply, use an auction. Auctions tend to be used if demand for spectrum is likely to exceed supply. Otherwise, you need to choose between conflicting demands for a finite amount of spectrum.
- There is no perfect auction, but experience shows that well-designed auctions are generally better at achieving a regulatory agency's objectives (as spelt out in section 5.1) than other approaches noted later.
- As a mechanism it is fair, objective, transparent, and robust. These are great attributes rather than unfair, subjective, opaque, and dubious. These latter descriptors describe some spectrum releases that have happened on the African continent in the past—and even some more recent ones! An auction is usually the most effective way to award the spectrum because it typically puts spectrum into the hands of those who value it the most. A good auction also leads to efficient allocation. This is because efficient allocation and revenue maximisation, more often than not, often go together, though not always.

- Auctions avoid prejudging what is the "best use" of that spectrum because the market (i.e., the eventual licensees of the spectrum) decides. This obviously requires the spectrum to be liberalised, i.e., service and technology neutrality must reign.
- Auctions implicitly assume that the market is more informed than the spectrum auctioneer, typically a spectrum regulator or some other part of government. This must be right.
- Economists also consider up front auction payments do not affect future market prices and that they are a *nondistorting tax*. This is because in well-designed auctions, bidders pay up front for their spectrum, and therefore, economically at least, these costs should be treated as sunk costs.[6] If bidders treat these up-front costs as sunk, then economic theory stipulates that they do not affect future market prices. Similarly, to the extent that an upfront auction payment is a tax, it is a nondistorting tax to the accounts of the licensees concerned, as these costs are sunk and irreversibly spent.

However, auctions are *not* without their detractors. Consider the following:

- Some argue that spectrum auctions are mechanisms to raise as much monies for governments as possible, allegedly by forcing bidders to pay high amounts. Such criticisms arose when some earlier auctions, including the UK's 3G spectrum auction in 2000 which raised £22.5 billion/€38.6 billion and the German 3G auction which took place a few months later in the same year and raised a staggering €50.8 billion. Yes these were incredible sums, but even all those who suffered the winners' curse (i.e., who "overpaid") now admit that their overvaluation stemmed mostly from wildly optimistic expectations

---

6 Sunk cost is an economic cost concept that measures costs already incurred in the past. So they are historic costs that are irreversibly spent and do not depend on the future quantity of goods or services supplied. A typical textbook example of a of a sunk cost is the cost of a marketing campaign for a new service. Once spent, this cost cannot be recovered regardless of whether the service continues to be provided.

about the future demand and supply conditions in the market during 2000. It was not due to the design of the auction itself that raised these gargantuan sums. Some of us who saw some of this firsthand thought at the time that the industry had taken leave of its senses. Therefore views that auctions are money-minting machines for governments are just simply wrong.

This does not mean that a very poorly designed auction may not force bidders to some degree to pay too much for spectrum. It could, but this is rare. Auction designs can minimise the winner's curse problem through a more gradual price discovery process—i.e., the prices are raised by the auctioneer more gradually, giving ample opportunity for more truthful bidding and price discovery, and by using the second price rule described later.

- Other detractors say high auction prices translate into high prices for services relying on radio spectrum. We have already addressed this to some degree by noting that upfront payments are essentially sunk costs and that sunk costs do not tend to influence market prices. The level of competition that we have emphasised throughout this volume is the biggest factor on the prices for services.

The main point is that most auctions are (or should be) designed to achieve the most efficient allocation of spectrum and hence achieve the best for society. In most cases, this happens. Bidders sometime complain, but in most cases they should look in the mirror if they think they suffered the winner's curse.

5.3.1 Should a Primary Objective on an Auction Be to Raise as Much Revenue as Possible?

In my four years as a senior regulator, I got this question umpteen times from the press, analysts, and other TMT industry players. Despite my protestations that not only did Ofcom's (UK) statutes explicitly *not* allow for this, but that any good regulator would (and should) shun this, I felt I was hardly ever believed. I decided on another way to answer the question, which seemed to be better believed. I noted Ofcom had some of the smartest economists and auction experts I had had the privilege of working with. If this was our mission—i.e., to maximise spectrum receipts—it would be very easy to create an artificial scarcity of spectrum. Demand soars, supply is limited, and price goes through the roof. The regulator and treasury get significant sums in.

In the long term, this is truly foolhardy. First, this will almost certainly *not* result in an efficient allocation of the spectrum. This is because some spectrum which should have been released into the market has been artificially "held back" and is not being put into productive use. So it fails both the tests of *allocative efficiency* (which ensures that spectrum gets into the hands of users who value it the most) and *productive efficiency* (which in this case means the spectrum is put into maximum productive use). It also fails on *dynamic efficiency* (i.e., the spectrum moves to its highest value use at any time). In the long term, all these inefficiencies are extremely costly to society. Secondly, any agency and/or decent regulator who tries to maximise receipts—assuming they do not end up in the courts, which they would deserve—would find their reputation thrashed. How can the regulator oversee an auction in which it (the regulator itself) has a principal interest? It would ride roughshod over good principles like truthful bidding and price discovery in the auction. Thirdly, it will not be transparent, objective, or fair. I could go on. Suffice to say good spectrum auctioneers and/or regulators must *not* be given an explicit duty to maximise receipts for the government.

5.3.2 Types of Auctions

The simplest way to understand the myriad of auction formats out there is to realise that they all derive from combinations of various different auction design rules and/or options.

- Is it a single round or multiple rounds of bidding auction?
- Is it an ascending (English) or descending bids (Dutch) auction?
- Is there a "clock"? That is, there is a standing high bidder, and bid prices and quantities are made or placed at announced prices

(clock). A clock round is good for price discovery, i.e., it allows bidders to learn from each other about the value of the item, e.g., some spectrum band. The auctioneer sets bid increments.

- Is information disclosed, i.e., open (transparent) or closed (sealed) bids? Sealed bids allow for no price discovery process, as bidders do not engage in learning from each other about the value of the item as happens with a clock process.
- Are bids for individual items or for combinations of items or blocks (package auction)? For example, like in the UK auction, bidders could bid for a combination of both low frequency spectrum (sub-1 GHz) for coverage and high-value spectrum (e.g., 2.6 GHz) for capacity.
- What activity rules are in place? E.g., as prices rise in ascending auction, bidders are not allowed to increase bid quantities.
- Rules to prevent collusive behaviour. There are always these.
- What is the pricing rule: first price or second price? First price rule ensures the bidder who pays the highest bid wins the item. Second price rule ensures the bidder pays the highest losing bid. Why is the first price or second price rule important? The reason is because of *bid shading*. Bid shading happens because bidders are incentivised in some circumstances to shade their bids, i.e., not to reveal their true values. Bid shading reduces their chances of winning, but the incentive is there to do so because it increases the bidder's payoff if the bidder *does* win because the bidder pays a lower price. The real problem is that bid shading introduces inefficiency into the auction because the bidder who values the item (e.g., spectrum) the highest may fail to win because of bid shading. The second price rule encourages bids to reflect true value, i.e., encouraging truthful bidding. There really is no incentive with the second price rule to bid shade (i) because it reduces the bidder's chances of winning and (ii) there is no payoff dividend because the price depends only on bids made by other bidders, which they have no control over. The best strategy with the second price rule is truly to bid truthfully.

- How many stages are there, one or two—or even more? First stage decides on who wins how many items or blocks of spectrum. Second stage decides on position in band.

Using these design rules and/or options, the following auction formats accrue and more. It is arguably easier to capture in summary form as a table—table 2. This table draws from Cave *et al.* (2007),[7] chapter 5, as they provide good examples of how these formats have been used for spectrum auctions around the world and from other research too. Please refer to this book chapter for more details.

Auction Format	Brief Description	Example(s)
First-price sealed bid auction	Simple auction design that is easy to design and implement (and completes quickly) in which the bidder who posts highest bid wins the spectrum lot. It is simple, quick, and good for small packages of spectrum wherein the bidder receives one license in a given geographic area. It is also good for competition. However, being first price, bidders may shave bids. Also bidders winning similar spectrum lots may pay different prices, flummoxing them along with other	Used in New Zealand in 1991 for FM, UHF, AM, and DMS frequencies for local licences throughout the country. United Kingdom (Ofcom). Low -power spectrum GSM/ DECT[8] guard bands.

7 Cave, M., Doyle, C., and Webb, W. (2007), *Essentials of Modern Spectrum Management*, Cambridge: Cambridge University Press.
8 1,781–1,785 MHz/1,876–1,880 MHz (GSM/DECT guard bands)

	government officials. No price discovery as a sealed bid. So may not be that efficient. Very high risk of winner's curse.	
Second-price sealed bid auction (also called Vickrey auction)	Similar in most respects to first-price sealed bid but uses second-price rule. A further downside is that if there is a wide gap between what successful bidder posts and the highest posted losing bid, this could also embarrass political masters. Interestingly, this happened in New Zealand, and they later used a first-price sealed bid for the later auction above for this poor reason. May not be a very efficient auction either, but no risk of winner's curse.	Used in New Zealand in 1989 for UHF frequencies. United Kingdom/ Ireland (for 1,785–1,805 MHz).
Simultaneous ascending auctions (SAA)—also called simultaneous multiround auction (SMRA)	Bidders submit bids round by round, successively bidding up until a round when no bids are received. Auctioneer decides on minimum bid increment and activity rules, minimising shading of demand, etc. Being simultaneous, can support many blocks of spectrum (including substitutes and complements). It is strong	United Kingdom (April 2000) 3G auction which raised €38.6 billion; 52 days, 150 rounds. Germany (August/2000) 3G auction which raised €50.8 billion; 19 days, 173 rounds.

	on competition. However, could take a long time and resource intensive to implement and could be prone to tacit collusion. Applies second price rule.	Switzerland (December 2000) 3G auction; one day. Sweden (April 2008)—2.6 GHz auction. Germany (May 2010), 4G auction of 800 MHz, 1800 MHz, & 2.6 GHz.
Ascending clock auction	It is very similar to SAA. Bidders submit their demand in response to auctioneer's announced prices and continue until demand is equal to the number of supply of licenses on offer. Auction experts assert that it is likely to be more efficient than SAA. There is a risk here of the auctioneer overshooting valuation of bidders, in which case two auctions may be required.	Nigeria (in 2001)—auction of 3 GSM licenses.
Revenue share auctions	Variants of other auctions with the added twist of revenue share between auctioneer and bidders. However, this means market prices include royalty tax.	Hong Kong (2001), 3G auction.

Hybrid auctions	Combines auctions with other release formats, such as beauty contests.	
Combinatorial auction/combinatorial clock auction (CCA)	Complex auction for auctioneer and arguably for bidders too with bids based on different combination of blocks. Multiple stages. Clock stage very similar to ascending clock auction, which continues until supply equal demand. Bids are for a combination of quantities of lots (e.g., two lots of 800 MHz and five lots of 2.6 GHz). Any of bidder's combinations could win, though only one can win. If bid combination wins, bidder gets all lots in that bid combination. Supplementary bid stage follows to decide on where bidders can also state other further bid combinations they would happily win and how much they would pay. Final assignment stage decides on specific frequencies in the bands.	United Kingdom 4G auction (February 2013) which raised £2.34 billion; fifty-two clock rounds.

	The second price rule typically applies in CCA. Winning bids are combinations of bids that produce highest total value. Efficient auction format.	
Anglo Dutch auction	Like SMRA auction but followed by a sealed bid auction using first price rule. Sealed bid element is to ensure if one or more licenses are unsold after SAA/SMRA clock round.	United Kingdom (2004)—3.4 GHz public fixed wireless access (PFWA) licenses.

Table 2—Simplified Table of Auction Formats

There is a lot of more complex literature on auction formats, but the table above suffices for understanding the options out there.

5.3 Other Approaches to Releasing Spectrum: Grants and Beauty Contests

Lest you believe that auctions are the only way to release spectrum into the marketplace, there are other approaches too. Two principal ones are spectrum grants and beauty contests.

- **Spectrum Grants:** Grants typically happen as first come, first served. In this case, licenses are awarded (subject to applicants meeting some minimum criteria, such as they are a bona fide applicant for a license, etc.) in the order in which they apply. There is no competition with grants. Many low-value, "commodity" type, and plentiful licenses are awarded as grants. It may result in very inefficient allocations, but the downside risks are small, as there are typically plentiful licenses.

- **Beauty Contests:** This is the approach to deciding *who* should have a spectrum license, where those who want the license make a case as to *why* they should have it. Therefore, licences are assigned to the bidder that best satisfies some predetermined strategic priorities identified by the regulator. The regulator or the spectrum agency decides which case is most convincing by carefully studying the strength of the cases made, covering their business plan, their sustainability, and other broader social value elements. Beauty contests are also competitions where the selection criteria and weightings are set and published/consulted on in advance. In the United Kingdom, as in other European countries, there were few contenders for the original mobile licenses in the early 1980s, allowing a beauty contest approach to be simply applied.

It is, however, the case that in more recent years, as demand for spectrum had been exceeding supply in some areas, use of "beauty contest" meant that governments or regulatory agencies had to choose between competing would-be service providers. By the time 3G licenses were auctioned in Europe, things were very different. In the UK 3G auction in 2000, there was an international field of thirteen applicants. A fair and transparent beauty contest would have been virtually impossible in these circumstances. In the United States too, such beauty contests, indeed command and control decisions, were increasingly subject to legal challenge, leading initially to the use of lotteries to overcome this problem and then eventually to the use of auctions. Other countries soon followed suit.

Earlier on in this chapter, it was noted that where demand for spectrum licenses exceeds supply, auctions are preferable. This is indeed true. However, it does not mean that where beauty contests are used, there cannot be more demand for those licenses than there is supply. More specifically, where much of the value to society is mostly in the externality[9] called *broader social value* (as is typically the case with some broadcasting activities) and not necessary in the core demand, beauty contests come into their element. Nevertheless, transparency can always be an issue, or losing bidders make the regulator feel it is an issue. Most national and regional TV and radio licenses are awarded through beauty contests.

5.4 Auction Logistics

The complexity of the auction logistics is clearly a function of auction format chosen. However, in general, there are four main stages to most auctions: an invitation stage; a prequalification stage; the main auction stage (which could comprise various substages); and, lastly, the grant of license stage.

The *invitation stage* commences with the publication of the information memorandum (IM), which really fires the starting gun for the auction. The IM details the "products" or various spectrum bands that will be auctioned, the auction rules, the application forms, and all the prequalification criteria.

The *prequalification stage* is the stage where "unqualified" bidders are screened out. The criteria for qualification are usually objective, transparent, and not burdensome. Cave *et al.* (2007) report on how the Nigerian GSM auction prequalification criteria included deterring those engaged in money laundering or other illegal activities from participating. Prequalification processes ensures bidders meet ownership rules, preempting a top company owning two companies who are applying to be bidders. Some say there is a beauty contest

---

9 Externality in this context is the means by which the service in question, e.g., broadcasting, provides huge value. But not much of it is monetisable. People do not want to pay for news programmes or cultural affairs programmes, for example, but they inform, they educate, they help create a sense of inclusion in society, they inform our democracies and foster cultural understanding, they articulate "social bads," etc. These are incredibly important to the broader social value which cannot be captured as private value, i.e., via profits and consumer surplus.

element to this stage too because bidders are vetted as to whether they can truly provide the telecommunications services they seek to provide. There is also always a significant deposit to deter frivolous or speculative bidders.

The *main auction stage* is covered in table 2 above.

Lastly, the *grant stage* is when the successful bidders are issued the licenses subject to all monies having been paid to the auctioneer.

These following summarise some main logistics issues to attend to with auctions during the main stage:

- Raising awareness of the auction: it is important to stimulate interest in auctioned licences and in the transparency of the process.
- Regulations: the prior consulted-on procedures and rules for running an auction need to be clearly set out.
- Information memorandum: This is the key legal document that details the spectrum on offer and the auction rules. It is most important that this document is signed off with care.
- Develop website: A website should be set up to convey public information, such as the above, on the auction in a timely fashion.
- Develop IT systems: most auctions in the second decade of the twenty-first century will be automated with sophisticated auction software. This includes accommodating remote bidding and processing of bids.
- Develop auction procedures: i.e., checking applications, contact with bidders, etc.
- Testing the auction design: the auction design and system must be tested in advance of the real deal, such as in-house laboratory simulations by expert designers.
- Training bidders: this must be done by conducting mock auctions.

As regards resources, a multidisciplinary auction team is required. Specialist advice may be needed to ensure a robust auction design. Choice of auction format needs skilful matching to the licence product on offer. Experience shows that auction design can go wrong, so getting advice is crucial. Bidders are likely to hire advisers to test auction design and rules—and so it is best the auction design is right. Most importantly from the perspective of this volume, the broad desired policy outcomes must be correct too, as this is what truly maximises the net economic value to consumers and citizens or both private value and broader social value. To achieve this, significant advice may be required too.

5.5 TMT Key Spectrum Release Recommendations for Africa and Emerging Markets

Spectrum release into the market is an important element towards widespread availability of quality mobile voice, mobile data, and mobile Internet. The following recommendations emerge from the sections above. For all of these, it is important advice is taken from competent professionals who have done it before and from those who have overseen such projects.

1. *Be clear on the desirable outcomes for releasing spectrum into the market:* Section 5.1 covers the desirable outcomes areas for releasing spectrum into the market towards widespread quality mobile voice, data, and Internet. To arrive at the desirable outcomes for every market does take a lot of thinking and deliberation amongst professionals within the regulator and/or various government departments. This will take a fair amount of time to debate internally and eventually consult externally.

2. *Liberalise where possible existing 2G spectrum in the hands of incumbents:* In order to begin addressing the 3G/4G data problem, the first and most obvious thing to do is to explore (and implement) the options of liberalising some of the spectrum already in the market today across Africa and emerging markets. By liberalising, constraints from their current licenses would go, and in its place would come in technology

and service neutrality clauses. Such liberalisation not only promotes market-based mechanisms into spectrum management (which is good) but also helps towards the goal of optimal use of our spectrum airwaves by driving more allocative, productive, and dynamic efficiency. Such liberalisations must not be automatic and must always be subject to competition checks, though not necessarily onerous ones. Liberalisation may also be accompanied by a review of the annual spectrum fee payment arrangements for this spectrum and/or the length of the licenses.

3. *Seek opportunities to refarm spectrum from existing use for mobile use:* Remember refarming assesses current use of a band by existing users with respect to international harmonisation initiatives or with respect to other competing uses. This redesignating of spectrum from one use to another is called refarming. There is a case for refarming some of the 800 MHz, (from CDMA), 700 MHz (from broadcasting), and other bands for mobile broadband and data. Looking towards the 2020s, refarming must be an important option across the continent and elsewhere. Refarming may also happen via the market where private operators buy out the spectrum rights from other operators, like what is happening with some 800 MHz spectrum on the African continent. As noted in the previous chapter, any informed analysis of the 800 MHz band in 2013/14 would quickly lead to the conclusion that LTE/4G is arguably the more optimal use for the African economy than for CDMA/2G/3G. So a change of use from CDMA to LTE/4G is a likely outcome of such a study. A recommendation in the last chapter suggested approaches the regulator could engage in in order to refarm such spectrum—particularly if the spectrum is in recalcitrant hands: encourage spectrum trading, introduce spectrum pricing, use regulatory clearance, or use an incentive auction approach.

4. *Prioritise releasing more spectrums into the market:* The GSMA believes that governments and regulators do not know how to release spectrum and do not see the importance of prioritising the release of spectrum. Governments and regulators should seek the right advice and help to address this problem.

5. *Carry out mobile and TMT sector competition market assessments and other relevant studies (e.g., technical ones):* You should by the end of this chapter now understand the primacy of very well carried out competition market assessments as a precursor to designing truly competitive TMT sectors for the 2020s. Mobile sector assessments are also invaluable to any future auctions or spectrum releases that happen on the African continent and some emerging markets. It is recommended that these market assessments are carried out by competent economic consultants and others who fully understand the policy objectives for the country. The relevant technical studies covering technologies, passive and active infrastructure sharing studies, and coverage studies. As coverage studies are being carried out to inform the extent of coverage obligations, it is recommended that work on how the obligations would be measured and enforced are also carried out.

6. *Carry out auction design and implementation preparations:* I will assume here that you now also agree that, more likely than not, any new spectrum releases into the market for mobile broadband and data would be via auctions. You have seen there are a myriad of auction formats out there. As seen, a good auction design in incredibly important to realising the most benefits to society. Preparing for and designing an auction which draws on all the prior recommendations is very time consuming. Even the logistics preparations needs thinking through.

Like in chapter 4, it is the case that some of these recommendations are hard to achieve, as they require significant up-skilling of spectrum policy professionals within regulators.

7. *Obtain good advice* is the last recommendation of this chapter.

CHAPTER 6

TV WHITE SPACES FOR
AFFORDABLE RURAL BROADBAND

"If spectrum is the oxygen of the wireless world, broadband is definitely the oxygen of the Digital Economy."[1]

"The global village is real, but not inclusive."[2]

This chapter is on how to optimise the widest possible availability of broadband in Africa and other emerging market economies, including rural broadband. Microsoft is right to note that broadband (whether via mobile Internet or otherwise, i.e., fixed) is the oxygen of the digital economy. Nevertheless, this chapter and other chapters preceding it explain that the market, left to itself, is most unlikely to deliver mobile Internet for the masses, not least because of the naked mobile data problem and its implications for coverage (see figure 3). It is, therefore, up to independent regulators and/or governments in Africa and other emerging economies to preempt this problem. One way to achieve this preemption which this volume has mentioned several times already is the license-exemption of TV white spaces technology.

Why do we need to care about ensuring widespread availability of mobile Internet—or mobile Internet for the masses in Africa and

---

1   Adapted from Julius Genachowski's "Spectrum is the oxygen of the wireless world" and Microsoft's "Broadband is the oxygen of the digital economy."

2   From a presentation, *Wireless Everywhere*, by Dr. Daniel Reed, Microsoft, at Cambridge TV White Spaces Trial: Results Meeting, United Kingdom. April 25, 2012.

elsewhere? There are a couple of important answers to this, and they are set out in the quotes I used to start this chapter.

Firstly, as noted in the first quote introducing this chapter, "if spectrum is the oxygen of the wireless world, broadband is definitely the oxygen of the digital economy." Africa and other emerging economies do not *only* need to become digital economies—these countries need their masses to join too. Remember from chapter 1 the 2011 study by Ericsson and Little[3] that found that both broadband availability and speed of broadband are strong drivers in an economy? They concluded that for every ten percentage point increase in broadband penetration, the GDP increases by 1 percent. Furthermore if speeds are doubled, then GDP increases by 0.3 percent. Chapter 1 notes that since these research findings were derived from developed economies, these figures would likely be doubled for African and some emerging market economies, i.e., 2 percent GDP increases for every ten percentage point increase in broadband penetration and 0.6 percent increase in GDP if speeds are doubled. It therefore makes economic sense to broadband connect the vast African unconnected and then speed up the broadband speeds.

Secondly, Microsoft's Dan Reed also rightly notes that the global village is *real*, but not *inclusive*. The International Telecommunications Union estimates that mobile broadband is unaffordable for 2.6 billion people and does not cover 3.8 billion people. The reality is most Africans fall into the *not-covered* number of 3.8 billion, as well as the majority of them too fall into the *unaffordable* 2.6 billion. This "double whammy" problem of coverage and affordability needs radical technological solutions and new commercial business models. This is the promise of TV white spaces technology and its emerging business models.

Returning to TV white spaces technology, preceding chapters made the case that as new spectrum is being released for 3G/4G to fuel mobile voice and mobile data/Internet in the dense urban and urban areas, TV white space technology could be ideal for semirural and rural areas. This chapter therefore aims to get the reader (particularly

---

3 http://www.telecompaper.com/news/doubling-broadband-speed-leads-to-03-gdp-growth-in-oecd--829373 (accessed June 2013)

government policy or regulatory decision makers, but also entrepreneurs and rural communities) to appreciate and act on the potential of TV white spaces in Africa and other key emerging economies. This is to enable them to ensure that, as regulators and governments plan to release more spectrums, they should think more broadly about coverage and affordability. Therefore the sort of questions this chapter seeks to address includes the following:

- What are TV white spaces? Where are these TV white spaces?
- How much of TV white spaces exist in most African countries?
- Why TV white space technology? Why is it attractive? How will it deal with the coverage problem?
- What are the use cases for TV white space Technology? How does TV white space technology work?
- What does TV white spaces presage for UHF spectrum policy in Africa and other emerging economies in particular, and for TMT Policy in general?
- How would TV white spaces deal with the affordability problem?
- What should governments and regulators do to enable TV white spaces? Should TV white spaces be license exempted or light licensed? What do these terms mean?
- What is the relationship between TV white spaces and Universal Service Funds?
- What are some key disclaimers about TV white spaces and rural broadband?
- What are the important recommendations going forward for white spaces for Africa and some emerging economies?

6.1 What and Where are TV White Spaces?

Section 4.2 has already answered the "what are TV white spaces" question (please refer back to it). It explains that the way TV networks are designed and built in Europe (mostly in UHF) leaves what is usually referred to as *geographically interleaved spectrum* in most areas.

Channel	21	22	23	24	25	26	27	28	29	30	31	32
Frequency (MHz)	470-478	478-486	486-494	494-502	502-510	510-518	518-526	526-534	534-542	542-550	550-558	558-566

33	34	35	36	37	38	39	40	41	42	43	44
566-574	574-582	582-590	590-598	598-606	606-614	614-622	622-630	630-638	638-646	646-654	654-662

45	46	47	48	49	50	51	52	53	54	55	56
662-670	670-678	678-686	686-694	694-702	702-710	710-718	718-726	726-734	734-742	742-750	750-758

57	58	59	60	61	62	63	64	65	66	67	68
758-766	766-774	774-782	782-790	790-798	798-806	806-814	814-822	822-830	830-838	838-846	846-854

Figure 38—Where TV White Spaces Are Found

(Source: Ofcom, Colour codings in this figure should be ignored)

TV white spaces are therefore the unused channels at a given location, as shown in figure 36 in chapter 4. The TV white space channels also reside within the UHF spectrum—as shown in figure 38—from 470 MHz to 790 MHz (i.e., band IV channels 21 to 60), or more like 470 MHz to 694 MHz (or channels 21 to 48) if 700 MHz is cleared across Africa for mobile broadband at the World Radio Congress in 2015.

The likelihood is that a significant number of UHF channels (each of 8 MHz bandwidth) on the African continent are already "white space" across most countries' national territories. The few channels that are being used for analogue TV today will be cleared out June 17, 2015, or by 2020 and be replaced by probably just a couple to three multiplexes using a UHF channel each to host between twenty and sixty digital channels. This is because each 8 MHz UHF channel can support an entire multiplex of up to 20 television channels, requiring the use of only two to three UHF frequencies to provide up to sixty TV channels. As is noted in chapter 4, some of these new digital channels may not even be in Band IV UHF (as they will go into Band III) which means in some countries, most of the entire set of UHF channels from 470 MHz to 694 MHz may be mostly white space everywhere. Indeed, a key question to be asked is, if technologies like white spaces technology are not employed for UHF in Africa between channels 21 to 48, what would they really be used for?

The preceding paragraph also begins to answer the question of how much white space channels exist in most countries on the continent. The answer is that it depends on (i) how many channels are reserved for digital TV in Band IV UHF, (ii) whether local TV channels are required, (iii) whether single frequency or multifrequency,[4] i.e., SFN or MFN digital broadcast networks, are deployed, and (iv) whether there is an extended period of dual illumination of both analogue and digital channels. Dual illumination is a special and transitory phase where the same channels are broadcast both in analogue and digital, and the analogue transmissions would be switched off at some time. However, assuming four UHF channels average in most countries (which is plentiful, as it can host up to eighty TV and radio channels), this suggests that twenty-three UHF channels may be vacant in most places across the nations, or 184 MHz of spectrum in most places up to 27×8 MHz or 216 MHz where there is no TV in UHF at all. In practice, it will be less than these numbers if spectrum is reserved for other services like local TV and due to international coordination reasons.

---

4 A single frequency network (SFN) is an analogue or digital broadcast network where several to many transmitters simultaneously transmit over the same frequency channel. A multifrequency network (MFN), in contrast, is one in which multiple radio frequencies are used for broadcasting. One way to visualise it is to imagine a chessboard with a transmitter in each square. In a SFN, all transmitters will be using the same frequency, whilst in a MFN, no two same frequencies will be adjacent to one another on the chessboard. SFNs are therefore more efficient on use of radio frequencies at the expense of likely self-interference, resulting in likely smaller coverage per cell/square due to the use of the same frequency in all cells.

UHF ASSIGNMENTS

| Channel | UHF Band | | Operator | Frequency | Location |
	Video Carrier	Audio Carrier		Assigned (MHz)	
21	471.25	476.75			
22	479.25	484.75			
23	487.25	492.75			
24	495.25	500.75			
25	503.25	508.75	CFC	503.25/508.75	Blantyre
26	511.25	516.75			
27	519.25	524.75	ABC	519.25/524.75	Lilongwe
28	527.25	532.75			
29	535.25	540.75			
30	543.25	548.75			
31	551.25	556.75			
32	559.25	564.75			
33	567.25	572.75			
34	575.25	580.75			
35	583.25	588.75			
36	591.25	596.75			
37	599.25	604.75			
38	607.25	612.75			
39	615.25	620.75			
40	623.25	628.75			
41	631.25	636.75			
42	639.25	644.75			
43	647.25	652.75			
44	655.25	660.75			
45	663.25	668.75			
46	671.25	676.75			
47	679.25	684.75			
48	687.25	692.75			
49	695.25	700.75			

Figure 39—UHF Assignments in Malawi as of May 2013

(Source: Malawi Communications Regulatory Authority [MACRA])[5]

You should be able to see for yourself the amount of white space available in Malawi as per May 2013. Apart from a couple of assignments in channels 25 and 27 in Lilongwe (the capital) and Blantyre (the other main city in Malawi apart from Lilongwe), you can see the spectrum is mostly "white," suggesting the sort of quantum of white spaces across the continent noted above. Even if the quantum is only half this or even a quarter, this is a lot of valuable sweet spot spectrum going vacant.

6.2 Why TV White Spaces? Why Is It Attractive?

TV white spaces can help satisfy the appetite of wireless connectivity. Leading innovators in the USA and United Kingdom principally

---

5 MACRA—Jonathan Pinifolo, *The Role of White Spaces in Universal Access*, TV White Spaces, Africa Forum 2013, Dakar, Senegal.

have already technically demonstrated the potential that TV white spaces can have for meeting Africa's and some emerging market's broadband needs. The idea of using it to deliver broadband (or wireless Internet) to rural parts of the continent and elsewhere is most exciting. Indeed, it is one of the most important and recent contributions to maximizing the spectrum efficiency below 1 GHz. The best pictorial answer I have come across to the "Why is TV white spaces attractive?" question is courtesy of the BBC, as per figure 40.

Why is TV White Space Attractive?

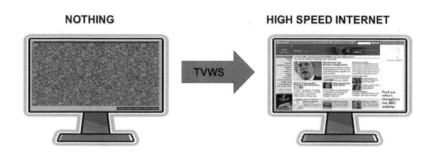

Figure 40—Why is TV White Spaces Attractive?
(Source: BBC)[6]

In essence, there are several reasons why TV white spaces in Africa and in some emerging market countries are particularly attractive.

- *Little Opportunity Cost:* There is little opportunity cost for this to happen in most African countries, as most of UHF may be "free" anyway. Figure 40 says it all about the almost zero opportunity cost.
- *Coverage and Affordability:* Providing the widest possible coverage of broadband at affordable prices is an important policy

6 From a presentation, *Cambridge Whitespaces and the BBC*, Mark Waddell, BBC, at Cambridge TV White Spaces Trial: Results Meeting, United Kingdom, April 25, 2012.

outcome, and TV white spaces promise to offer these both. Figure 41 shows some distances and broadband speeds achievable using TV white spaces. The speeds are by no means puny: at 10 km away, speeds of 2 Mbps are achievable with a sweet spot area between distances of 2 and 8 km.

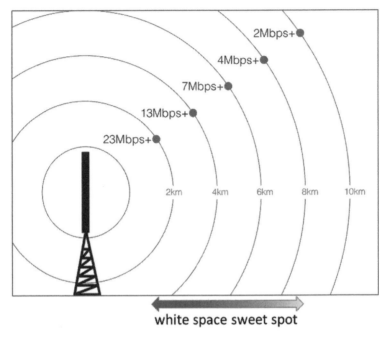

white space sweet spot

Figure 41—Achievable Downlink Speeds in a Single 8-MHz TV Channel at Various Distances from Base Station
(Source: TTP)[7]

• *Overarching African Challenges:* The end of chapter 3 noted some truly big challenges about Africa in particular: the sheer size of the continent, its population distribution, and the fact that 70 percent of Africans live in rural or semirural hinterlands of the continent. TV white spaces–based rural broadband promises to be part of the solution to these challenges, in addition to other solutions.

---

7 Ibid.

- *Socioeconomic Benefits:* White spaces can maximise socio-economic and environmental benefits that can be generated through the use of radio spectrum, as pointed out earlier on in this chapter.
- *New Spectrum for Broadband:* Addressing increasing demand for spectrum driven by mobile data means alleviating demand for more scarce spectrums. TV white spaces UHF spectrum ticks these boxes excellently, and this is prime sweet spot UHF spectrum. It will also ensure radio spectrum contributes to broadband targets.
- *Wireless Innovation:* New spectrum for broadband will no doubt foster more wireless innovation in Africa and elsewhere, particularly because this spectrum will be used in rural areas too. Who knows what apps and new services will emerge to meet the needs of rural Africans?
- *Dynamic Spectrum Management and Spectrum Sharing*: Another (albeit more general but most relevant and important) reason which is arguably more critical for developed economies is that new technologies like TV white spaces assists regulators to develop new regulatory frameworks to improve on the optimum use of spectrum. This is not only because TV white spaces by definition targets the usage of interleaved spectrum which is currently "white," i.e., not being used, but also because it promises to usher in an era of dynamic spectrum management. Even in the developed world, most spectrums are not being used in most places most of the time. This is not a good fact to hear if you are a good spectrum regulator. The current traditional approaches for spectrum allocation encourage such subefficient usage. The notion of being able to move from static to dynamic allocation of spectrum—where spectrum can be used dynamically for some time by User A and returned into the "pool" for User B to use the same spectrum the next moment—is one which many spectrum regulators truly aspire to. Furthermore, spectrum sharing is being enabled by TV white spaces. *Spectrum sharing* generally refers to a "secondary" use of the same spectrum, though it could also refer to a "co-primary" use. In this

case, the same spectrum TV white spaces can either be used as a secondary use for mobile broadband whilst the primary use remains for TV, or both mobile broadband and TV could be designated as primary users of the same spectrum.

Dynamic spectrum access (DSA)'s time has come, i.e., a dynamic way of accessing spectrum in contrast to the current static approach. TV white spaces would be one such instantiation of dynamic spectrum management, and it promises to help connect hundreds of millions to billions more people and devices to the Internet.

I have also been on record that dynamic spectrum management is the nirvana[8] for any good spectrum regulator: "the nirvana of dynamic spectrum regulation should be something all regulators should aspire to...in order to drive up spectrum efficiency."

6.3 What Are the Use Cases for TV White Spaces? How Does It Work?

Rural broadband is obviously the "biggest draw" for TV white spaces, but it's by no means the only one. The following are the main use cases driving TV white spaces work.

- *Affordable Rural Broadband and How It Works:* Thanks to the physics of low frequency spectrum, particularly spectrum in the lower UHF range as depicted in figure 38, TV white spaces technology's central *promise* is offering enhanced ranges and higher speeds (see figure 41) at affordable prices to rural areas. It must be admitted that as of December 2013, the affordability claim has yet to be proven, and that is why it is still a "promise." I believe it will be proven, but only through a public-private-partnership (PPP) model. As of the technology itself, that has

---

8 "Africa and TV White Spaces: The ghosts in the machine could provide additional spectrum at low cost," *Telecoms, Internet and Broadcast in Africa*, issue no. 575, October 7, 2011, http://www.balancingact-africa.com/news/en/issue-no-575/top-story/africa-and-tv-white/en (accessed November 2013).

been proven in multiple trials and pilots across the globe in the USA, United Kingdom (Cambridge, Isle of Bute), Germany (Munich), Finland, Singapore, South Africa, Kenya, etc., with many more started or planned in countries like Korea, Japan, Philippines, Brazil, Uruguay, Nigeria, Ghana, etc. The more countries who adopt the same standard of TV white space technology and the same way it will work, the more economies of scale will drive down the prices of the technology and make it even more affordable.

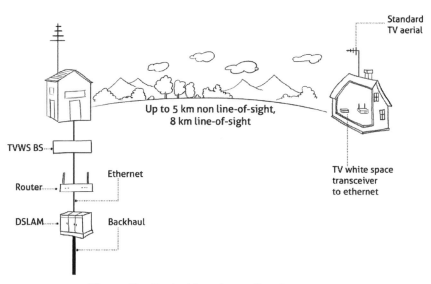

Figure 42—Typical Rural Broadband Use Case

Figure 42 shows the typical use case with the clear TV white space link from the top of the transmission mast which "houses" the TV white spaces base station, i.e., the technology that converts digital information into direct-to-TV white spaces signals using TV frequencies, which propagate much further, as shown in figure 41. These signals are then transmitted from a point-to-point (PTP) or point-to-multipoint (PMP) radio antenna across 5 to 8 km to customer premises equipment (CPE) on top of the *remote* house. At this customer premises end, you can also see that a standard receive aerial is used along with some component called the TV white space transceiver (or converter) which converts the TV white space signals back to standard digital ethernet. This standard ethernet can be distributed by Wi-Fi inside the house or by a local access network (LAN) within the customer premises.

All the technicalities aside, the main message to the technically challenged on how this works is that broadband Internet content is transmitted across TV white space spectrum, which travels much farther than other higher frequency broadband spectrum, thereby enabling rural broadband and broadband for the masses. In this scenario, TV white space provides the middle long-distance TV white spaces "several miles," whilst Wi-Fi or TV white space (TVWS) technology[9] provides the "last hundred yards." Another likely scenario, slightly modifying figure 42, is the middle several miles gets distributed via a "standard middle-distance backhaul transport" technology, such as a point-to-point microwave distribution up to the last hundred yards, and TVWS is only used in the last mile or hundred yards. TVWS itself also distinguishes itself as an effective point-to-multipoint technology.

- Extension of Fibre Footprint: TVWS could also be used as an extension of the fibre footprint, particularly as fibre backbones are extended into the hinterlands. For example, it really makes little sense to run fiber to serve just a hundred people. TVWS, and admittedly other wireless technologies, could be used in such a scenario,

- *Urban Broadband—Super-Wi-Fi Hot Spots:* Admittedly this chapter is titled "White Spaces for Affordable Rural Broadband." However, there are use cases for TV white spaces too for urban

---

9 It is more likely WiFi since the latter is embedded in so many devices already, notably PCs, tablets and mobile phones.

broadband in the cities. The reason rural broadband is emphasised is because this volume has noted in several places that the market would almost certainly provide for wireless broadband in urban areas, as the economics likely works in urban areas. The urbanites can also afford it, in the main. Having noted this, the rapid growth in data traffic area in urban areas and cities like Cairo, Accra, etc., need to be dealt with. This clogs our wireless public networks, leading to poorer quality of service for all—this is an experience many Africans and others in emerging markets experience daily. One way to deal with such traffic is to "off-load" much of this data traffic onto Wi-Fi, traffic which would otherwise be carried on our public 3G and future 4G networks, leading to poor quality of service. This is happening today at Wi-Fi "hot spots" over many African cities. TV white spaces signals, which travel much farther than Wi-Fi (which operate at much higher frequencies)[10] allows for what we term super-Wi-Fi hot spots, i.e., Wi-Fi hot spots which offer much broader radii than traditional hot spots. TV white spaces would be able to provide Wi-Fi for an entire business park, or an entire university campus or stadium, or the central district of an entire city. However, this will require TV white space devices if Wi-Fi is not the "last mile" technology[11]. This is why it is likened to "Super Wi-Fi."

•   *Location-Based Services:* This is another use case that follows on naturally from the super-Wi-Fi use case. If one indeed has a super Wi-Fi hot spot which covers an entire city centre, then providing location-based services content makes much sense. Content would be provided which is truly local, emphasising local amenities, schools, hospitals, churches, etc. With a mobile device that is moved around by its owner, services can be tailored to locations. Restaurant bookings (reservations), route finding, and location information are perhaps services with no

---

10 Wi-Fi operates at 2,400 MHz (2.4 GHz) and at 5 GHz compared to TV white spaces at 470 MHz to 694 MHz. Remember: the lower the frequency, the farther it travels.

11 A non-WiFi "last mile" technology will not be quick and will not initially be cheap compared to the scale economies for standard WiFi chips.

fixed world competition. Imagine being able to ask, "Where is the nearest cinema to where I am right now in Douala?" or "Navigate me from where I am to the nearest petrol or gas station to fill up my car." This is the power and promise of location-based services, which TV white spaces would enable.

- *Distribution of Local Content:* TV white spaces can also obviously be used for distributing local broadcast content, like local TV, for that particular local area. This could drive some local "broadcast" advertising sectors.

- *Machine to Machine Communications/Internet of Things:* Perhaps less so in Africa and some emerging economies in the first instance, but machine-to-machine communications will be rife in Africa post the 2030s. Many people in the Western world do not realise that the "Internet of Things" is already emerging around them every day: traffic sensors all around the city which measure the level of traffic and send these data to a control nerve centre from which computers adjust traffic light sequences across the city accordingly; weather sensors in the city feeding data into a central meteorological station; city lighting coming on and off at night and day, respectively conserving power and making our streets safer; remote car monitoring video cameras which can facilitate the opening of gates to let cars through at tolls and charge their drivers' accounts accordingly; smart meters for electricity, gas, and water wirelessly transferring their readings to remote billing centres. These are just examples of *machines* (i.e., sensors, smart meters, etc.) "talking" to *other machines* (e.g., central computers, billing stations). TV white spaces providing for super-Wi-Fi across a city would offer opportunities for such machine-to-machine communications.

6.4 TV White Spaces and UHF Spectrum Policy across Africa and Emerging Economies

All good regulators have a duty to ensure optimal use of the nation's frequency airwaves. A good regulator would have to interpret its statutory duties, and because all regulators are ultimately economic regulators (see chapter 11), "optimal use" is typically interpreted as "efficient use," and efficient use in turn would be one that maximises total "value" to society, including broader social value (BSV); see chapter 11 for more on the concept of economic regulation.

6.4.1 The Case for License-Exempting TV White Spaces

Recall that some communications equipment use frequency bands that have been allocated for unlicensed use in the ISM band. New acronym—ISM stands for industrial, scientific, and medical. License exempt also means the licensing for unlicensed use. A good example here is Wi-Fi or Bluetooth radio built into most phones today and certainly in tablets and phablets.[12] These users of such Wi-Fi devices—that is, typically you and me—do not require a special license from the regulator to use the ISM bands' 2.4 GHz and 5.8 GHz that have been allocated internationally for unlicensed use. The important point for this section is that most other parts of the electromagnetic spectrum are tightly controlled (or regulated) by licensing regulation, with licensing costs, processes, and bureaucracy being massive economic factors. This is the case for TV frequencies practically everywhere in the world. This subsection makes the case for exempting some of this TV spectrum from licensed use (i.e., license exempt), allowing it to be unlicensed or only lightly licensed. The concept of light licensing is explained in a few paragraphs' time.

From these basic premises, and from prior chapters, one concludes the following:

Auctioning 3G/4G Spectrum: Such spectrum in UHF (i.e., 700 MHz, 800 MHz, and 900 MHz if liberalised for 3G) should be auctioned, as demand for such spectrum will almost certainly exceed supply, and maximising value to society here in a transparent way is best achieved via auctions.

---

12 Phablets are devices which pass for both phones and tablet computers, typically used for Internet access.

TV White Space Spectrum Release via License Exemption/Light Licensing: The major question is: how is such TV white spaces spectrum released to maximise total value to society, including broader social value? The immediate right answer is partitioning, such that some of it is commercially auctioned (i.e. >700 MHz where demand will exceed supply), and some dedicated for rural broadband on a license exempt basis for broader social value reasons. Remember, true TV white spaces spectrum is plentiful and has almost zero opportunity cost on the African continent and elsewhere. Demand clearly does not exceed supply, and hence auctioning such spectrum is not sensible. Returning to what is covered in the spectrum 101 of chapter 4, remember there are three main regulatory approaches to spectrum, namely, command and control, market mechanisms, and licence exemption. Command and control is getting passé, and as already argued, market mechanisms such as auctions do not really apply to true TV white spaces (even those within auctioned bands). What is left then is the license exemption approach. License exemption is the approach to licensing spectrum wherein operators are able to operate electromagnetic communications equipment using frequency airwaves without having to hold a license from the regulator. Without a license, they also operate on a best efforts basis with respect to interference issues. This is a strong contender for what should happen to this TV white space spectrum across Africa and the rest of the world. License exempt regulatory frameworks across the globe are *sine qua non* to achieving affordable TV white spaces–based broadband (both rural and urban) across the continent.

The case for license exemption in general derives from the following:

- License-exempting spectrum has a very good history of generating substantial value to society for only tiny bits of spectrum. Wi-Fi is the poster child for license exemption. By the end of 2011, 25 percent of homes worldwide used Wi-Fi, according to Strategy Analytics, a well-regarded research house.[13] The key

13 Andrew Burger. "Report: Wi-Fi Households to Approach 800 million by 2016." Telecompetitor, n.d., http://www.telecompetitor.com/report-wi-fi-households-to-approach-800-million-by-2016/.

features of license exemption for TV white space spectrum would be the following:

◦ There would be minimum (low or no) barriers to use and therefore quick access to spectrum.

◦ There would be no quality of service guarantees.

◦ TV white space equipment would operate at low power, enabling many users.

◦ Congestion may be mitigated with a geographical white space database approach—we do not describe the details here. However, the principle is that white space devices would request from a centrally maintained white space database by providing its coordinates. The database would return the frequencies and channels the device can use at the device's particular location and at the maximum power the device can transmit. This is how dynamic spectrum allocation and management could be achieved[14].

• Thanki[15] (2012), in his excellent piece of work, provides a very strong case for license exempting spectrum in general, exemplifying it with Wi-Fi. His analyses indicate that by enhancing the value of fixed home broadband, Wi-Fi generates approximately $52–99 billion of consumer surplus each year. Without this, Richard Thanki notes that the effect on the value of fixed broadband would be lower and would result in the disconnection of perhaps 50 to 114 million fixed broadband connections around the world. Thanki's report also suggests a range for Africa of $69–901 million from an estimated one half to one million Wi-Fi connections on the continent. We can only expect this number to be growing exponentially over the medium term.

---

14 Light licensing is also applicable here and is mentioned later in this chapter in section 6.4.3.

15 Richard Thanki (2012), "The Economic Significance of Licence-Exempt Spectrum to the Future of the Internet," June 2012, file:///C:/Users/Sama/Downloads/Economic%20Impact%20of%20License%20Exempt%20Spectrum%20-%20Richard%20Thanki%20(3).pdf (accessed December 2013).

- TV white spaces would add billions of value to this too. This is not least because absent TV white spaces, arguably, no or little broadband would/may be deployed in rural Africa. The number of extra sites that would need to be deployed too absent TV white spaces super-Wi-Fi would be huge. Thanki estimates that with current data growth worldwide, absent Wi-Fi, 140,000 to 450,000 extra sites would be needed at a cost of $30–90 billion. Africa hardly registers in these numbers but would do so by the 2020s. TV white spaces would preempt this.

6.4.2 The Further Case for License Exemption Specifically for Africa in Particular and the Next Five Billion Unconnected in General

As this book so far testifies, I am very outcomes oriented in my thinking and arguments. The economics for providing broadband for the next one billion to be connected is more difficult than for the current 2.6 billion who are already connected. The economics for the further one billion (post the next one billion) will be even harder, and so on. The naked data problem (see figure 3) clearly puts the brakes on the limit of the how far the market will go, coverage-wise in particular. The next chapter covers and illustrates this clearly. However, the key arguments for Africa in particular and the next five Billion in general include the following:

- The next chapter shows a 250-MHz gap in spectrum between African and European markets for mobile communications (see figure 49). Africa has some stringent broadband goals and timescales to meet. The amount of spectrum in the pipelines for release on the continent today would hardly plug this 250-MHz gap. License exempting some spectrum would be quite beneficial to putting more spectrums into the market just like auctioning, though license exemption is arguably much faster to drive innovation.
- I also note that—thanks to the nonexistent fixed Internet infrastructure on the African continent—Africa totally relies

on wireless. For this reason, this 250-MHz gap needs to be doubled at least to compensate for the absolute lack of fixed Internet, i.e., 500 MHz of more mobile spectrum is needed. The case for regulators license exempting spectrum on the continent only grows as another means to get spectrums into the market in addition to auctions.

- Recalling the end of chapter 3, Africa is an incredibly large continent, and unlike other much smaller continents, like North America, Canada, and Australia, Africa does not have its populations "bunched" together in specific corners of the continent as much—and the population of Africa is one billion strong (in 2013/14) and growing at the fastest rate of any other continent. What this means is that much more terrestrial networks need to be built in Africa, but at the same time the low African ARPUs today in 2013/14 would not sustain this. Indeed, the ARPUs would get lower as new revenue-diluting customers join the mobile revolution. It stands then to reason that more sub-1 GHz spectrum is needed to be released for the continent. Most of Africa's TV frequencies are hardly used in most parts of the continent. And these frequencies propagate so much further. Therefore, yes, we need more licensed spectrum like the 700-MHz band, which will be released and reassigned to mobile post 2015 on a licensed basis. However, we also need license-exempt sub-1 GHz spectrum too where the opportunity cost of the TV white spaces spectrum is so low on the continent that its opportunistic use for broadband Internet makes eminent sense. Figure 42 is a good illustration of how the middle several miles for rural broadband would be achieved using TV licensed-exempt spectrum in addition to the last mile being covered by licensed-exempt Wi-Fi.

- Following on from the last bullet, new business models for broadband are needed to connect the remaining five billion. License exempting sub-1 GHz spectrum enables and facilitates such new business models because the low opportunity cost of TV whitespace spectrum is recognised commercially and exploited for broadband—and along with other innovations like solar and wind power, as well as lower backhaul costs—the next five billion have a better chance of being connected than otherwise. We cannot rely on just one business model—the current licensed spectrum–based business model. We need a mixed ecology of business models in order to address connecting the next five billion. There is no guarantee that these models would evolve easily, but surely by sub-1 GHz spectrum being license exempted, the prospects of the viability of new broadband Internet models for the next five billion improves.

- Developed economies' thinking and leadership typically lead the communications sector, as is the case with most other sectors. Nevertheless, for reasons enunciated above, there is a strong case that mobile should be different. My minor beef with the European/American-led mobile industry is that they frequently ignore this fact. A developed market-only spectrum view will constrain emerging economies' mobile markets in places Africa. This is why I have been on record on the continent and beyond arguing that the licensed vs. license exempt as regards TV white spaces is simply facetious: we cannot let the best be the enemy of the good. The next five billion need both to work towards widespread availability and affordability of broadband Internet.
- Lastly, there is a strong case for regulators to provide a level playing field for different approaches and business models to "attack" the access and affordability problem. It cannot be right that just one business model is given the chance to address this problem.

Importantly too, African and emerging market regulators need to read, hear of, and understand such counterarguments and make independent decisions for the benefits of their respective consumers and citizens. In summary, I state strongly and unapologetically that broader social value and affordability are arguably the strongest arguments for license exemption of some TV white space spectrums.

6.4.3 Light Licensing TV White Spaces Is an Alternative

There is also an argument for light licensing the TV white space frequencies. The light licensing approach to TV white spaces management would work as follows:

- The regulator or the spectrum agency keeps records but does *not* manage the TV white space frequencies per se. Incumbents like TV stations can be protected through records keeping and/ or through implementing exclusion zones.
- TV white space transmitter owners can also self-coordinate on a first come, first serve basis to ensure their deployed base stations do not interfere with one another. In this case, they carry out interference analyses and coordination using spectrum management tools. The regulator or spectrum agency would be informed but not necessarily manage it. In some cases, the regulator/agency would manage the light licensing process.
- Light licensing is better than license exempt if there are relatively few users and if they are relative fixed too as opposed to mobile. This is the case with TV white spaces frequencies where the number of users in some geography would be maximum of about a dozen, say. The transmitter sites would also be tractable. The technology would be homogenous, i.e., TV white space technology. So light licensing is a clear and viable approach.

Indeed, a light licensing approach may be implemented by the regulator or spectrum agency via a geographical database too.

Sophisticated spectrum users would sometimes prefer a light licensing approach because it sets up *a priori* a set of processes for some minimum self-coordination, record keeping, and interference management if interference cases arise.

6.4.4 Exclusive Licensing for Mobile Spectrum and TV White Spaces

I am fully aware that there is a fear from some influential stake-holders that efforts towards innovations like TV white spaces could deflect attention for further efforts to exclusively license further spectrum for mobile broadband. Ann Bouverot[16] of the influential GSMA (whose data and research findings are replete in this book) writes in *The State of Broadband 2013*:[17]

> As mobile technologies have proliferated, demand for access to radio spectrum has intensified, generating considerable debate and advocacy for new approaches to spectrum management, including proposals for the use of TV "whitespaces" and other spectrum-sharing arrangements. While these innovations may find a viable niche in future, pursuit of these options today risks deflecting attention from the release of sufficient, licensed spectrum for mobile broadband. Exclusive licensing is a model that works, and it underpins the undeniable benefits of mobile technology.

As a former senior spectrum regulator, I completely understand the GSMA's concerns—after all, I led the clearance and auction of the 800 MHz and 2,600 GHz spectrum and the 4G auction in the United Kingdom in 2013. However, as noted above, let us not allow the good to be the enemy of the best: they are both on the same side. TV white spaces for rural broadband could and would be a "niche" as much as unlicensed Wi-Fi is a niche today! More exclusive spectrum is no doubt needed for mobile, and I make this argument too umpteen times in this volume, not least because of the 250- to 500-MHz gap of licensed

---

16 Dr. Ann Bouverot is currently director general of the influential GSMA (www.gsma.com).

17 *The State of Broadband 2013: Universalizing Broadband,* A Report by the Broadband Commission, September 2013, http://www.broadbandcommission.org/documents/bb-annualreport2013.pdf (accessed September 2013).

spectrum in Africa vis-à-vis Europe and North America. And TV white space spectrum, which is mostly unused in Africa, also needs to be put to good use. Both exclusive licensing and license exemption/light licensing efforts for mobile broadband should continue simultaneously.

As of the "deflecting attention" argument, I submit this is a decision for regulators like I once was, and not for GSMA to decide on their behalf. Broader social value and affordability imperatives compel developing economy regulators to look at low-cost broadband models seriously. African and emerging market decision makers and regulators must understand both sets of arguments (and more) and make their own independent decisions. African economies, in particular, cannot wait forever for Western mobile data business models to work in Africa. I have argued clearly that the nature of the African mobile data problem is different, requiring different economic models. If these arguments are sound, then critics should address the solution (and quickly) rather than shoot down others trying others trying to connect the next billions unconnected.

Lastly, this I make no apologies for encouraging the levelling of the playing field such that other business models and approaches to addressing the African and other emerging countries (e.g. Bangladesh) broadband affordability and accessibility problem should be given a chance. If all the TV white spaces achieve in the end is to facilitate and hasten the traditional mobile industry to properly address the access and affordability for the next five billion broadband unconnected—and fast—it would have been worthwhile. This is what competition of approaches and business models do.

6.4.5 Responses to Some Other Objections to TV White Spaces

Some objections and responses follow.

1. Using TV white spaces frequencies will cause interference into TV and other services. The response to this is simple. Any good regulator will take this concern very seriously. They will always consider how best to secure the most efficient use of

spectrum in such a manner that harmful interference is not caused. The geographical database approach is explicitly designed to address directly the risk of harmful interference being caused to existing licensees. This database will also be dynamically updated.

2. Using a licensed-exempt approach or a light licensing approach is either irresponsible, ill-advised, or both. The answer is that Africa and other developing economies need more spectrums for wireless services and whether they are licensed or licensed exempted is an important but secondary issue. African consumers do not care today that they are using 2G/3G (licensed) and Wi-Fi (unlicensed); they just want to enjoy wireless Internet services—as long as there is no interference into their services. The previous section also answered the "exclusive" licensing question.

3. Where are the devices that will be used? This is a fair question, but a chicken-and-egg one. Until enough countries legislate and allow for the license exemption (or light licensing) of TV white space devices (thereby ensuring a potential large demand for white space devices [WSDs]), there will not be a good incentive for device suppliers to manufacture these devices in volume. The more demand, the more the volume manufactured is, and the lower the prices, making them even more affordable. TV white spaces can also just be used for the backhaul, and Wi-Fi can be used for the last mile or hundred yards in the short to medium term. Clearly then, initial solutions will use TV white spaces for the last ten miles say, but will convert to WiFi for the last one hundred meters in order to mitigate the devices question and optimise the affordability one through low cost WiFi-enabled devices. In summary, the WiFi ecosystem provides superb devices for TV whitespaces today.

4. Why should Africa lead the way here when many European countries have not yet adopted TV white spaces? This is another good question. The simple answer is that Africa's (and other emerging economies') need for wireless radio spectrum for broadband is greatest by far. And this approach guarantees access (much better propagation by the laws of physics) and

promises affordability than any other approach to date. As of 2013 these were are promises, but it is important to give this approach and business model a chance too. I am involved in trying to make this promise a reality, and if you are interested , or know of some funds or individuals who are interested, please get in touch with me.

5. Why TV frequencies in particular and why only them? The approach will also work for other bands; the TV bands just happen to be one of the most sought-after frequencies which are poorly used in the spectrum sweet spot bands. Furthermore when I am asked this question, I also note that the "TV white space" label is sometimes a red herring. All the TV white spaces approach is ultimately about is the *opportunistic* and *shared* use of spectrum which otherwise has a low opportunity cost, i.e., spectrum not being used most of the time. The approach acknowledges implicitly that there is a likely primary use of the spectrum, e.g., in the case of TV white spaces for television. However, if it is "white," surely it should be "shared," and a secondary use could and should exploit it. The fact that this also ushers in a new era of dynamic spectrum management is a true bonus.

6.5 What Is Affordable Broadband?

This is a tricky question, but there appears to be an emerging answer to what constitutes affordable Internet globally. That said, the affordable broadband problem has no easy and straightforward prescriptions, and any suggestions to the contrary from me would be misleading. However, we can be clearer on what is affordable and what *clearly* is not. We can look at different approaches to postulate an affordability range for monthly broadband Internet, which I put at US$1.50 to $5 (2013 prices) for the continent of Africa.

- Firstly, it is self-evident that given average revenues per month (ARPUs) in the mobile industry today (for voice mostly) on the continent are in the US$6–10 per month range, we can say with some high certainty that any figures close to this for mobile data/broadband would be simply unaffordable. Indeed, I suggest that affordability would have to mean consumers pay about half the voice ARPUs, i.e., circa $3–5 in 2013 prices.

- Secondly, developing countries studies by Cisco show that 2–5 percent income threshold is where broadband starts to flourish. Cisco notes: "generally, when the annual broadband expenditure is priced at more than 2 percent to 5 percent of a household's income, broadband is considered unaffordable."[18] Similar academic studies have also corroborated this, for example, Dr. Raul Katz at Columbia Business School, USA.

- Thirdly, there is another justification for the circa US$5 monthly affordability "cap" limit in Africa on average (as per 2013). The ITU-mandated Broadband Commission for Digital Development came up with four broadband targets for all countries to achieve by 2015; these targets are noted in the next chapter, chapter 7. Target 2, which emphasizes affordability, recommends that broadband services should cost less than 5 percent of monthly income. Looking at figure 22 for sub-Saharan Africa shows a picture of many countries with a GDP per capita of circa US$1,000–2,000, but also with many large population countries as well either in the less than $500 grouping or in the $500–1,000 grouping. A "weighted average" by population GDP per capita feels right at circa $1,200. An annual GDP per capita of $1,200 means $100 per month, and 5 percent of this number is US$5. Even countries doing relatively well, like Ghana, had a current GDP per capita of US$1,500 in 2013/14. On the other hand, one has to have another look at the reality of some of the bigger countries, like Tanzania with a population of close to forty-five million people but with a GDP per capita US$500, and it is even smaller in DRC. This is why a circa US$1.50 price should also be sought after.

---

18   Handler, D., and Grossman, P., "The Role of Income Distribution and Broadband Penetration in Developing Countries," http://www.cisco.com/web/about/ac79/docs/pov/Income_Distribution_POV_ 1123_1207FINAL.pdf (accessed October 2013).

If you consider how far removed $1.50 to $5 is from today's reality, then you better appreciate the affordability problem on the continent. Take Nigeria for example wherein ninety percent of those who access the Internet do so via their mobiles as of 2013. Many more Nigerians have access to the Internet via smartphones, however mobile data rates are really expensive, e.g., N200 ($1.25) for only one day limited to 50 MB or up to N8000 ($49.60) for a monthly 5 GB data plan for computers or iPads.[19] When will it ever be affordable for Africans to pay $49.60 a month *for the majority of rural Africans*, and just for data? Most Europeans do not even pay this! To conclude this section, without just looking at one country, you should see for yourself the size of the affordability challenge from the ITU table below.

Broadband Prices as % of GNP per capita		
	Developed	Developing
Fixed Broadband	1.7%	30.1%
Mobile Broadband	1.4%	11 - 25%*
* dependent on plan		

(Source: ITU Facts and Figures, 2013)

Both fixed and mobile broadband are just unaffordable in most developing countries. Paying 11–25 percent of monthly income for mobile broadband is just not affordable, and as for fixed broadband, what can one say?

6.6 How Would TV White Spaces Deal with the Affordability Problem? The Mawingu Project in Kenya Example

So clearly, achieving a data monthly ARPU of US$1.50 to $5 would be a major challenge, but just think for a moment of the development impact in rural Africa of providing Internet access to rural communities

---

19 Source: MTN Nigeria website, http://www.mtnonline.com/products-services/internet-services/data-bundles (accessed September 2, 2013).

that currently have no telecommunications or even electricity infrastructure. Let us consider schools, clinics, local government offices,
libraries, and hospitals at *affordable* rates to consumers and citizens of
$1.50 to $5 per month. Yes, I am not asking you here to consider—yet
alone ensure—Internet access to all individual rural-based Africans
(or similar in other emerging economies) or the "poorest of the poor."
Nevertheless, as Eric Wilson[20] notes, TV white spaces promises to put
Internet—like in the Nanyuki example mentioned later—within the
reach of many institutions that "intermediate" with the least well-off:
schools, clinics, councils, municipalities, councils, churches, women's
associations, and many more. Wilson rightly notes that by using these
intermediaries, rural farmers would (or could) have access to market
pricing information before they decide to transport their produce to the
market. Like with the iCow innovation in Kenya which uses texts on
mobile phones to educate rural farmers on how to look after the general
well-being of their cows from birth to sale, farmers would be able to
access this information online. Information on droughts, flooding, and
other disasters could be disseminated online to rural areas.

Schools would access a waterfall of information online, including educational aids and test papers as they have never seen before.
Clinics could implement just-in-time procurement of supplies. Rural
people would be connected via VoiP or Skype to friends and families
in the cities, if not abroad in London or California. Central, regional, and local governments would be better connected to their rural
administrators for better coordination and logistics. Headmasters or
headmistresses of schools could e-mail their weekly reports to their
district education inspector bosses rather than jumping on the back of
unsafe motorcycles to take the paper reports by hand twenty kilometres every Friday for two-plus hours. This is a real scenario that was
happening in Nanyuki before the trial, and that no longer happens.
How do you get this headmistress back to going by road to deliver

---

20 Eric Wilson is a friend and colleague in a new venture, Impact Broadband Ltd,
who has also worked as an advisor with Indigo Telecom. Indigo Telecom Ltd., a
local Internet service provider in Kenya who have provided engineering design and
networks construction and management and coordinated the local content for the
"subscribers" in the Nanyuki white space trial in Kenya.

her weekly reports if the trial network is switched off? How do you explain to her the sudden loss of productivity of such a move? In Haiti, disaster recovery and tax collection are the two key drivers to the government for driving rural broadband.

So how would white spaces technology address a problem that the market itself cannot currently address? How could it achieve $1.50 to $5 ARPU levels when most of the areas concerned hardly have any electricity, implying provisioning and maintaining for electricity also have to be borne in the costs in more inaccessible places? The true answer to all these questions is that a public private partnership must evolve to make this work—and one such partnership in evolution on the continent today in 2013/14 is the Mawingu project in Kenya described below.

6.6.1 The Mawingu[21] Approach

The Mawingu project aims to deliver low-cost, high-speed wireless broadband to locations not served by even electricity, connecting poor, remote, or low population areas, i.e., the sort of locations that lack basic infrastructure, such as electricity or paved roads, and are difficult to serve with existing wired and wireless technologies. The Mawingu network relies on unlicensed or license-exempt technologies, including Wi-Fi and TV white spaces base stations and WiFi-enabled end-user devices.

Peter Henderson (Chairman and founder of Indigo Telecom Ltd) and Malcolm Brew (who pioneered the technology in the Isle of Bute trials in Scotland) instigated the Mawingu project in Kenya. The Mawingu project[22] is supported in a partnership model including:

- Microsoft Corporation: providing financial and technical support, WiFi-enabled end-user devices, and cloud-based software and services, such as Microsoft 365. The Microsoft effort was led by friend and colleague Paul Garnett who has gone on to help found and chair the Dynamic Spectrum Alliance

---

21 Mawingu means "cloud" in Swahili.

22 http:// www.mawingu.org, (accessed September 2013)

(DSA) [23] – a global organisation rightly advocating for laws and regulations that will lead to more efficient and effective utilization of spectrum.

- Indigo Telecom Ltd. (a local Internet service provider in Kenya): providing engineering design and network construction and management and coordinating the local content for the subscribers' "walled garden." The services include basic and premium Internet access, plus a recharging facility for devices where access to electricity is limited.

- Communications Commission of Kenya (CCK): Kenya's very good converged communications regulator who issued the necessary test and development licenses.

- Government of Kenya (Ministry of IT and local government): providing support for the project and supporting initial pilot sites.

- Additional support and grants were provided by development aid agencies, such as USAID, providing some needed equipment for the pilot network, such as radios, solar panels, and batteries.

Figure 43—On the left, a typical classroom at a Kenyan rural school; on the right, the new classroom with a server and multiple monitors— students at Gakawa School now have a computer lab and teacher training and are connected to the world. (Source: Eric Wilson, Impact Broadband Ltd.)

---

23 www.dynamicspectrmalliance.org.

When the network is complete, it will cover sixty-seven thousand people. The Mawingu project in Kenya illustrates the art of the possible through public private partnership. The initial pilot project in Nanyuki provided first-time Internet connectivity for a number of secondary schools and the Red Cross office as well as the local provincial governor's office and a midsized flower farm. The project has subsequently been expanded to more users.

The deployment at the school included USAID funding for radios and batteries, and the project also included the remodeling and refurnishing of a classroom at the Gakawa secondary school (see photos above).

The connectivity to the World Wide Web is provided through the television white space radios on the mast that link the school back to the central base station, which is in turn connected to the optic fibre backbone in Kenya. Further access is provided in the surrounding community for local hot spots through point-to-multipoint radios on the mast at the school, providing connectivity for subscribers within a radius of up to 10 km, as described earlier in figure 42.

Figure 44—Internet connectivity provided through local base station
(see the mast in the photo); this is a scenario of the "middle several miles"
TV white spaces being distributed via a "last mile"
point-to-point network at Gakawa School
(Source: Eric Wilson, Impact Broadband Ltd.)

Such dramatic reduced economics in the cost of Internet access are based on the use of the "white spaces" in ultra-high frequency (UHF) bandwidths for backhaul, together with renewable energy power for the access network and Wi-Fi for the last mile/hundred yards. Using these low frequencies allows for fewer base stations covering greater distances (See figure 35 for a reminder), while using solar power removes the need for generators and diesel fuel costs, thereby enabling an overall lower cost structure for the network. Seventy-five percent of Kenyans lack access to electricity, and using devices charged by solar energy is just natural.

The Internet service would also provide access to both local content information (for agricultural market information, weather, educational apps, etc.) as well as links to cloud-based applications, such as through the Microsoft Azure platform, providing cloud-based Windows applications, such as Office 365. This solution can be implemented readily where governments have provided the appropriate regulatory environment, such as license-exempt or light licensed models to enable the access to the TVWS spectrum for such initiatives.

The social impact promises to be significant if Mawingu achieves its aim of reducing access costs and bringing more people online, affordably, via e-health, education, improved communications, etc. Mawingu is already delivering teacher training and other educational advantages by computer labs and tablets, as can be seen in figure 43. Since it was set up in February 2013, broadband has now reached three remote schools, a Red Cross outpost, a health clinic near Nanyuki, an Internet kiosk, and local government offices.

6.6.2 The Mawingu Technology

Malcolm Brew[24] is the true brains behind the technology assembly in Mawingu. Malcolm is the former technical director of Bushnet

---

24 Malcolm Brew is one of the pioneers, along with Peter Henderson of Indigo Telecom Ltd., of connectivity in Africa. One of the first trials of white spaces in Europe—indeed in rural Bute, Scotland—was instigated by Malcolm Brew.

Ltd[25] in Uganda and a real pioneer of making TV white spaces happen. As argued above already, white spaces in Africa and some emerging markets present a unique opportunity, as it is the first time such a large amount of high-quality spectrum could be made available for unlicensed use.

Using white space spectrum in Nanyuki (Kenya), Malcolm Brew and his team have shown broadband can be delivered to remote and difficult-to-access areas with a combination of the following:

- *Solar- and wind-powered towers,* which are truly unique, rather than the typical unaffordable (for these purposes) two-diesel-generators configuration across the continent. The base stations are solar powered (or hybrid solar-wind). They are robust and cheap to manufacture and install. Tests in Scotland have demonstrated that base stations can withstand high winds of up to 90 km/h and can last for five days on battery alone.
- *Automated and remotely configurable base stations* so that engineers do not have to frequent inaccessible sites.
- *White space spectrum* for transmission and connectivity to the Internet as per figure 42.
- *High throughput broadband* at speeds of up to 20 Mbps down to 2 Mbps as per figure 41.
- *Very low cost per megabyte compared to other technologies*, which is the key argument for having this technology in the first place.

From their experience in Kenya, the Mawingu team have found it necessary to draw the important distinction between Wi-Fi networks (Wi-Fi hot spots) and white space networks.

- Wi-Fi is the means by which end users will connect to their hot spots or access points. It is a radio frequency transmitted at 2.4 GHz and/or 5 GHz.

---

25 Bushnet Ltd. (Uganda) has been offering Internet services to Uganda's rural areas. See http://www.bushnet.net.

- Wi-Fi radios are onboard all Wi-Fi enabled devices, like smart-phones, tablet computers, laptops, and wireless routers.
- Wi-Fi range is typically limited and usually only workable at distances of 150–200 metres outdoors.
- White space, on the other hand, is the available frequency of 470 MHz to 790 MHz and used for long-range transmission of data from base station to base station, and from base station to hot spot.
- White space base stations can cover between 6 and 10 km, depending on terrain.

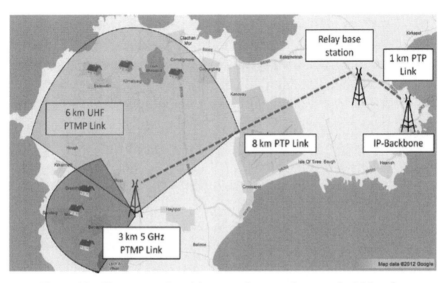

Figure 45—Key ranges for white space base stations; typical 8 km for point-to-point (PTP) backhaul link and "last miles" 6 km for point-to-multipoint wide area cover (or hot spot) (Source: Indigo Telecom Ltd.)

The base stations provide the link to hot spots. The base stations act as both the connection for end user hot spots and as the *backhaul network* for base stations that are located up to twenty hops away. Base stations can transmit up to 6 km away and without the need for line-of-sight communications. The white space base stations have two ranges to consider (as illustrated in figure 45):

- from tower to tower (point to point): 8 km
- from tower to user hot spot (point to multipoint): 6 km

The Internet backbone is the final hop for base stations. This can be provided via connection to a fiber node and/or possibly with a Ka band[26] satellite receiver dish for additional redundancy if desired. Figure 45 also ilustrates how other frequencies, e.g. 5GHz, can also be used albeit with much limited ranges requiring more base stations (i.e. higher costs). Such high frequencies are also less effective for non-line-of-sight coverage.

6.7 The White Space Public Private Partnership, Universal Service Funds, and Entrepreneurs' Mini-ISPs

The evolving business model in Kenya allows for subsidised services for the schools and clinics, while a tiered Internet access service and cloud-based premium services are provided for consumers, local government, and small businesses, which may be marketed through a network of local agents and hot spot managers.

In general, as I write, the business and commercial model for making white space technology—along with solar and wind power (and generators perhaps in some cases) as sources of power—is very much being evolved and developed. One thing is certain though—it will have to be a public private partnership. It is recommended policy makers and regulators not only license exempt the spectrum or light license it, but also that Universal Service Funds be used to facilitate such public private partnerships (PPP).

I can think of no better use of these funds than to to bridge the divide of the communications/digital "haves" and "have-nots." If you have some doubts, see what an example law stipulates of its universal access/service fund—that of Nigeria, which is the runaway

---

26 Ka Band refers to the frequencies from 26.5 to 40 GHz, so very high frequencies. Being so high means they allow for high bandwidth communications, and therefore they are favourite frequencies for satellite communications.

largest telecommunications market on the African continent. The 2003 Nigerian Communications Act, which establishes NCC as the independent regulator, mandates it to

> consider, design and determing a system which shall promote the widespread availability and usage of network services and application services throughout Nigeria by encouraging the installation of network facilities and the provision for network services and application services to institutions and in un-served, underserved areas or for the underserved groups within the community Universal Service Provision (USP).[27]

It is true that in some countries these funds are used to contribute to the submarine cable initiatives or for the fibre backbone distribution, as is the case in Cameroon. These are very worthy initiatives, but white space PPP would be a great addition to this list too. The term "universal" connotes several other elements, including availability, affordability, and accessibility. Operators are typically taxed a certain percentage, typically less than 1 percent, (e.g., 0.2 percent of gross revenue for Kenyan operators, though it is currently 3 percent in the case of Cameroon) of their annual revenues which go into this fund.[28] Such funds can be "tapped" to build and subsidise communications to uneconomic areas.

Remember it is reported in chapter 1 that Calandro *et al.* (2010) broadly conclude that many African countries are failing on their universal service obligations. They conclude, although several countries have established UAFs[29] and often dedicated agencies to ensure their implementation, these have not yielded the intended results."

---

27 Nigerian Communications Act, Part IV—Universal Service Provision, Clause 112(1), http://www.ncc.gov.ng (accessed October 2012).

28 In Nigeria the fund is called the Universal Service Provision Fund (USPF); in Sierra Leone, the Universal Access Development Fund (UADF); in Ghana, the Ghana Investment Fund for Electronic Communications (GIFEC); in Kenya, the Universal Service Fund (USF); in Cameroon, the Telecommunications Special Fund (TSF); in Uganda, the Rural Communities Development Fund (RCDF), in Tanzania, the Communities Services Access Fund (CSAF), etc.

29 Anagram for universal access funds.

White space PPPs would be a very good start for African countries to redeem this position. However, it is also true that there must be competent and credible private partners with true commercial plans to work with these funds to make this happen too, as is the case with the evolving Mawingu partnership in Kenya. Commercial planning and business development are all afoot to achieve $1.50 to $5 monthly ARPU pricing using such PPP models. It is nontrivial to be too prescriptive on how the Universal Service Funds must be used, as they could be deployed and used in many ways depending on the circumstances in the country. It must be noted that every USF fund will have clear guidelines on how they can be accessed and what sort of activities are bona fide uses of these scarce funds—and which are not. It is possible that if the current rules of the fund cannot be interpreted to allow its use for TV white space–type activities, then this must be something that perhaps should be addressed first—lobbying the government on consulting on a new set of rules which includes TV white space–type projects. This is the case in at least one country I know about. However, if the rules of the fund allow, the monies may be used in many ways as follows (this is meant to be illustrative of many ways in which USF funds can help facilitate rural broadband through TV white spaces):

- Some monies from this fund could be drawn to set up "regulatory pilots" described later to help inform many questions that regulation should preempt.
- Some monies could go as a one-off into the capital expenditure (capex) to roll out the nationwide network of thousands of TV white space base station sites and their connection to the national electricity grid and/or backhauling back into the Internet via fibre nodes.
- However, my personal preference from some experience from TV Whitespace business modelling from Kenya would be to use such private funds to purchase customer premise equipment (CPE) of solar panels and battery kit costing circa US$ 800, radio/WiFi/antenna ($800) and devices/tablets/phablets. These are in 2013 prices and are too unaffordable. The base

stations costs are much more affordable relative to their mobile counterparts.

- The private partner may pay for the capex whilst the Universal Service Fund pays for the ongoing operational expenditure (opex), e.g., power, security, etc., for an initial period until the project becomes self-financing.
- Alternatively, the fund many be used to provide grants on a selective basis to help set up broadband in specific communities. The grant monies could pay for just capex, just opex, or both, depending on the merits of the proposal made by those requesting the grants.
- The USF fund may be used to provide "matching" fund grants—i.e., whatever monies get raised by some deserving community aspiring to have access to the Internet could be matched (dollar for dollar) by monies from the fund, subject to the some limits.
- I think sensible compromise options for such funds is that they are used (1) to pay for the CAPEX and for the CPE access equipment and solar panels for select communities, e.g. schools, clnics and government offices as well as provide the devices and computer equipment, and (ii) to pay for the interconnect backhaul costs too.
- There are many other combinations of the above and others that are also applicable.

So how could $1.50 or $5 monthly ARPUs be achieved? This is where entrepreneurship and the PPP model "collide." Consider a scenario that could evolve from the Mawingu example, provided the government and the Kenyan regulator eventually license exempts TV white spaces devices in Kenya. The public private partnership (PPP) venture(s) would deploy the national or regional TV white space network of transmission sites, relays, IP backbones, etc., which provide *wholesale* Internet capacity. The small rural entrepreneur—operating using a large cargo container kitted out with power and maybe several computers connected to the Internet via TV white space technology—becomes the small Internet service provider (ISP) in the village. His/ her clients pay $1.50 to $5 or more for "reasonable" access to the

Internet or some other tiered plans. Depending on the number of clients he/she has—let us say thirty to fifty—this "mini-ISP" is now earning revenues of up to $100–150 a month with true profits of, say, a third of this. More creatively, his clients have the right to go recharge their client devices in this entrepreneur's Internet café or container—remember that they almost certainly have no power access otherwise. The entrepreneur may even have a separate retail business next to his/her "café."

In three years, the entrepreneur could pay back his/her initial loan outlay (probably from the bank or from some established rural broadband fund) to set up his/her mini-ISP. However, most importantly, the value of the service the business is providing to the community is incalculable: his/her clients and families are now connected to other family in the cities and abroad; they now have access to a waterfall of information as never before; the entrepreneur who may have left for the city to become a migrant worker (or fully emigrated) is now gainfully employed, providing much-needed services to his/her community which he/she is passionate about; other benefits here are clear for all to see. This model does not yet fully exist. However, provided TV white space devices and base stations are licensed exempted and licensed respectively, it will be a matter of *when* such model evolves and not a matter of *if.* Sure, such models will take some time to evolve, and some may fail in the first instance.

6.8 How Rural Broadband Changes Real Lives

Before we conclude the Mawingu case study, it is arguably equally as important for you to hear the voices of the beneficiaries of this trial project. They are given here verbatim so you can see what happens when technology is put in the hands of people—even in the rural areas. Indeed, they are provided to emphasise the point made in the preface of the book—on why rural Africans should not be deprived of having access to the Internet just because the economics of broadband is not in the favour of rural areas. These notable quotes speak to access and inclusion better than I have arguably managed to in this volume.

"I touched a computer for the first time in this lab and I have been very eager to discover everything I can about them." —Ishmael Maina, a Form Three student at Gakawa Secondary School (Source: Daily Nation)[30]

"It has helped me to do revision work. When we did not have computers, I was not able to come and copy some questions from the computers. But now I'm able to copy and revise well." —Judy Muchoki, pupil at Gakawa Secondary School

"Eight months ago there was no electricity in this school. But thanks to solar power and a little technological magic, Gakawa Secondary School in Kenya's Nanyuki Region now has dozens of computers connected to the Internet." —voice-over, eNCA[31] video via Reuters

"The issue of me commuting to town was not working. I spent a lot of bus fare and wasted time, yet was not gaining anything. But here [at Mawingu] I do not have to go far. When I want to come here to do work, there is no problem. I can come here direct, do my research when I want to." —John Mutesh, local musician, eNCA video via Reuters

"Mawingu is all about revolutionizing. It is through a project like Mawingu that we allow the African continent to give back to itself." —Malcolm Brew, Project Mawingu chief engineer

---

30 "Idle TV spaces deliver Internet to School, Daily Nation, Tuesday November 19th, 2013. http://www.scribd.com/doc/185346148/Daily-Nation-19-11-13 (accessed December 2013)

31 Source: http://www.enca.com/africa/free-wireless-access-kenya-improve (accessed November 2013).

"For Internet access we had to travel the 10 kilome-teters to Nanyuki and it would cost 100 Kenya Shillings (approx. US $1.20) to get there. Internet access is a life changing experience and it's going to give both our students and teachers added motivation for learning", Beatrice Nderango, Headmistress Gakawa Secondary School.[32]

6.9 Recommendations — What Governments and Regulators Must Do in Order to Enable TV White Spaces Broadband to Happen

There are many things that government and regulators across Africa and some emerging economies should start doing. Some key ones are the following:

1. *Awareness:* They should start by reminding themselves what the outcome they cherish is—and it is towards widespread availability of affordable high-quality mobile data and mobile Internet for the masses. It is sometimes easy to get lost in the fog of what key outcomes are. Given this outcome, govern-ments and regulators would quickly realize that their current plans towards this important outcome are incomplete if they do not have a TV white spaces element or equivalent. So the first thing governments and regulators should do is to be *aware* of the potential of TV white spaces towards achieving this key outcome.

2. *Proactivity:* The twin issues that should ring in their ears are both the *widespread* and *affordability* issues. There are things they can largely leave to the market, like they did for 2G voice. Not so mobile data because of these two primary issues! This

---

32 Source: "Microsoft brings solar Wi-Fi to rural Kenya", *New Scientist*, 13th February 2013, "Microsoft brings solar Wi-Fi to rural Kenya", *New Scientist*, 13th February 2013 (accessed December 2013).

leads to a simple inescapable conclusion: governments and regulators need to be proactive to realise this outcome, i.e., they need to specify, design, plan, regulate, and implement for it.

3. *Understand and weigh the arguments:* It is my hope that independent ministers, decision makers, and regulators in emerging market countries (particularly in Africa, some Asian countries, and some Latin American companies) would understand the aguments proffered in this chapter as they get bombarded by the views of the established mobile industry. By doing so, and mindful of their duties to their consumers and citizens (and not to big businesses), they are likely to decide to license exempt their TV white space frequencies for mobile broadband to add to the limited spectrum ecology. Or they may just choose to allow a level playing field to ensure other approaches and business models also have a chance at addressing the broadband access and affordability issue.

4. *Legislation and regulation are in the hands of national regulators:* Following on from the latter, governments and regulators could/should (be minded to) work to update their spectrum legistations and regulations respectively in order to be able to enable TV white spaces–based mobile Internet to emerge in Africa and other key emerging economies. The good news is that the ITU World Radio Conference of 2012 concluded that the current international regulatory framework can accommodate dynamic cognitive radio systems and hence dynamic spectrum access without any changes to current frameworks. Therefore the ITU asserts that concepts such as TV white spaces are essentially in the hands of national regulators in every country. So each regulator needs to look at the national legislations, regulations, and rules to see what minor changes they need to make to accommodate TV white spaces.

For example, the emerging regulatory approach of accessing TV white space spectrum in the pioneering countries of the

United Kingdom and USA is through a geographical-based database in order to minimise the little risk of harmful interference. African and emerging economies should/could adopt this stance too. The simple idea of geographical databases (without getting too technical) is the following.

A white space database will be set up for each country such that the "white" or free frequencies in every town or village—i.e., not used for TV, mobile broadband, or for something else—are recorded in this database. Let's say Channel 36 is white or free in Johannesburg but not free in Cape Town. The database will record this fact, and white space devices (WSDs) would query the database and be allowed to use Channel 36 in Johannesburg, but not in Cape Town. Similarly, if at the time when another WSD queries to use Channel 36[33] at some geographical location (e.g., a coffee shop) when another WSD has already been allocated that channel to use, that channel will not be allocated until that WSD has finished with it and released it back to the database. It is akin to an occupied hotel room not being able to be allocated to a new guest until the current guest has vacated the room though the guest is not there most of the time as she may be in meetings in town. Clearly, this is no way to run an internet service business. For example, if Mawingu offers a fixed wireless service to a government office or hospital or school, it is not tolerable to have that channel disappearing for large periods of time. Therefore you can see how a geographical database enables *dynamic spectrum management,* wherein the same channel (or hotel room) can be used by multiple WSDs at different times of the day at the same location, e.g., the same coffee shop. This is in contrast to *static spectrum management* where the channel (or room) is allocated indefinitely to one user or WSD. It is clear to see

---

33 Strictly speaking, it will not be the entire Channel 36 of 8 MHz. Channel 36 will be split into subchannels which will be requested by WSDs.

which is more efficient in the use of spectrum. Light licensing models would also apply here.

Based on Ofcom consultations over the past four years, Ofcom's view is that licence exemption in the TV band provides an appropriate balance between promoting innovative applications and services, while ensuring that current users of the band are protected. Note that we are dealing with a different flavour of licence exemption than those encountered before as in Wi-Fi, say (i.e., the licence-exempt WSDs will be subject to the control of white space databases described earlier). These WSDs will not be subject to licensing by regulatory authorities, in just the same way as your Wi-Fi smartphones are not subject to licensing obligations. They are *licence exempt*, and hence you pay no license fees for using the state's finite resource of Wi-Fi spectrum.

So what have all of these details on geographical databases, WSDs, and license exemptions got to do with legislation and regulations? This is a good question. There are several answers. Firstly, much current national legislation in existence in Africa, as elsewhere, were written in a world of static spectrum management, not dynamic, so they may need revisiting. Secondly, hardly any of the current legislations and regulations would state that such valuable TV spectrum could/should be license exempted to WSDs. Indeed, and thirdly, white space devices do not even exist in all these national regulations. Fourthly, the flavour of licence exemption through a white space database concept does not also exist in these regulations too, yet regulators would have to license TV white space databases, for example. For these core reasons and more, legislations and/ or regulations (may) need to be updated, and these processes usually take time, sometimes up to a couple of years—and this is subject to legislative room. The earlier these processes are started, the earlier the outcome desired of widespread and affordable broadband can be reached. Drafting good legislation/regulations requires consultations with stakeholders.

Regulators would have to consult on how they intend to implement the legislation via general consultations and later on draft statutory instruments (SIs), e.g., a draft SI on how to licence exempt WSDs by 2015, say. These all take time.

5. *Harmonisation, standardisation and cooperation:* Harmonisation and standardisation are key to WSDs achieving economies of scale and scope, allowing for roaming across African country borders and enabling a common African and emerging economies market—if not a global market. Frankly and bluntly, such harmonisation and standardisation is being driven elsewhere in Europe and the USA. However, Africa must cooperate to ensure that the protocols (i.e., the rules) on how their white space broadbands work are fully harmonised. This way, the way the database works in Ghana will be largely consistent to the way it works in South Africa. The data in the database would be different, but the protocols should be standard. Those promoting TV white spaces should be under no illusion that harmomised spectrum and global standards have enabled mobile telephony to reach seven billion subscriptions and two billion for mobile broadband. Achieving economies of scale is no mean feat.

6. *Regulatory pilots*: It has already been noted that technical pilots have already "proven" the white space broadband concept, technically. Regulatory pilots are therefore recommended for the folowing reasons:

    i. It encourages regulators and governments to be proactive about TV white space–based broadband, as they should be.
    ii. It enables and facilitates the crafting of good regulation to enable TV white space–based broadband to emerge. Such regulation would now include concepts of WSDs, white space databases as regulatory tools, licence exemption (or light licensing), and dynamic spectrum management.
    iii. Such a regulatory pilot should invite future stakeholders and industry players to partipate and learn about how the

whole new regulatory approach and scheme will work. Such experience would be vital when it goes fully live.

iv. It would offer opportunities for the regulator to decide on issues such as: Who would run the databases, and how many different companies should be allowed (*and licensed*) to run databases? How many of these databases would exist in the country? How are these databases synchronised? Does the country want to prioritise certain catergory of users, such as emergency services—and perhaps only in certain locations? What services are already in UHF in which geographies that need to be protected? How much TV white space is there across the different geographies of the country? How does the regulator deal with roaming across borders? What about rogue WSDs? What cooperation needs to take place with other countries? Who are the credible partners who could work together with the government in fruitful PPPs in order to maximise widespread and affordable broadband to rural areas? Such questions and more should be answered in such a pilot.

7. *Public private partnerships and Universal Service Funds:* I have already made the case in section 6.6 that there is a strong synergy between TV white space–based broadband, Universal Service Funds, and viable PPPs. These need to be explored, developed, and put in place. The partners who can truly make this happen would be few and far between. Indeed, there may only be a couple or several credible multinational partners (more likely investment funds) who would be able to partner with any specific country's Universal Service Fund to truly make white space–based mobile Internet happen in that country.

8. *Small entrepreneurs must be encouraged to be engaged with TV white space–based broadband:* Like Wi-Fi, TV white space–based broadband would typically spin off hundreds if not thousands of entrepreneurs: the set of agents selling or

marketing TV white space–based broadband, village hot spot managers, Wi-Fi–enabled point of sale payment systems, rural content providers, rural market information intermediaries, small, rural ISPs, rural maintenance of solar panels, etc. The list is endless. The Mawungi trial in Kenya has already begun to enable these sort of entrepreneurs to emerge and more. Education, media literacy, and suitable training are strongly recommended to enable these, again perhaps partly funded by Universal Service Funds.

6.10 A Long Road Ahead for Standardised Rural Broadband Based on TV White Spaces

In summary and for the avoidance of doubt, rural broadband based on TV white spaces has a long journey ahead of it in order to achieve the right economies of scale and low costs across Africa and emerging markets. However, this volume is setting up the sector for the 2020s, which is why we need to start now in 2013/14. As we have seen,

(i)   the regulations have to be clear, either license-exempt regulations (preferred on balance) or lightly licensed ones;

(ii) standards need to be agreed upon (e.g., how do devices "talk" to the TV white space database, for example?);

(iii) chipsets (ASICS and/or FPGAs) will need to be developed for TV white space technologies once the regulations are in place and the standards are agreed upon;

(iv) then following from above, radios using TV white spaces will need to be developed in volume; and

(v)   lastly, and most importantly for Africa and emerging markets, the business models need to be evolved in order to make broadband 2 percent or 3 percent, say, of customers' monthly incomes.

These are the typical steps that underpin the commercialisation of all radio technologies, and TV white spaces is no different. They need clear regulation and standardisation such that economies of scale can kick in the costs of chipsets and radios. The steps taken in Nanyuki described above are very early steps with yet-to-be-defined regulations around spectrum, with bespoke standards and early demonstration chipsets and radios.

And for the many critics who are already pronouncing TVWS as a failure, I respecfully note the following: the first TVWS policies and regulations anywhere in the world were only put in place by the FCC in the United States of America in December 2013. That is (i) above has just been promulgated in one country which would trigger standards, chipsets, etc. How can they honestly expect (ii), (iii), (iv) and (v) above to happen without (i)? Furthermore, Ethernet and WiFi took ten years from policy to commercialisation. How can they pronounce TVWS a failure a month after one country only has published their policies and regulations? The road ahead for TV white spaces is still long but most promising.

6.11 An Important Disclaimer: There Are Other approaches to Affordable Rural Broadband

It is important we end our tour of TV white spaces with this key disclaimer. The focus of this entire chapter is widespread and affordable broadband. It is the case that to achieve this laudable goal, the issue of affordable rural broadband must be addressed. This volume is *not* proposing that TV white space technology is the *only* promising approach to achieving affordable rural broadband. As it is evident from the chapter, what the TV white spaces approach essentially ensures are the following:

- finding creative ways to minimize and optimise some of the major cost drivers and items to broadband provision, principally power/electricity, capex-funding minimisation, and backhaul optimization (using TV frequencies for the middle several miles)
- an approach to accessing spectrum at almost zero cost; this is because the spectrum is license exempted like Wi-Fi or lightly

licensed and used on a best efforts basis. The reason the spectrum is licensed exempted in the first place is because the opportunity cost of the spectrum is minimal, not because the spectrum is free! This is an important distinction. It also makes eminent sense to achieve broader social value of economic development with such spectrum as it is illogical to raise the cost structure for building networks in low affordability areas.

- the use of TV bands frequencies which propagate much farther and hence reduce network costs via minimizing number of base stations. The catch to date (as per 2013/14) is in the CPE and installation costs.
- an approach that finds creative business models to make rural broadband affordable

Other approaches which try to address these problems, e.g., using other license-exempt spectrum at 2.4 GHz and 5GHz, could/would be viable, but, by the laws of physics, their ranges would be much less, even though their capacity would be much higher.

In no way should this chapter be seen as the only widespread and affordable rural broadband approach there is. TV white spaces just happens to be one of the most promising I have engaged in, but I am also very supportive of all other efforts to drive widespread and affordable broadband on the African continent and beyond. The next chapter also touches on other low-cost approaches, including mesh Wi-Fi networks, low-cost cellular open-source networks, and low-cost hybrid satellite/GSM networks.

Indeed, if the TV white spaces license exemption approach (along with new business models) spurs the mobile industry to optimize its spectrum costs, backhaul costs, power/electricity costs, opex, and capex to be able to achieve US$1.50 to $5 monthly ARPUs for Africans and others to be able to enjoy affordable broadband, those enjoying it would hardly ask what the technology underneath "the bonnet" is.

CHAPTER 7

TOWARDS WIDESPREAD AVAILABILITY OF AFFORDABLE HIGH-QUALITY MOBILE VOICE, MOBILE DATA, AND MOBILE INTERNET

"One key to strengthening education, entrepreneurship and innovation in communities... is to harness the full power of the Internet, and that means faster and more widely available broadband."

—President Barack Obama, September 21, 2009[1]

"We, the Ministers responsible for Information Communication Technologies (ICTs) in our respective countries in Africa, assembled in Cape Town from the 4th–7th of June 2012 for the Inaugural ICT Indaba[2]...hereby declare our common desire and commitment to eradicate the barriers of poverty through the promotion and use of enabling ICTs to build and foster a

---

1   As quoted in National Executive Council (NEC) Broadband Report, December 21, 2009, http://broadbandbreakfast.com/wp-content/uploads/2009/12/NEC-Broadband-Report.pdf (accessed September 2013).

2   "Indaba" is a Zulu word for a council or meeting of indigenous peoples of southern Africa who meet to discuss an important matter.

> *people-centred knowledge-based economy in Africa....We declare access to broadband communication as a basic human right in Africa and commit to increasing broadband penetration to approximately 80 per cent of the population by 2020. This common vision draws its basis from the positive impact exerted on economic growth through increasing Accessibility, Affordability, and Availability to broadband by all.*"[3]

This is the last of four chapters in this volume towards *widespread* availability of *affordable* high-quality mobile voice, data, and mobile Internet for the masses—a most desirable outcome but also one which I set myself up to fail. As such, it is the "catch all" chapter of this section of the volume. As a reminder, the first of the three chapters (chapter 4) of section III provides an introduction to spectrum, which Julius Genechowski coined as the oxygen of the wireless world. Chapter 5 is about spectrum auctions and other ways to release spectrum into the marketplace because the mobile market definitely needs more spectrum than it has today in order to achieve widespread mobile voice, data, and Internet. Chapter 6 introduces TV white spaces for rural mobile broadband as a potential way of commencing to address not only the widespread availability of broadband but also its affordability. However, I am very aware that the sum of these individual preceding three chapters, i.e., put another way, the sum of their individual parts, does *not* amount to a whole solution to addressing "towards widespread availability of affordable high-quality mobile voice," "towards widespread availability

---

3 Inaugural ICT Indaba: African ICT Ministerial Declaration, June 7, 2012. In June 2012, African ministers for ICTs attended the inaugural Indaba in South Africa event and set themselves the target of achieving broadband penetration of approximately 80 percent by 2020.
http://www.ictindaba.com/2012/images/ICT_Indaba_2012_African_ICT_Ministerial%20Declaration_07June2012.pdf (accessed October 2013)

of affordable high-quality mobile data," and "towards widespread availability of affordable mobile Internet."

For example, none of the preceding three chapters mentions "quality" or quality of service, nor mobile penetration rates, nor coverage of voice on the African continent—the latter two of which are both clearly pertinent to "widespread availability," etc. Therefore, this "catch all" chapter is only but a poor attempt at providing some semblance of a "whole" solution towards this desirable outcome by justifying a bit more the last three chapters, whilst "rounding out the whole" through a miscellaneous set of other important areas.

Keep in mind the three overarching challenges at the conclusion of chapter 3: that of Africa's sheer size, Africa's population distribution, and the fact that 70 percent of Africans live in the rural areas.

7.1 Towards Widespread Availability of Affordable High-Quality Mobile Voice

It is instructive to quickly review where Africa is broadly in 2013/14 on "towards widespread availability of high-quality mobile voice." What indeed is the brief scorecard of findings to date? Following from the findings, what other initiatives should or could be pursued in order to achieve widespread availability of affordable high-quality voice?

7.1.1 Mobile Voice Findings to Date

This section draws from GSMA Intelligence and Deloitte (2012)[4] and other GSMA research and intelligence and is not meant to be exhaustive. It proceeds to make additional observations and recommendations.

---

4 GSMA Intelligence (2012), *Sub-Saharan Africa Mobile Observatory 2012*, http://www.gsma.com/publicpolicy/wp-content/uploads/2013/01/gsma_ssamo_full_web_11_12-1.pdf (accessed September 2013).

1. *Mobile connections/penetration have grown substantially— do the omens look good for "widespreead" voice?:* This fact was indeed already covered in chapter 1. However, it is the case that mobile penetration has increased incredibly in the last thirteen years in sub-Saharan Africa (SSA)[5]— according to GSMA Intelligence and Deloitte (2013)—it has grown from just 1 percent in 2000 to 54 percent in 2012, representing a compound annual growth rate of 36 percent. Indeed since 2000, mobile penetration has grown in Africa by the highest rate than any other continent: 43 percent in Africa as a whole compared to 34 percent for developing regions and only 10 percent in developed regions. Perhaps better is the fact that GSMA Intelligence research finds that it is common to share mobile phones in SSA or to use public mobile phones, demostrating that mobile services extend well beyond penetration levels. As figure 46 depicts, it is expected that penetration will continue to grow steadily, reaching 75 percent of the population and 700 million connections by 2016. It must be noted too that mobile penetration varies markedly across the continent, from 119 percent in southern Africa to less than 30 percent in Niger, say. Countries such as Gabon, Botswana, South Africa, Gambia, and Namibia have penetration levels similar to those witnessed in Europe, i.e., above 100 percent.

---

5 GSMA Intelligence and Deloitte (2013) define SSA in this context as comprising forty-seven countries out of fifty-three countries in Africa and a population of 831 million people—practically more than 80 percent of Africans.

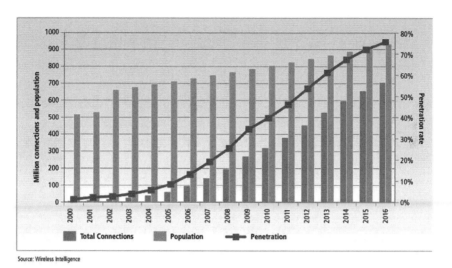

Source: Wireless Intelligence

Figure 46—Mobile Connections, Population, and Mobile Penetration in
Sub-Saharan Africa of 47 Countries (2000–2016)
(Source: GSMA Intelligence (2012);
reproduced with permission of the copyright owner)

2. *"Two thirds of Africans yet to join the mobile revolution*[6]
    *(GSMA Intelligence, 2013)"—widespread voice may not be
    that widespread after all, or is affordability the real prob-
    lem here, or both?* So the penetration rates above are hiding
    a key fact: the true *unique* penetration rates are much lower.
    GSMA Intelligence on behalf of GSMA calculates that only
    one in three of the African population is currently subscribed
    to a mobile service. They calculate that the total "unique" in-
    dividual mobile subscribers in Africa stood at 356 million in
    Q4 2012, representing just 33 percent of the population. The
    reason for the 33 percent is allegedly explained by the fact that
    "cost-conscious African consumers hold two SIM subscrip-
    tions each on average" (GSMA Intelligence, 2013).

---

6 GSMA Intelligence (2013), *Two thirds of Africans yet to join the mobile revolution: African mobile penetration set at 33%; multiple SIMs driving growth*, https://
gsmaintelligence.com/analysis/2012/11/two-thirds-of-africans-yet-to-join-the-mo-
bile-revolution/357/ (accessed September 2013).

Overall, the research shows that Africa's subscriber penetration rate is the lowest in the world. So even though connections continue to grow at 15 percent per year across Africa, connections growth continue to be driven largely by multiple SIM ownership—clearly alluding to an affordability problem. Africans hold 1.96 SIM cards each on average, higher than a global average of 1.85. Like elsewhere, this is due to Africans holding prepaid SIM cards in order to access as many low-cost deals as possible. GSMA Intelligence found that the highest multiple SIM ownership is in Nigeria at 2.39 SIM cards per user on average, second only to Indonesia on a global basis at 2.62 SIMs per user. They quote from MTN Nigeria, who in Q2 2012 reported that "only 25 percent of the gross additions in the market were first time subscribers. The other 75 percent was mainly attributable to rotational churn and multi SIMs in the market."

3. *Coverage increases are improving widespread availability:* Increasing widespread access has been made possible by mobile operators across the continent investing and increasing their network of base stations. However, more base station rollouts are hampered through unreliable electricity supplies, base stations being primarily powered by diesel generators, poor road infrastructure, etc. Despite these, nearly 76 percent of SSA was covered by mobile services in 2012, up from 65 percemt in 2009. Figure 47 shows the coverage levels achieved by 2012 across selected sub-Saharan countries by 2012.

It can be seen that South Africa and Burkina Faso have managed to achieved 100 percentage population coverage, whilst Mali still has a long way to go, being sub-50 percent.

4. *The importance of mobile network infrastructure for voice, data, and Internet in Africa cannot be overstated:* This is certainly the case. Whatever the limitations of penetration levels, levels of coverage, or low level of unique subscriptions on the continent, Africa has come to rely incredibly firmly on

its mobile network infrastructure. Though mobile penetration across the SSA region at 54 percent in 2012, fixed teledensity is at approximately 1.7 percent. GSMA Intelligence (2012) therefore conclude that there are twenty-eight mobile subscriptions for every fixed line in SSA. This clearly demonstrates the importance of mobile infrastructure across the continent today for voice, data, and Internet.

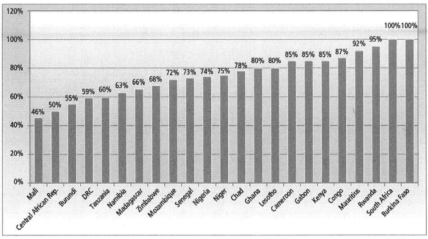

Source: Wireless Intelligence. Data for available countries

Figure 47—Mobile Coverage in Selected Sub-Saharan African Countries (2012)
(Source: GSMA Intelligence [2012];
reproduced with permission of the copyright owner)

5. *Affordability of voice is clearly a concern:* Africa has some truly diverse markets with significant economic and social differences. Whilst the average annual income per capita stands at US$2,439, GSMA Intelligence and Deloitte (2012) note that it varies markedly from a meagre $216 in the Democratic Republic of Congo (DRC)—the poorest country—to $14,660 in Equitorial Guinea, the richest country. There is some correlation between how rich the country is and ARPUs achieved in the country. The affordability challenge is a core reason why only a third of Africans to date are subscribers. GSMA Intelligence (2013) note how monthly

ARPU stands at below US$5 in markets such as Burundi, Rwanda, Uganda, and Egypt.

6. *Handset prices and other factors:* Miscellaneous other factors also impact widespread availability of affordable voice on the continent: these include prices of services (lower call prices or price reductions drive up usage and penetration), increased availability of affordable handsets or lower cost of ownership of handsets (frequently as low as thirty dollars), competition, etc. Indeed, handset prices are a major barrier to affordability on the continent, as is discussed next.

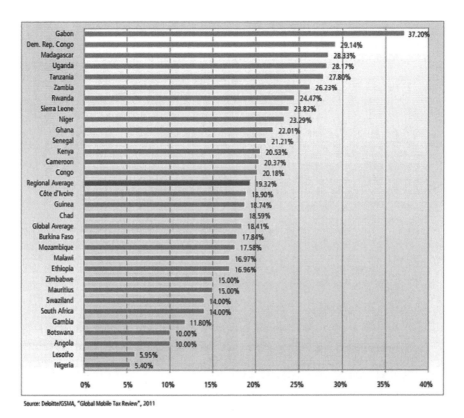

Source: Deloitte/GSMA, "Global Mobile Tax Review", 2011

Figure 48—Mobile Taxation as a Proportion of Total Cost of Mobile
Ownership in Sub-Saharan Africa (2011)
(Source: GSMA Intelligence [2012];
reproduced with permission of the copyright owner)

7. *Taxation on mobile consumers and operators reduces service affordability:* Many African countries sadly tax mobile telecommunications in general at rates amongst the highest in the world via a series of mobile-specific taxes on mobile consumers and mobile operators. Taxes on handsets and usage are of real concern on the continent. Handsets are frequently considered "luxury" items, attracting luxury taxes and custom excises. Airtime excises are also applied to usage, fixed contributions on connections, handsets, and rental. Add on to these sales taxes, VAT, etc., and the result in so many African countries is tax as a proportion of a user's total cost of mobile ownership (TCMO) is amongst the highest in the world in 2011, according to GSMA Intelligence and Deloitte. I ask you to see figure 48 and literally weep for some of the countries at the top.

The TCMO for Gabon was at an incredible 37.2 percent in 2011, according to GSMA Inteligence and Deloitte, due to a VAT rate of 18 percent; a customs duty of 30 percent imposed on imported handsets plus an additional five-dollar fixed tax applied on each handset; and an airtime excise of 18 percent. Across SSA, the average is an incredible 19.32 percent tax. This is regressive, as it drives up the cost of doing business in the region, constrains customer affordability, impairs productivity, and ultimately constrains job creation. Ghana in August 2013 dropped plans for a Communications Service Tax (CST) Bill[7] which planned to slap an additional 6 percent interconnection fee on incoming international calls and which also proposed to reintroduce a 20 percent import tax on mobile handsets, ostensibly in order to protect local manufacturers of mobile phones. So you would have payed a levy in order to call to do business in Ghana. They should also move to remove the National Health Insurance Levy (NHIL) on international calls—yes, in case you are wondering, I also have no idea what

---

7 "Ghana drops plans for 6% communications tax," *Africa Telecom & IT*, August 2013, p. 27.

this levy has got to do with telecommunications. The current CST in Ghana already levies 15 percent value added tax (VAT) on communications in 2013, and Ghanaians have billed the CST the "talk tax." The point is all these taxes impact affordability, and governments will earn more in the long term from many people more being included and services being affordable.

8. *Quality of voice service is truly variable across the continent, but overall poor:* Perhaps one of the best assessment of quality of service is Calandro *et al.* (2010), where they assessed sixteen countries and only found four as being perceived as slightly above the bar for efficiency. In general, they found that the quality of service is a reflection of the oveall regulation within the sector in the country and that it is also influenced by the level of investment in infrastructure and network roll-out, the number of competitors, and the prevailing interconnection regime. In the few instances like in Ivory Coast where QoS is perceived as efficient, they found conformity of equipment/terminals to GSM/ITU standards for mobile telephone and conformity of technical equipment to GSM standards, call quality, connection speeds, and good enforcement regulatory regime.

7.1.2 Initiatives Towards Even More Widespread Availability of Affordable Voice

The findings above are clear for all to see. Some key takeaways—which reinforce earlier recommendations in this volume, particularly in chapter 3—are the following:

1. *Liberalisation and Competition:* The key takeaway is: liberalisation of the telecommunications sector has been a major success. It has increased competition and hence increased affordability. Achieving even more widespread availability of voice at affordable prices requires the liberalisation to continue. This is why the blueprint in chapter 3 majors so much in

several places on the benefits of liberalisation and competition. There are clearly more paying subscribers to be connected on the African continent with only a third of us being unique subscribers. More competition and increasingly richer African countries will see more subscribers, albeit at lower ARPU rates overall. The more competition there is in markets, driven by the number of licensed operators and good regulation, the more widespread and affordable services will become. Chapter 3 also rails at the risks of "choking off" the benefits of liberalisation and competition. Governments should really be wary of choking of liberalisation policies that have worked so well.

2. *Emphasise and address access and affordability concerns even more, as chapter 3 emphasises:* Remember Calandro *et al.* (2010) conclude that national objectives of achieving universal and affordable access to the full range of communication services have been largely undermined by a range of issues, including poor policies and even regressive taxes on usage. Universal access funds have a role to play here.

3. *Reduce and/or eliminate the regressive telecommunication taxes (VAT, excise, custom, airtime, connection taxes, corporation taxes, etc.):* GSMA Intelligence and Deloitte analysis clearly show an increase in the number of countries levying such taxes. Rwanda and Tanzania increased airtime taxes to 12 percent in 2012! Governments have a major role to play here as taxation policies have a significant impact on the value accrued to society from mobile services. It is good to see, for example, that Kenya recognised that handset prices represented a barrier to the development of the sector, and they removed the 16 percent VAT on mobile handsets in August 2009. The result was dramatic: even though this VAT elimination only reduced the tax as a result of the total cost of mobile ownership from 25 to 21 percent, handset purchases have increased by 200 percent in Kenya since the removal of the VAT, and mobile penetration increased from 50 to 70 percent between 2009 and

2011. GSMA Intelligence and Deloitte rightly argue that this will in turn generate an increase in government tax revenues through the positive impact on mobile operators' revenues and the overall economy. Other countries wedded to such taxes can and should learn from this Kenyan example. Corporation taxes for mobile are also highest in Africa at circa 29 percent compared to 23 percent for the twenty-seven nations of the European Union (EU).

4. *Rural coverage network rollout commercial models would need to be evolved, which does not fall foul of regulatory concerns:* Some countries, exemplified by Tanzania and Uganda, have very large percentage of their populations living in rural areas, at 74 percent[8] and 87 percent, respectively. This helps explain the low penetration rates in these countries because of the sheer poor economics of rural network rollout. Costs spiral rapidly up whilst income levels are much lower. One network operator could roll out for rural network coverage with the regulator's blessing subject to this operator providing regulatory access (where the regulator regulates access and ongoing rental charge) to its competitors and/or roaming. Alternatively, other super-low-cost models being tested and developed on the continent by the likes of Movitel in Mozambique or VNL in Ghana must be supported. These include do-it-yourself (DIY) low-power solar solutions, solar chargers, or the "village telco"[9] concept—an initiative to build low-cost community telephony network using open-source hardware and software. This is briefly described later on.

5. *Revenue-dilutive incremental subscribers mean network infrastructure, spectrum and site sharing are on their way, as well as build operate transfer/lease (BOT/L) models*: As

---

8 Some other sources say 80 percent, e.g., from Prof. John S. Nkoma, director general, Tanzania Communications Regulatory Authority (TCRA), personal communication, November 2013.

9 http://villagetelco.org/ (accessed September 2013).

mobile operators add to their networks (i.e., the two-thirds of Africans who are not subscribers), they are increasingly reaching out to harder-to-reach segments, poorer subscribers, or multiple-SIM owners. This means earnings and margins are being diluted. Typically 50 percent of the revenues come from 10 percent of the base station sites, and 80 percent of the revenues come from 30 percent of sites. The last 50 percent of the sites would typically only raise 10 percent of the revenues. The inescapable conclusion is that two mobile operators may have to share sites, radio access network equipment, backhaul—and subject to competition checks, even spectrum—thereby sharing operational and capital costs, particularly for the sites generating less revenue. Furthermore, third parties, like tower companies, may build, operate, and transfer/lease sites to mobile operators, which improve coverage beyond what individual operators would choose to do commercially. Regulators may be wary of such moves on competition grounds, but, however, these approaches would be important to driving more widespread availability of voice at affordable prices. Sharing at sites level—what is sometimes termed *passive sharing*—is already commonplace on the continent. *Active sharing,* where some of the electronics on the sites, like antennae, transmission/backhaul and even spectrum, are shared, is less common but would now have to be considered subject to regulatory approvals and amendments to regulatory guidelines. Not many regulators on the continent in 2013 had acts and/or regulatory guidelines which encouraged active sharing. These need to be revisited fast. Remember the problem of the size of the African continent at the end of chapter 3. The case for spectrum and infrastructure sharing on the continent is growing stronger by the day.

6. *Power problems need to be alleviated in order to support extension of coverage to rural areas:* Extending coverage to rural areas presents operators with significant challenges due to unreliability and quality of power supply. GSMA Intelligence

(2013) note the fact that Tanzania, Uganda, and Kenya collectively had a total network of 13,225 base station sites as of Q3 2012, of which 9,957 were connected to the commercial grid power supply, and the remaining 3,268 were off grid. Nevertheless both on-grid and off-grid base stations still rely on expensive diesel generators due to poor power infrastructure or limited grid power. Furthermore, the situation in east Africa is much better than in western Africa, where deployment in countries like DRC are truly hampered due to lack of electricity and/or roads through which to service diesel-based generators.

7. *Quality of service—indeed quality of experience—needs real attention on the continent:* In, frankly, most countries on the continent, quality of service is perceived as poor or very poor by users, driven by increasing number of subscribers using inadequate infrastructure. In many countries too, the regulatory oversight for quality of service is just poor. For example, Calandro *et al.* (2010) report of a "regulatory impasse" in Cameroon or in Senegal where the latter's regulator (ARTP) responsible for monitoring QoS does not work closely with the consumer's association. Therefore, consumers experience poor quality of service, yet are not aware of regulatory redress. Benin, Ghana, Namibia, Kenya, and Nigeria are plagued by low signals, dropped calls, traffic congestions, and poor reception, amongst many other woes. In Uganda, QoS results were not being published in a meaningful way to enable subscribers to exercise choice, but the regulator—the Uganda Communication Commission (UCC)—is now rightly adopting its "name and shame" policy, which compares the performance of different providers across a number of metrics in the public media. This is after the UCC had claimed that none of the nation's six operators were meeting minimum QoS requirements. In Ethiopia, QoS has been failing due to lack of competition. Botswana provides a good example of how QoS works where operators are required to submit monthly network performance

reports to the regulator detailing performance parameters and status of their networks. This has apparently resulted in a positive perception of the regulator as regards QoS. The regulator also carries out investigations on telecommunications equipment, ensuring conformity of equipment/terminals to GSM/ITU standards.

In general, this is arguably the biggest problem on the continent today with mobile network operators. The reasons are many and varied. In Nigeria, for example, operators blame amongst other things vandalism of their backhaul fibre, base station sites, and other assets. Type approval problems are definitely a significant contributor which needs to be addressed. One can summarise that there are three categories of issues here at play with QoS: demand side, supply side, and regulatory.

Demand side issues: There is no doubt that there is the exponential increase in demand from consumers for voice and increasing data-hungry applications.

Supply side issues: Are there enough spectrums in the marketplace? This chapter suggests not. Are the spectrums in the right hands? The answer to this is mixed. Is there enough sharing of spectrum and infrastructure at play? Is there enough backhaul spectrum or fibre links, and are they secure? Is there enough dimensioning for the capacity needed? Are small cells solutions like Wi-Fi, picocells, and femtocells being used to off-load traffic from macro networks? Are right-of-way issues hampering network rollouts?

Regulatory issues: Is there enough competition in the marketplace? Are enough measurements being made and operators being named, shamed, and occasionally fined for breaching QoS KPIs? Do mystery shopping exercises take place? What information remedies are in place? Are go-type approval processes in place by both the operators and the regulator?

In conclusion, and in my experience, QoS—indeed from a customer's perspective it is quality of experience (QoE)[10]—tends to correlate with the overall regulation of the sector and country. In other words, regulators should first look at themselves when it comes to quality of experience issues, as their polices, regulation, and enforcement influence investment, rollout, number of competitors, intensity of competition, interconnection regime, and so on.

7.1.3 Other Wireless Voice Network Platforms: Satellite Voice Networks

Africa and other emerging economies also need more competition in wireless platforms in addition to fixed in order to achieve widespread access to voice. Mobile networks are not the only networks than can provide such wireless voice services. Satellite platforms, as described in chapter 2, can also do the same. They may not be that affordable, but they offer choice and may be the only option for broadband in rural and remote parts of the continent.

Though some countries like Burkina Faso can boast of 100 percent population coverage, the geographical coverage is much lower. So if there is a disaster in part of a country where there is justifiably no commercial mobile operator network, satellite wireless telephony will provide an important alternative. Many news organisations use satellite phones for close to 100 percent global coverage.

7.2 Towards Widespread Availability of Affordable High-Quality Mobile Data and Mobile Internet

The quote used to begin this chapter from President Barack Obama is most apt here: "one key to strengthening education, entrepreneurship and innovation in communities...is to harness the full power of the

---

10   The last thing customers need are operators providing evidence of esoteric technical readings and measurements in erlangs achieving even more esoteric KPIs, yet their quality of experience (QoE) is terrible.

Internet, and that means faster and more widely available broadband." In this same speech, President Obama argues how he truly believes that the rapid expansion of Internet across Africa could transform how Africa trades, learns, and holds political power accountable. However, perhaps even more pertinent in this section is the second quote at the start of this chapter—i.e., that from the inaugural ICT Indaba African ministerial declaration of June 7, 2012. In it African ministers declare access to broadband communication "as a basic human right." They emphasise "increasing accessibility, affordability and availability to broadband for all," and they set a target of 80 percent broadband penetration by 2020. These are all very laudable, but executable plans need to be put in place to make 80 percent access to affordable broadband happen on the continent.

Furthermore, the ITU set up a multistakeholder commission—the Broadband Commission for Digital Development—comprising over fifty top-level global leaders who helped define four critical targets that that all countries are expected to push to attain by 2015:

- Target 1: Making broadband policy universal. By 2015, all countries should have a national broadband plan/strategy or should include broadband in their universal access/service definitions.
- Target 2: Making broadband affordable. By 2015, entry-level broadband should cost less than 5 percent of average monthly income.
- Target 3: Connecting homes to broadband. By 2015, 40 percent of households in developing economies should have Internet access.
- Target 4: Getting people online. By 2015, Internet user penetration should reach 60 percent worldwide, 50 percent in developing countries, and 15 percent in least-developed countries.

I would hardly disagree with such targets in a section on making broadband widespread and affordable. To the extent that they help move broadband to the top of the political agenda, these targets are invaluable. Whether most African countries can meet them by 2015 is a moot point. It is looking unlikely from the vantage point of late 2013 and early 2014.

7.2.1 What Are Broadband, Mobile Internet, and Mobile Data?

I can also almost hear you beginning to ask what the difference is between "mobile data/broadband" and "mobile Internet." Indeed, what is broadband in the contexts of Africa and some emerging markets?

Broadband in the African context is the delivery of Internet IP bandwidth at speeds of 256 Kbps or more in 2013/14 (in Europe it is 2 Mbps or more). Yes, millions of Africans will metaphorically die for 256 Kbps! For mobile broadband, 256 Kbps is a realistic start particularly if the 70 percent reality of rural Africans is considered. Ditto for Pakistan, Bangladesh, Haiti, Burma, etc. Other purist analysts would disagree, but with large fractions living in the rural parts, it is hard to argue otherwise. Broadband also includes the content, services, and applications that consume this capacity. Given the lack of fixed broadband infrastructure, mobile is the main gateway to the Internet for Africa and many other developing countries. Over 70 percent of Africans today who manage to access the Internet actively do so over a 2.5G or 3G mobile connection. Furthermore, as figure 4 (in chapter 1) depicts, between 5 and 28 percent of these Africans with access to the Internet use their mobiles to browse it, depending on the country concerned. Other countries, e.g., Bangladesh in 2013, access the Internet only via 2G use, with most people using the Internet over a 2G connection via feature phones or low-end smartphones.[11] This suggests a strong latent demand for *mobile Internet access* that will accelerate via the availability of 3G (and later 4G) and the enhanced user experience gained through a higher speed connection with lower latency.

---

11 This situation in Bangladesh should change over the next few years after their most recent 3G auction of September 2013.

Therefore, *mobile Internet* refers to the means of accessing the Internet—or achieving broadband—over a mobile 2G, 3G, or 4G connection. However, beyond core access to the network, mobile operators are providing mobile-enabled services targeting specific segments (e.g., low-income populations are making use of mobile data), typically through apps, but also via the mobile Internet. Apps and services have been accelerating on the continent since 2011 and in other emerging markets, particularly covering education, health, banking services, money transfers, social data communications like the Facebook app, eGovernment, etc. Therefore, *mobile data* refers to rapid traffic growth on mobile networks driven by apps, the proliferation of data-enabled devices that allow mobile Internet connectivity, and better connectivity by successively better radio interfaces, as in 4G being better than 3G which in turn is better than 2G. So for example, the increase in 3G connections, along with the proliferation of data-enabled devices, has led to a massive growth in the use of mobile data. Total mobile data usage has more than doubled on average every year from 2005 to 2010 in almost every developing country. In western European countries, it grew by 350 percent. Indeed, mobile operators in all regions of the globe continue to show impressive data volume growth rates as more and more people connect to the Internet via mobile. In emerging markets like Africa, growth will be driven by the increased penetration of smartphones and years later by increased download speeds made possible by new technology such as 4G.

In fact, total traffic volumes in 2012 alone exceeded all the previous years combined, and globally data is projected to grow by 66 percent per annum through to 2017. This process is sometimes referred to as the *democratisation of data*, as this data growth has no real demographic identity. President Obama's quote at the beginning of this chapter refers to such a democratization phenomenon with the Internet, mobile or fixed.

There is clear latent demand for broadband access and infrastructure to drive broadband inclusion across all strata. It is instructive to quickly review where Africa is broadly in 2013 on "towards widespread availability of high-quality mobile Internet and data," as we did for voice.

7.2.2 Mobile Internet and Mobile Data Findings to Date

This section also draws from GSMA Intelligence (2012).[12] It proceeds to make additional observations and recommendations.

8. *Mobile has the potential for delivering the benefits of the Internet across Africa and is set to grow twenty-fivefold in four years:* According to GSMA Intelligence and Deloitte,

> Mobile broadband has the potential to further expand this transformative experience by bringing the Internet to consumers in SSA. The lack of affordability, coverage and reliability of fixed networks across the region means that mobile broadband is the only way for the vast majority of consumers to access the Internet.

I could not agree more. Thanks to this basic point, they also point out that the proportion of web browsing using mobile technology relative to fixed lines is the highest in the world. Citing Statcounter they note for 2011 58.1 percent of web traffic in Zimbabwe was mobile based, 57.9 percent in Nigeria, and 44 percent in Zambia, compared to a global average of 10 percent. Zambia is the country ranked fifth in the sample by mobile-based Internet browsing. Thanks to the extremely poor coverage of fixed line networks and the high associated cost of computers, mobiles are quickly becoming the main platform for Internet browsing. These figures put these countries at the top of global mobile web browsing, followed by India and Sudan. These figures are well above the world average, currently at 10 percent, and indicate that Africa is a leader in mobile versus fixed Internet browsing. Demand for

---

12 GSMA Intelligence (2012), *Sub-Saharan Africa Mobile Observatory 2012*, http://www.gsma.com/publicpolicy/wp-content/uploads/2013/01/gsma_ssamo_full_web_11_12-1.pdf (accessed September 2013).

connectivity and web-based information is very high in the region and can be addressed by accessible and affordable mobile broadband. This growth in mobile broadband is predicted to soar twenty-fivefold over the next four years, driven largely by lower income groups. Like with broadand elsewhere, mobile broadband in Africa would drive economic productivity via better information flows, reduced travel time and costs, and improved business efficiency.

9. *The predicted growth in mobile data necessitates more spectrum being released in Africa—a core reason why chapters 4 and 5 cover spectrum 101 and spectrum release/auctions respectively:* Figure 49 captures this graphically and excellently.

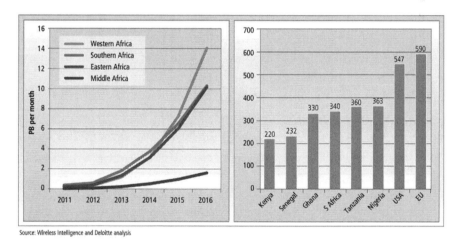

Source: Wireless Intelligence and Deloitte analysis

Figure 49—Estimated Total Mobile Internet Traffic in Sub-Saharan Africa, by region (2011–2016) and assigned spectrum for leading SSA countries in MHz (2011)
(Source: GSMA and GSMA Intelligence [2012]; reproduced with permission of the copyright owner)

This traffic increase is becoming unsustainable on current network infrastructure, and operators have already started to experience significant congestion. This congestion is expected to increase significantly as mobile services are used as a substitute for fixed Internet services due to the high cost of rolling out fixed infrastructure. Operators are already expressing concerns about their lack of access to the low-frequency spectrum that they require to expand coverage, particularly in rural areas. Therefore, GSMA Intelligence (2012) note that while demand for mobile broadband is expected to be strong and forecasts show increasing connections, the extent to which this is realised will depend on resolving these constraints on the supply side.

As total mobile penetration in SSA has increased from only 1 percent to 54 percent in twelve years, and as the fixed line network often remains undeveloped and unavailable to the majority of the population, mobile services have become the universal provider of communications services. These significant penetration increases have made basic mobile services available to millions of people across all income levels and have affected greatly the economy as a whole.

You can see in figure 49 the predicted assymptotic growths in data across all regions in Africa, bar middle Africa. Even more important, given Africa would rely even more on mobile broadband for access to the Internet as noted in the previous finding, the graph on the right-hand side is also not good for Africa: Nigeria for example has 363 MHz of mobile spectrum in MHz vs. 547 MHz and 590 MHz in the USA and EU, respectively. Yet, Nigeria and the rest of Africa will see more mobile Internet traffic growth than any other continent. You can see clearly why this volume majors in chapters 4 and 5 on spectrum 101 and on spectrum releases on the continent. Africa needs to have more spectrum released for mobile than the USA and EU. Governments in Africa risk undermining their broadband and development goals unless levels of spectrum similar to EU and more are made available in Africa. Previous chapters have made this point.

10. *The good news is that more 3G networks are being developed on the African continent to usher in the mobile data era. The not-so-good news is that 3G penetration will be minimal in the short to medium term.* GSMA Intelligence and Deloite report that 3G networks were available in thirty countries in sub-Saharan Africa in 2012, compared to only ten in 2008. However, though they note this investment in 3G network roll-outs, penetration is only predicted to reach 15–16 percent in 2016, as shown in figure 50.

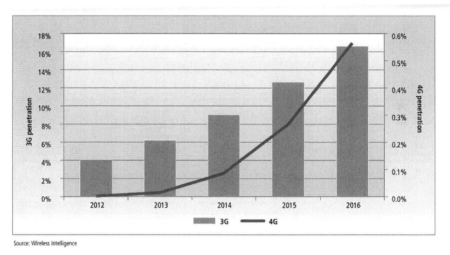

Source: Wireless Intelligence

Figure 50—3G and 4G Penetration in Sub-Saharan Africa (2012–2016)
(Source: GSMA Intelligence [2012];
reproduced with permission of the copyright owner)

Whilst figure 50 shows good news for networks investment, 16 percent penetration is also a real story in this picture. In practice what this means is that only circa 10–15 percent of the base stations in most countries will be lit for 3G, i.e., 3G radio equipment will only be rolled out in the most dense urban areas. The reason? Well, you remember the naked mobile problem of chapter 1 (figure 3). As data starts dominating, the revenue-per-bit of traffic drops off a cliff, and revenues flatten off and coverage suffers. We need to understand this inevitability and preempt it. Figure 50 also shows the emergence of 4G networks on the continent on the right-hand side of the graph—but only to a paltry 0.6 percent penetration by 2016. This is covered next. Figure 50—being an average across all sub-Saharan African countries—is a pessimistic generalisation in some countries on the continent, like South Africa, Rwanda, Kenya, or Egypt, where 3G is currently higher or where 4G/LTE would be rolled out before 2015. The reputable GSMA projects 0.5 million, 1.1 million, and 2.5 million 4G/LTE connections in Kenya, Nigeria, and South Africa respectively in 2015. Nevertheless, the key message of paltry 3G/4G capacity still stands across the continent, as depicted in figure 50 above. Nigeria has a 4.2 percent 3G penetration in 2013, well below the average 6 percent shown in figure 50, whilst South Africa has 18 percent.

11. *Plans to release more 4G spectrum must commence now, and we must preempt the data "haves" and the "have-nots" on the continent—hence why chapter 6 unapologetically introduces TV white spaces for rural broadband:* Thanks to the naked data problem, 3G networks which are not optimised for data would need to be supplanted and/or added to by 4G networks. However, both the 3G and 4G networks' coverages are unlikely to ever go beyond the urban populations centres. Three clear messages emerge here. First, figure 50 is yet another illustration of why 3G spectrum must be liberalised or released on the continent. Second, it also reemphasises why 4G spectrum needs to be released as soon as possible and why chapter 5 argues strongly for 4G spectrum releases across the continent, preferably by auctions. Third, the risk of the data "haves" and the data "have-nots" is real. If collectively 3G and 4G networks do not ultimately extend beyond the population centres on the continent due to the economics of data—the naked mobile problem—what are those in the rural areas meant to do? What about countries like Tanzania and Uganda with 74 percent and 87 percent rural populations? It is precisely to preemt the data have-nots on the conitinent that chapter 6

proposes and argues for TV white spaces for rural broadband across Africa and emerging economies.

12. *Affordability is a major problem still on the continent. The last chapter on white spaces tries to address it. It is important that initiatives like this and more are progressed on the continent:* You do not need to take this from my. Listen to the ITU. Brahima Sanou, director of the Telecommunication Development Bureau (BDT), made this point aptly at the ITU11:

> Broadband is still too expensive in developing countries, where it costs on average more than 100 per cent of monthly income, compared with 1.5 per cent in developed countries...Countries without affordable broadband access run the risk of falling behind in the global information society.[13]

100 percent of monthly income is patently unaffordable anywhere! This position has improved with the landing of more and more submarine cable capacity on the continent, but as we saw in the last chapter in the case of Nigeria, say, reasonable broadband consumption over a month still costs over forty US dollars, which is simply unaffordable.

13. *Adopt and properly execute on all the Broadband Commission for Digital Development targets:* The four targets recommended by the ITU-mandated commission listed above are truly laudable, albeit I question whether most African countries would meet them by 2015. However, they are extremely sensible recommendations which all countries, including African ones, must adopt and properly implement. Some countries like Rwanda are well on their way, and they are moving forward with delivering

---

13 "Measuring the Information Society 2011," published by the International Telecommunications Union (ITU),
http://www.itu.int/ITU-D/ict/publications/idi/index.html (accessed October 2013).

broadband via 4G, whilst Kenya has unveiled a US$2.9 billion broadband strategy to bring Internet services by 2017.

7.2.3 Other Views towards Even More Widespread Availability of Affordable Mobile Data and Internet

All of the recommendations towards widespread availability of affordable voice of section 7.2.1 also apply for mobile data and the mobile Internet, including liberalisation, competition, access and affordability, reduction in regressive taxation, preempting rural coverage, addressing power problems, etc.

Like before, we add several below which largely reinforce earlier recommendations in this volume, particularly in chapters 5 and 6:

14. *Mobile broadband and the mobile Internet would be constrained by spectrum scarcity, so efforts must be made to liberalise existing spectrum and start releasing spectrum by 2015 when digital switchover completes in many countries (at least this is the optimistic timetable):* This is not a new recommendation but worth reemphasising, particularly after the evidence shown in figure 49. As figure 49 also depicts, the data growth is more acute in western, southern, and eastern Africa, with countries like Nigeria expected to see 132 percent growth in data year-on-year. So the demand side is clear, and the supply side must be addressed, and the biggest gating factor on the supply side is spectrum scarcity. Mobile spectrum on the continent is low for its needs! Europe is already at almost 600 MHz of mobile spectrum, with clear plans aiming towards 1,000 MHz. African countries are at 200 to 300 MHz and yet rely on mobile for the Internet more than Europe and any other continent in the world. You can see—yet again—why chapters 5 and 6 are important to this Africa TMT story. The recommendations in these chapters should be heeded and 2G spectrum liberalised in the hands of incumbents for 3G/4G (subject to competition) and more spectrums released and/or refarmed for 4G. Peter Lyons of GSMA observed, "governments and

regulators are not prepared for the coming growth because they have been dragging their feet in allocating spectrum to support mobile data networks."[14]

15. *The spectrum released must be harmonised spectrum—"in summary, the combined effect of the Digital Dividend (700 MHz and 800 MHz) and 2.6GHz bands and re-farming the 1800 MHz band would have a US$33.6 billion impact on GDP between 2015 and 2020, leading to the creation of 14.9 million jobs in the top six markets"* (GSMA Intelligence and Deloitte, 2012). Yet again, not a new recommendation but worth emphasising with GSMA Intelligence and Deloitte evidence and/or prediction: Do all these spectrum bands (700 MHz, 800 MHz, 2.6 GHz) read familiar? If they do, it is because they were all highlighted in chapters 5 and 6. The top six SSA markets GSMA Intelligence and Deloitte refer to here include Nigeria, South Africa, Ghana, Kenya, and Tanzania. The impact of $33.6 billion between 2015 and 2020 is yet another clear signal that spectrum releases must be happening in 2015 or shortly thereafter. Mobile data usage would—as argued several times in this volume already—improve economic productivity and growth. Remember Deloitte and GSMA Intelligence's study mentioned in chapter 1 that concludes that a doubling of mobile data use leads to an increase in GDP per capita of 0.51 percentage points? They proceed to extrapolate for SSA in GSMA Intelligence (2012) that GDP could increase by forty billion US dollars over the next four years, representing approximately 0.5 percent of total GDP of this region over that period subject to *harmonised* spectrum being released in a timely fashion. They also support chapter 5's recommendations that liberalizing spectrum has the potential of providing an effective short-term solution, allowing operators to deploy technology for mobile broadband whilst they wait for 4G spectrum to be

---

14   Peter Lyons of GSMA is quoted in "Spectrum hoarding hampers African telecoms growth," *Africa Telecom & IT*, January 2013, p. 40.

released. It is indeed scary they also report that it has been estimated that failure to achieve spectrum harmonization in SSA can increase device costs by up to US $9.30 - an 18 percent increase on an affordable smartphone's costs.

16. *Taxation should not stifle the development of the mobile Internet:* Africa has the highest taxes as a proportion of TCMO. Taxes on smartphones, mobile broadband usage, etc., just make little sense. GSMA Intelligence (2012) rightly rails against Kenya— the world leader in mobile banking services with M-PESA— announcing in 2012 a new 10 percent tax on money transaction services. GSMA correctly argues that it is threatening Kenya's vanguard economic and social development initiative.

17. *Planning permissions (rights-of-way) for base stations and fibre rollouts must be simplified and standardized:* Mobile data and the mobile Internet will require significant base stations and fibre rollout across the continent. Planning and approval processes must be streamlined, and complex uncoordinated national and local regulations must be harmonized and standardised. Otherwise called "standardisation of rights-of-way," this is a significant gating factor for investment in 3G and 4G networks. Indeed, many mobile operators on the continent have known mobile "not spots" (i.e., areas in cities where subscribers have no mobile reception) in major cities like Lagos, Douala, or Cairo. Frequently, it is because they cannot find an appropriate site to locate a mobile base station to fill this not spot as they struggle to obtain "right-of-way" with landlords. The establishment of a national central information repository for such right-of-way procedures and permissions—perhaps by the communications regulator or the department driving the TMT business plan—is strongly recommended.

18. *TV white spaces for rural broadband:* Need we say any more? Chapter 6 says it all. We must preempt and minimise the haves and the have-nots with mobile data and the mobile Internet.

19. *Rollout of national and regional fibre backbones:* Without national and regional fibre distribution of landed capacity, countries will continue to rely on expensive satellite for international connectivity. This is illustrated later in section 7.4. Not a new recommendation, but it's worth reemphasising.

20. *An approach of collaboration between governments, regulators, and industry would also be invaluable to making mobile Internet happen both in the urban and the rural areas across Africa:* This includes refarming and liberalizing spectrum and releasing new spectrum for 4G, and ensuring affordable smartphone devices are delivered for the continent, taxes are minimized, regulation is predictable (which encourages investment), and media literacy is enhanced. Even African governments and regulators should ensure their spectrum is harmonized as well as they work together to drive up similar devices being used across the continent—driving down device prices.

7.3 Wi-Fi and Small Cells Contributions Towards Widespread Voice, Data, and Internet

Wi-Fi, incredibly, stands for "wireless fidelity," but we can ignore this arguable historical misnaming and really define Wi-Fi to mean wireless local area network or WLAN. A local area network, or LAN, is also obviously a small cell network with a typical use case range of thirty-five metres indoors and one hundred metres outdoors, in contrast to larger 2G/3G/4G macro networks whose typical use case range are measured at circa one to two kilometres. Practically every laptop and broadband enabled device will be Wi-Fi–enabled, allowing users to be able to connect to the Internet via a wireless Wi-Fi access point or router. The vast majority of the readers of this volume would need no more introductions to Wi-Fi.

Suffice to say that in the context of this chapter, Wi-Fi is an almost neglected and underestimated orphan child in the delivery of mobile data and the Internet broadband, and it must not be ignored. Wi-Fi operates on a license-exempt basis at 2.4–2.483 GHz and at 5 GHz. In Europe, Wi-Fi small cell networks carry more than twenty times as much Internet data as all cellular networks combined, and more than half of all smartphone traffic is routed over Wi-Fi. Wi-Fi data traffic is growing four to six times faster than cellular. This trend towards mobile data off-loading to Wi-Fi and other smaller cell solutions, such as femtocells[15] and picocells,[16] will only grow as Africa and emerging markets consume more and more data.

Small cell solutions like Wi-Fi, femtocells, and picocells are inside-out solutions (i.e., they are designed for small, indoor-type use case scenarios that can "grow out") in contrast to the outside-in solutions of the external macro network. Small cells networks provide capacity and coverage where needed, increasing use of smartphones and tablets plus more data-intensive applications which would otherwise place strain on macro-cell capacity. Small cells need to be properly integrated into the mobile network operator's network to ensure a transparent end user quality of experience (QoE) femtocells and/or Wi-Fi. Mobile operators and consumers in developed markets are increasingly using home femtocells, office picocells, home Wi-Fi, or Wi-Fi hot spots to off-load data from the macro network. Seventy-five percent of video is typically off-loaded to Wi-Fi.

So if Wi-Fi is carrying so much traffic already, why can it not be used for even larger radii, e.g., a village? The answer is it can, and some use Wi-Fi with much larger radii. So, Wi-Fi hot spots could also cover quite large areas if higher powers are used than in mostly indoor or 100-metre outdoor use cases. One can have a village Wi-Fi solution unlike what most mobile network operators would acknowledge. However, a Wi-Fi solution is not designed for wide areas, being an inside-out solution. Wi-Fi could also provide a platform for voice-to-voice communication using voice-over IP (VoiP) via applications such

---

15 A femtocell is a small, low-power cellular base station typically designed for use in a home or a small business. It is normally used to augment poorer indoor coverage from the outside macro network and/or to provide more capacity.

16 Picocells are also small cellular base stations which cover larger areas that homes or small business but slightly larger radii, such as shopping malls, train stations, or airport perimeters.

as Skype, Viber, Tango, WiCall, and more—but not a scalable and widespread one.

7.4 Low-Cost Mesh–Wi-Fi and Cellular Networks for Affordable Voice and Data

Affordability, particularly for the rural parts of Africa, demands low-cost optimised models which cost optimises practically all cost elements of the fixed or cellular network operator model.

Cost optimising a more expensive fixed network is the main idea behind a mesh–Wi-Fi type model typified by Steve Song's "village telco"[17] implementation. The idea is people living in a small village who want to talk to one another—instead of resorting to expensive mobile/cellular calls which they can hardly afford—use a network of simple Wi-Fi devices that talk to other simple Wi-Fi devices. People can connect ordinary phones to these devices, enabling people to make free calls to all others on the "village" network. Any type of phone can be "hooked up" to this Wi-Fi device, as long as the Wi-Fi devices are connected up into a "mesh" of Wi-Fi devices. If the mesh devices are also linked to the Internet and/or other telecom operators, apart from to each other, then the people are now able to access the web as well as make cheap long-distance calls. This is essentially a do-it-yourself telecommunications tool kit which has no major network vendor lock in, no regulatory overheads, and no masqueraded fees. The key other need is power, and typically low-power solar solution and solar chargers are preferred to keep costs down, in addition to open-source hardware and software to run the telecoms operations.

Similarly, there are also cost-optimised variants of cellular networks using commercial open-source cellular systems. Such a network would allow for making and receiving local/global calls, sending and receiving local/global SMS text messages, and building on open-source software and generic wireless IP backbone without expensive cellular-grade interconnections, software, and hardware.

---

17 Source: http://villagetelco.org/ (accessed September 2013).

7.5 National and International Roaming and Infrastructure Sharing Towards Widespread Mobile Voice, Data, and Internet

Within a country or even within a continent, one obvious approach to enhance (and make widespread) mobile voice, data, and Internet from the vantage point of a consumer is via national and international roaming. Suddenly, that customer is able to have seamless widespread service within his or her country or even within his/her continent.

National roaming refers to the arrangements or agreements (commercial led or regulatory imposed) where one national operator (A) allows the customers of another competitor national operator (B) to use A's network for a fee. International roaming is a form of mobile roaming offered by mobile operators that allows customers to use their mobile phones abroad (or outside their country). International roaming depends on the home operator having agreements with foreign operators that allow customers to make and receive calls, send and pick up SMS messages, and use some of the other mobile services (such as access to voicemail or topping up credit on prepay phones). The exact services available and the charges for their use vary amongst operators.

Infrastructure sharing is where Operator A may be obliged to share its passive infrastructure (sites, masts, towers, etc.) or even active infrastructure (transmission equipment, backhaul equipment, etc.) with Operator B. Alternatively, it may be a commercially agreed arrangement of which the regulator would have to approve or be informed.

Therefore national/international roaming and infrastructure sharing obligations are all areas that the regulator has significant jurisdiction over. In general, if the market is found by the regulator to be competitive across voice, data, and Internet services, then the regulator would have no business in imposing a national roaming obligation (for any service, e.g., voice, SMS, data, etc.) on any operator. However, if Operator A is found to be dominant, the regulator may choose to impose roaming obligations where Operator A has to accept roaming requests from Operator B. Other examples or scenarios include:

- 3G mobile licenses may make it compulsory for existing mobile operators to offer 2G roaming to a new 3G market player. This is a case of an *ex ante* regulation imposed on existing licensees for competition reasons.
- 4G mobile licenses make it compulsory for existing mobile operators to offer 2G (voice) or 3G data (or both) roaming to a new 4G market player. Ditto as above.
- All mobile operators in some mobile markets are obligated by regulation to accept all reasonable requests for national roaming agreements from new entrants or MVNOs.
- If the regulator designates a provider as having significant market power in the market for access and call origination on public mobile telephone networks, that network operator would be obliged to meet all reasonable requests for national roaming access, MVNO access, and even co-location and infrastructure sharing on their sites.
- Two commercial firms may contract for roaming services commercially without involvement from the regulator; however, regulation could provide a safety net for the "weaker" operator who needs the roaming access. It could include terms for the dominant operator not to discriminate with respect to prices and other terms and even the terms by which prices for national roaming should be based.
- There may also be no obligation on operators to provide national roaming. It may be that operators that do not have coverage in all areas can negotiate commercial agreements to roam onto others' 2G networks.
- A regulator may choose to work with mobile operators to develop national roaming for emergency calls, as has happened in the United Kingdom.

All these scenarios clearly demonstrate how, whether via regulatory diktat or by commercial negotiation, customers can experience more widespread voice, data, and Internet coverage both nationally and internationally, well beyond the footprint of sites and coverage of their specific network operator.

It is up to the regulator to decide what is right for each local market. Ideally, for the regulator at least, roaming should be driven commercially both nationally and internationally. Bharti Airtel's "One Network" roaming in east Africa covering Tanzania, Uganda, and Kenya is ideal—and consumers are the key beneficiaries. This means customers do not experience bill shock, a scenario where they return to their countries to a massive bill for the misfortune of having roamed onto an international network. However, the market is not working in this way in most of Africa, which means regulators may need to be intricately involved.

In such a case, it is important regulators work on anti-bill shock and transparency regulations. Ideally, a super-African regulator (akin to the European Commission for the EU) or a conference of regional regulators may choose to work on measures such as the following:

- Establish wholesale access price caps (or maximum pricing) for voice, SMS, and data that take full account of latest estimated maximum wholesale costs.
- Implement retail caps establishing a downward glide path with headline reductions in caps for voice (i.e., calls made), e.g., from ten cents (US dollars) to six cents, say, ten to five cents for SMS, from fifty cents to twenty cents per MB of data, etc. Such a glide path will result (even at the caps) in substantial reductions in roaming tariffs for consumers.
- Consider establishing a retail/wholesale markup, in the EU of at least a multiple of three, to make competitive entry sufficiently attractive for some entry to occur.
- Institute anti-bill shock and transparency regulations—the latter referring to clear rules on being very transparent to consumers what the tariffs are per MB, per minute, etc., with no hidden charges in opaque footnotes.

What the above bullets is meant to show is that regulating for roaming is regulator intensive and very time-consuming, but where needs must, so be it. A voluntary commercially negotiated solution offers a better prospect of working and being implemented successfully with significantly less legal risk than a mandated regulatory solution to roaming or even infrastructure sharing. For these reasons, regulators eschew them, but roaming and infrastructure sharing must be part of the mix towards achieving widespread affordable high-quality voice, data, and Internet on the continent. I will always urge and encourage African countries and elsewhere (i.e., governments and regulators) to explore the use of market incentives that would lead to significant reductions in national and international roaming charges.

7.6 Satellite International Connectivity for Universal Broadband Access: An Introduction

I am a champion of giving consumers and citizens as much choice as possible, both across *inter-platforms* (e.g., wireless vs. cable vs. fibre) and *intra-platforms* (e.g., intra-wireless, as in terrestrial 3G/4G solutions vs. satellite-based broadband solutions vs. hybrid solutions).

As an Avanti-sponsored Commonwealth Telecommunications Organisation (CTO) report (CTO 2012)[18] rightly notes, satellite is the only viable means of providing universal broadband access beyond the reach of terrestrial transmission networks. In this report, it is claimed that in June 2012, a total of 341 million people in sub-Saharan Africa lived beyond a 50-km range of an operational fibre optic network, which they rightly point out is greater than the population of the USA. Besides, the 50 km figure is based on an assumption that WiMAX broadband access can theoretically reach 50 km. A more realistic range of 25 km increases the number of people outside the range from 341 million to 518 million, according to the report, which in turn is greater than the population of the European Union. The case the report makes is that only satellite can reach this population. What is not clear is how much of this number will be covered by terrestrial wireless networks. Nevertheless, the

---

18 CTO (2012), October, *The Socio-Economic Impact of Broadband in sub-Saharan Africa: the Satellite Advantage*, http://www.cto.int/wp-content/themes/solid/_layout/dc/ptojects/Socio-Economic_Impact_of_Broadband_The_Satellite_Advantage.pdf (accessed October 2013).

report makes a good point in the sense that only satellite can offer international bandwidth back into the Internet in many parts of the continent—remember from the end of chapter 3 how large the continent of Africa is. The implication being that even if there are terrestrial 2G/3G/4G or TV white space networks covering some of these 518 million people, they may still have to rely on satellite for international bandwidth in order to connect to the Internet. Satellite bandwidth capacity is expensive, though the report notes that in the last decade costs have fallen from a high of US$12,500 per Mbps per month to as low as US$500, and even less in some places.

A key point of note here is that satellite will always provide complementary services towards universal broadband. Even if it is a terrestrial network which provides access to customers, the terrestrial network may require satellite for international connectivity or backhaul if there is no fibre or microwave. The report points out that in June 2012, eight countries remained 100 percent dependent on satellite for their international connectivity, as they do not have an operational fibre backbone. They include Burundi, Central African Republic, Guinea Conakry, Liberia, Sao Tome and Principe, Sierra Leone, Somalia, and South Sudan. This is yet another reason why national backbones are important to distribute landed submarine capacity. To illustrate the importance, Sierra Leone was—until the landing of the ACE submarine cable in October 2012—wholly reliant on Ku and C[19] band satellites for international connectivity. These satellites delivered 155 Mbps in 2011 for a population of 6.35 million people. This resulted in Sierra Leone having some of the highest satellite costs in the world at between US$4,000 and $5,000 for 1 Mbps per year, compared to US$200 in the USA or US$500 in east Africa. With such costs, broadband will never be affordable. The arrival of ACE should change this affordability equation in Sierra Leone as it has in other countries like Kenya, Uganda, or Tanzania.

Furthermore, more satellite capacity is being provided by launched satellites in the Ka band,[20] which each have a capacity of 450 MHz per

---

19 Ku band is between 12 and 18 GHz. C band is between 4 and 8 GHz.
20 Ka band is between 26.5GHz to 40Gz.

transponder, compared to 72 MHz and 36 MHz for Ku and C band satellites, respectively.

In summary, there is no doubt that satellite's contribution to universal or widespread availability of broadband is invaluable. Affordability is another matter. Satellites also truly complement the services offered via terrestrial networks in our quest to achieve widespread access to broadband. Low-cost satellites, complementing terrestrial and submarine cables being landed, are important to the widespread broadband availability on the continent—and contributing too to mitigating the affordability problem.

7.7 Satellite VSAT-Based Rural 3G/4G Voice and Data Solutions and Hybrid Satellite/GSM Solutions

After the above introduction, satellite-based rural broadband solutions are clearly an option which may compete with TV white spaces (i.e., it is a substitute) for rural broadband, or, more likely, it is a complement. Recently, some commercial companies have announced successful trials of a "cost effective" rural 3G mobile phone/ data service. The solution works by using capacity on satellites via terrestrial teleports.[21] The demonstration showed the ability to deliver a high throughput managed VSAT-based 3G solution through the dynamic allocation of capacity based on traffic demands. The solution requires using a fleet of satellites along with a terrestrial network in order to be able to configure the end-to-end solution. The terrestrial network typically includes a network based on Internet protocol/multi-protocol label switching (IP/MPLS),[22] thousands of miles of terrestrial fibre lines, teleports, and many points of presence (PoPs) or points

---

21 A teleport, ground station or earth station is a terrestrial station for communicating (i.e., transmitting and receiving) with satellites in orbits or with spacecraft.

22 IP/MPLS is a way in high-performance telecommunications networks to be able to get data from one network node or network type to another based on short path labels rather than long and complex Internet Protocol (IP) addressing. This reduces delay or latency.

of interconnection with other networks. In this sense, a VSAT-based rural 3G solution is really a hybrid satellite and terrestrial solution.

The attraction of such solutions is that despite the best efforts of 3G/4G terrestrial operators (and even with rural-based solutions like TV white spaces), there will still be millions of people outside coverage. Having solutions of this ilk for geographically dispersed sections of countries—or parts of rural Africa—are also important. They are, however, unlikely to be as affordable as TV white spaces promises, but they would likely provide complementary solutions. For example, in one country that I have analysed, it is possible that operators would roll out 3G to about 30 percent of the population and 3G/4G to about 45 percent, while TV white space–based rural broadband may extend this by another 30 percent to about 75 percent of the population, and satellite remains the only viable solution to take it 100 percent, not only of population but geography.

In this vein, I am happy to see African satellites are being launched and brought into use, e.g., the NigComSat-1R which was launched into space in December 2011 with a coverage beam of forty African countries. This is a Nigerian satellite that promises to deliver satellite broadband capacity to Nigerian underserved or rural areas. NigComSat[23] as a company has had a rough few years to 2013/14 but I hope it pulls through and eventually goes on to the public markets or into competent private hands.

NigComSat is not the only African-focussed satellite that has been launched. RASCOM,[24] for example, has launched RascomStar hybrid satellite/GSM solution. This pan-African satellite operator's C-band satellite uniquely claims to cover the entire African continent, though they also use Ku band too, which has a narrower coverage. Their model is to extend GSM operators' networks into rural areas by providing satellite backhaul wherein the operators only pay for satellite capacity they actually use via a revenue-sharing model. If the operators start seeing more traffic from the rural site, they can move on to lease a

---

23 Nigerian Communications Satellite Ltd, www.nigcomsat.net (accessed December 2013).

24 Regional African Satellite Commercial Organisation (RASCOM)—see http://www.rascom.org/ (accessed November 2013).

trunk circuit on the satellite. This hybrid solution has modified GSM signalling protocols to reduce the amount of GSM signalling traffic over their satellite networks.

7.8 Google's Loon & Facebook's Drones: Futuristic Projects

In June 2013, Google announced Project Loon's[25] ambition to provide broadband Internet for the two thirds of the world that does not have access to a reliable internet connection. This project plans to use a network of high-altitude, solar-powered balloons above the Earth, twelve miles high and out of the way of commercial flights and birds! The balloon would provide an Internet network built on the back of these balloons flying in the sky. They are networked with each other and the ground via radio transceivers. These Loon balloons would essentially compete with satellites and promise faster, cheaper and more widespread Internet solutions to large portions of the globe where it will never make sense to run fiber or build terrestrial networks. This is an ambitious project technically which so far makes for great public relations (PR), but any technical details are scanty. However, Google is currently (January 2014) trialling this futuristic idea in New Zealand using 2.4GHz and 5.8GHz spectrums where 30 super-pressured balloons were launched.

Not to be outdone, Facebook announced in early 2014 details to bring 'solar-powered drones, satellites and lasers' internet access[26] to the whole world using Internet.org. The drones at sixty thousand feet will stay in flight for months and beam data to Earth using lasers. Its founder Mark Zuckerberg announced that Facebook's Connectivity Lab aims to deliver Internet to everyone (specifically to 'the next 3 billion people') citing that work in the Philippines and Paraguay alone has doubled the number of people accessing mobile data.

---

25 https://www.google.com/loon/ (accessed January 2014)

26 https://www.facebook.com/zuck/posts/10101322049893211 (accessed March 2014)

SECTION IV

TOWARDS WIDESPREAD AVAILABILITY OF AFFORDABLE HIGH-QUALITY RADIO, DIGITAL TV, AND OTHER MEDIA

CHAPTER 8

TOWARDS WIDESPREAD AVAILABILITY OF AFFORDABLE HIGH-QUALITY RADIO, DIGITAL TV, AND OTHER MEDIA IN AFRICA

"Futura formare prospicere melius."[1]

"A problem well-stated is half-solved."
—*Charles Kettering*

The above Latin quote is so germane to the key message of this section of the volume that I just had to start with it. "It is better to *shape* the future than to *predict* it." Or another translation has it: "It is better to *shape* the future than to try and *foresee* it." This is quite apt for this section of this volume on media because I can think of no other sector/subsector of any economy—particularly in Africa and other emerging economies—which needs so much shaping. Yet and admittedly, it is genuinely nontrivial to shape!

The issues with the evolving new media sector on the continent, as you will see in this chapter, are even more complex, intertwined, technical, political, economic, cultural, uncertain, quite different in every country, regulator complex, and replete with misunderstandings. A significant percentage of decision and policy makers are also in the dark as to what is happening around them as regards the media

---

1 For those of us who are Latin challenged: "It is better to shape the future than predict it" or "It is better to shape the future than to try and foresee it."

than many uninformed citizens who at least experience new media around them daily through Facebook, Twitter, Skype, and other new media platforms. There is a good argument to throw your hand up in the air and decide the new media sector problem is just too hard—and just let it be, or just let it happen onto the economy without planning and shaping for it. However, this will be a mistake of monumental proportions to inflict on our economies. Even spaghetti-like problems (like the new media problem, frankly, is to most African and emerging economies) can be shaped. Indeed, they must be shaped. The alternative would be unadulterated media anarchy on the continent.

This is the first of just two chapters in this section of the volume. The first key goal is to try and articulate the complexity of the new media problem on the continent. The spirit in this part is truly one of a problem well stated is half solved, as Charles Kettering, the famous General Electric (GE) inventor opined. I leave it to you to judge how "well stated" the Africa new media problem is as described later. Unless the problem is reasonably well stated, there is no chance at shaping it. And shape it we must—otherwise what will African regulators be issuing audio-visual or electronic communications multimedia licenses for? What and for whose benefit would the media sectors on the continent be liberalised for? Why would international investors invest in uncertainty and absolute fog? How would the media sector in Africa get to employ as many people as technology and telecommunications combined, as is the case in London? These are just some of the reasons why the new Africa media problem should be stated *before* it is shaped. The second and key goal is to venture some clear recommendations towards widespread availability of radio, digital TV, and other media on the continent.

8.1 Defining the Africa New Media Problem Statement

To work towards stating the Africa new media problem statement, the problem is to try and understand at least five core areas:

- What constitutes the current African media sector? Where does the current African media sector come from? How relevant are they today?
- What are some of the key TV and radio platforms out there?
- What are the core drivers for African and emerging economies' media? What is happening with respect to these core drivers today on the continent, particularly the economic driver?
- Where is this sector going?
- What lessons can new Africa media learn from the rest of the world?
- Importantly, what are some of the key outcomes that African media should strive to achieve?

From addressing the above, one can take a stab at what the problem statement then is. Furthermore, from an analysis of the problem statement, a clear set of recommendations are ventured.

8.2 A Quick Overview of Radio and TV Platforms

It is important to have a quick overview of radio and TV platforms in order to understand much of what follows in the rest of this chapter, as well as the other chapters of this section of the book. You are forewarned that many new acronyms for various analogue and digital standards are introduced in this section, and you should not get befuddled by them all.

8.2.1 A Brief Overview of Analogue and Digital Radio and TV Platforms

Terrestrial broadcast systems, including terrestrial radio, have a very simple architecture.

ANALOGUE AND DIGITAL RADIO/TV TRANSMISSION

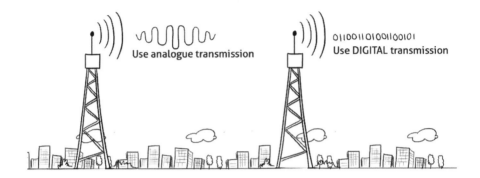

Figure 51—Analogue and Digital Radio/TV Transmissions

For analogue radio, a transmitter transmits analogue signals, as per figure 51, in either AM or FM mode,[2] with AM broadcasting operating typically in the medium wave but also in long wave and short wave bands (see figure 32 for a reminder) and FM broadcasting authorised in the much higher Band II, i.e., 87.5–108 MHz. AM and FM are examples of analogue techniques used to "encode"—or vary the frequency waves transmitted in such a way that it carries information (i.e., encoding happens) which can be "decoded" and understood at the receiving end.

Think of an example of having a series of codes that just you and your family members understand as to where each family member is. You could then use these codes and broadcast where you are going to, even in a crowded room, and *only* your other family members would be able to "decode" the messages received to know exactly where you are going. Encoding information into wave transmissions requires

---

2 AM and FM stand for amplitude modulation and frequency modulation, respectively. Modulation techniques are used to carry information in radio carrier waves, in the case of AM by varying the strength (amplitude) of the wave with respect to the information being transmitted; in the case of the FM, by varying the frequency of the radio carrier in relation to the information being transmitted.

varying the waves in an assorted myriad of waves to capture information which is then transmitted: in the case of AM and FM, using amplitude and frequency modulations, respectively. Radio sets can then be tuned either to AM or FM to pick up these transmissions. So these analogue radio signals are received via the radio set's aerial.

In the case of TV, similarly, a transmitter erected at a suitable location would broadcast TV signals (analogue or digital), encoding the pictures and sound information using various clever equipment and then transmitting the encoded signals via transmission equipment and antennas. For analogue, the analogue TV signals are received via a rooftop aerial or by a communal aerial broadcast distribution (CABD) system in the case of a block of flats/apartments, say. In some cases, analogue TV signals are received by set-top aerials, i.e., an aerial connected to the back of the TV but placed on top of the TV itself or nearby, rather than a rooftop aerial cabled to the back of the TV, as per figure 52.

A TYPICAL DIGITAL TV HOME CONFIGURATION WITH
SET-TOP BOX; IN THE CASE OF ANALOGUE TV, THERE IS NO SET-TOP BOX

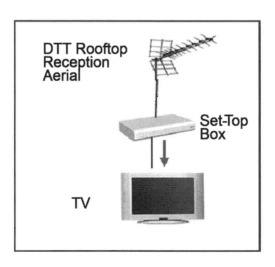

Figure 52—A Typical Digital TV Home Configuration with Set-Top Box;
In the Case of Analogue TV, There Is No Set-Top Box

For digital radio or TV, the transmitter transmits (as per the right-hand image of figure 51) as a series of zeroes and ones, albeit these binary digits carrying information that are "coded" within transmitted analogue waves travelling across the airwaves. In the case of digital radio, the digital radio signal is received via the aerial of the radio set and decoded within the set for listening. For digital TV, the signal is also received by the aerial and typically decoded for viewing on the TV set via some sort of a decoder, otherwise typically called a set-top box. Sometimes, this decoder is built into the TV, and there is, therefore, no need for an external set-top box. As is the case for analogue TV too, digital TV signals are also sometimes received via a CABD system.

There is another key difference of note between radio and TV networks. TV networks are designed for fixed—and typically rooftop—reception. Radio networks, on the other hand, even though originally foreseen only for fixed reception using rooftop aerials, now boast of receivers (i.e., radio sets) that allow for portable and mobile reception. This is because listening to radio is something people do whilst simultaneously doing other things, e.g., being at work, driving a car, at leisure, or even whilst jogging. Mobile and portable consumption of radio services now abound, and radio networks are now designed for mobile reception even at high speeds to accommodate scenarios of cars on the highways or trains.

Having briefly overviewed radio and TV systems above, we proceed to summarise some of the relevant and various analogue and digital radio and TV systems in Africa and some emerging markets. This is for completeness, and some readers may recall nostalgic technology memories of yesteryear.

Whilst reading the following, keep in mind that there is a difference between *transmission* standards (i.e., how to transmit over the airwaves) and *encoding* standards (i.e., how to capture information in the signals being transmitted).

- *Analogue Radio*—AM and FM analogue systems: Amplitude modulation (AM) and frequency modulation (FM) analogue systems have been covered above. These are still very much radio systems in use today across Africa and emerging economies.

AM and FM are transmission standards. For FM, one also typically sees a philosophy of "one frequency—one station—one programme" (Beutler, 2012).[3] This is a key feature of FM as it creates for unique coverage areas and associated quality of service for separate stations broadcasted on separate frequencies. This is not a feature of digital broadcasting where several programmes[4] are all bundled together on the same multiplex, resulting in identical coverage and quality of service for all the services throughout some service area. AM is falling out of favour in Europe due to its high operational costs and because of its long range, it also does not suit regional or local radio broadcasters. In Africa, it is still very much in vogue.

- *Analogue TV:* Analogue TV systems (like with radio above) refers to where the TV pictures and the associated sounds are encoded using analogue encoding techniques and then transmitted typically in very high frequency (VHF) or ultra high frequency (UHF) frequencies (refer to figure 32 again). Older readers may have heard about some of the analogue encoding techniques, including Phase Alternate Line (PAL), Sequential Colour with Memory (SECAM), and National Television System Committee (NTSC). NTSC originated from the USA and is still in use in some emerging economies in parts of Asia and South and Central Americas. France pioneered SECAM, and hence the majority of French-speaking African countries encoded their TV signals using the SECAM standards. PAL was (and still is as of 2013) the dominant analogue encoding standard in use in Africa. PAL, SECAM, and NTSC are encoding standards. Analogue transmission is typically planned for rooftop reception.

- *Digital Radio T-DAB:* T-DAB is an acronym for Terrestrial Digital Audio Broadcasting which, being digital, encodes audio content as a series of zeroes and ones. T-DAB is meant to replace analogue FM radio above in Band II, i.e., 87.5–108.0 MHz with T-DAB transmission in Band III (i.e., 174–230

---

3 R. Beutler (2012), *The Digital Dividend of Terrestrial Broadcasting*, Chapter 2, XVII, London: Springer Verlag, ISBN: 978-1-4614-1568-8.

4 Read: several radio channels.

MHz) and L-Band (1452–1479MHz). The United Kingdom is amongst several countries to have significant T-DAB digital radio networks but yet has not managed to shut down their analogue FM stations. There are three main reasons for this.

1. There are literally a hundred million FM receiving sets being used by British citizens out there, and making all these sets redundant by switching off analogue FM is a bold and courageous move by any democratic politician.
2. Following from the first reason, FM analogue systems are not broken—so why fix them? Nevertheless, they are ageing and are increasingly expensive to maintain.
3. Most importantly for me, there is little incentive to vacate Band II where FM currently resides, as there is not a higher value use of that spectrum to take its place. It is easier for you to vacate your land and sell off to someone who values it more than you do. This is not the case for Band II frequencies. No one is really pushing FM out of Band II.

For these reasons, there is hardly any digital radio in Africa and emerging economies, and this is likely to be the case into the 2020s. In other words, the benefits of digital radio—clearer digital signals leading to good sound quality, no *sshhh* sounds from interference with analogue signals, ability to also carry data, e.g., traffic information, etc.—do not outweigh the costs of a wholesale change from analogue to digital radio, particularly when the nonexistence of any digital dividend is considered. There are other improved variants of DAB called DAB+. DAB and DAB+ are transmission standards, whilst MPEG-1[5] is the encoding standard used with these transmission variants.

- *Digital Radio—DRM:* DRM stands for Digital Radio Mondiale, hence a digital transmission standard system. It

---

5 MPEG is an acronym for Moving Pictures Expert Group, who standardize compression standards for encoding and "compressing" information for more efficient transition. MPEG-2 is more efficient than MPEG-1; MPEG-4 is more efficient than MPEG-2.

is also a terrestrial radio broadcasting system designed as a substitute for analogue AM transmissions for use below 30 MHz, i.e., in the short- and medium-wave bands. However, AM radio broadcasting is also resilient in many African countries just as in other countries like Russia, China, India, and Brazil, as these countries prefer AM because it covers large areas. DRM shares in the AM bands the same sorts of digital benefits like T-DAB, including much higher quality of service almost as good as FM in Band II (Beutler, 2012). DRM is the transmission standard, and it employs MPEG-4 as its encoding standard.

- *Digital TV—Digital Video Broadcasting (DVB-T), Second Generation DVB (DVB-T2), and Digital Video Broadcasting-Handheld (DVB-H):* DVB is a set of internationally accepted and open standards for digital broadcasting which even includes standards for distribution by satellite, cable, radio, and even handheld devices. In addition, DVB-T was also designed to allow for TV reception for both indoor and outdoor portable reception. As with a digital radio, several TV programmes are grouped to form a programme multiplex which consists of video signals, audio signals, and pure data. All three content forms are encoded using MPEG-2 as the encoding standards, whilst DVB-T is the transmission standard. DVB-T+ (otherwise known as DVB-T2) is a more efficient transmission standard than DVB-T, yielding circa 33 percent more transmission capacity. DVB-T2 is the latest set of transmission standards developed by the DVB. If high definition TV services are required, MPEG-4 would be preferred to MPEG-2 to encode the content forms of video signals, audio signals, and data, and DVB-T2 would probably be preferred as the transmission standard.

Another typically used word for encoding is "compression." Ghana, for example, has chosen to adopt the DVB-T2 transmission standard and MPEG-4 for compression for both standard and high definition TV, thus ensuring the most efficient use of spectrum airwaves. Uganda, like other East African Community member states, has also adopted DVB-T2 as its transmission standard and is ordering the withdrawal of DVB-T1 set-top boxes from the market. This is truly good news on two fronts: first, the East African Community harmonizing on a single standard, and, second, Uganda's regulator (UCC) being firm on enforcing the standard.[6]

Analogue to digital TV switchovers therefore in Africa and some emerging economies involves doing away with the analogue encoding standards of PAL, SECAM, and NTSC in favour of MPEG-2/MPEG-4, whilst also ditching analogue transmission schemes for digital ones like DVB-T and DVB-T2. Much of Africa is migrating (or would choose to migrate) to the digital DVB transmission standards for their digital TV switchovers and MPEG encoding standards for the content. A few countries are having a dalliance with other transmission standards.

DVB-H is the DVB transmission specification to allow for mobile and portable reception so that TV can be watched on the move, in trains, in cars, and out and about.

Digital TV can be set up on a free-to-air (FTA) basis or on a pay basis (PayTV).

8.2.2 A Brief Overview of Satellite Radio and TV Platforms

Terrestrial broadcast systems are indisputably the most common form of broadcasting in Africa. Terrestrial radio broadcasting certainly annihilates satellite radio broadcasting on the continent (and frankly everywhere else). On the other hand, satellite TV is the second most common form of TV broadcasting in Africa after terrestrial TV broadcasting.

---

6 "Uganda bans outdated TV devices," *Africa Telecom & IT*, vol. 13, no. 11, November 2012, p. 36.

AN EXAMPLE OF THE LINKS IN THE CHAIN FROM VIDEO
TO VIEWER USING SATELLITE DIRECT TO HOME (DTH)

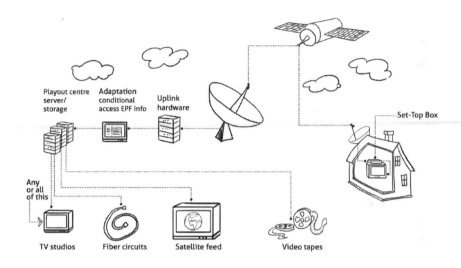

Figure 53—An Example of the Links in the Chain from Video to Viewer,
Using Satellite Direct to Home (DTH)

As shown with figure 53, with satellite TV, digital video and audio (delivered live from TV studios, fibre circuits, satellite feeds, or
tapes) first go through a content protection system (called conditional
access) to ensure only those who are allowed to will receive and view
the content at the receiving end. The content is uplinked from a large
satellite dish to a satellite, where it is broadcast to all consumers' satellite dishes throughout the satellite's footprint or area of coverage. At
the receiver end, satellite TV requires a satellite receiving dish and a
receiver set-top box at the customer end. In the case of satellite radio,
special receivers are required that are very expensive. Direct-to-home
(DTH) satellites typically operate in the Ku-band with uplink of frequencies in 14.0 to 14.6 GHz and downlink frequencies of 11.7 to 12.2
GHz. Since Ku-band satellites use much higher power than C-band
satellites, the receive antenna dishes required to receive their signals
can be quite small at 0.5 m diameter. Three equally spaced satellites

35,700 km above the equator can cover almost the entire surface of the earth. Therefore the biggest advantage of satellite is its widespread footprint. Other key advantages of the satellite TV/radio broadcasting are the high bandwidth of the downlink[7] (where it can accommodate up to two thousand channels) to the satellite receiving dish, and the relatively low cost of providing and operating a broadcasting infrastructure that can serve a large swathe of households and people. Furthermore, the opportunity of marginal costs of reaching extra customers being almost zero is a major attraction. So as a mass medium, it is very strong. Its main disadvantage is that broadband network access is not automatically included for interactivity, even though some would say this is not really that big a disadvantage. Another disadvantage is viewers can experience distortions under bad weather conditions, such as fog, heavy rains, and high humidity, where pixilation can occur.

The satellite TV broadcasting system can also split viewers into those who subscribe to pay satellite TV services or free satellite viewers or both. With respect to transmission standards, DVB-S is DVB's original satellite broadcasting specification, like DVB-T was in the case for terrestrial. DVB-S2 later followed in a similar way to DVB-T2 for terrestrial.

TV and radio broadcasting are really close to each country's culture, hence terrestrial broadcasting, which is in the gift and control of the country and tends to be preferred by most countries. A problem with DTH is that transmissions from one country threaten another country's sovereignty in broadcasting. Countries rightly fear cultural dilution, hostile propaganda, and other such perceived negative externalities. Some satellite content is more justifiably problematic, as in the case of pornography. DTH does truly present a challenge because it is virtually impossible to stop anyone tuning into foreign satellite broadcasts, irrespective of what his/her home country's diktats stipulate. Using tools like Satbeed or Satfinder to align a dish to a pirate satellite is quite easy to do.

---

7 Such large bandwidth has the capacity of distributing hundreds to thousands of channels.

8.2.3 A Brief Overview of Digital Cable and DSL

For completeness, we mention cable TV, arguably the largest TV platform in some countries, such as the USA. In cable TV, the video is distributed directly from some headend (control centre) to consumers' households via a wired terrestrial network of fibre of coaxial cables. There is hardly much widespread cable deployments in Africa, but there are small pockets in some new developments in some cities, hence it deserves a mention. One benefit of such a digital platform is that they offer the opportunity for triple play of TV, telephony, and Internet via such a platform. Digital cable platforms can also be used to deliver digital radio channels.

8.3 Colonial Old Media and the Africa Media Sector

Earlier on in this volume—specifically in chapter 2—I described the current African media sector as "colonial old media." It basically consists of radio broadcasting, TV broadcasting, and newspapers/press. This is the broadly short form answer to the questions: "What constitutes the current African media sector?", "Where does the current African media sector come from?", and "How relevant are they today?" The long form answer follows.

In the beginning, in precolonial Africa, there was no media sector in any sense of the word as we understand it today. The colonials have cometh and gone, and we were bequeathed across much of Africa with largely the colonial model of the media—consisting of radio, some TV (which came much later after independence in the case of many countries and only truly grew on the continent in the 1990s), and newspapers/press. This colonial bequeath—mostly from the British, and to a lesser extent the French (and even much less from the other colonials)—is largely still what exists across much of Africa today.

8.3.1 Radio Broadcasting in Africa

Graham Mytton's[8] "A Brief History of Radio Broadcasting in Africa"[9] is a crisp and excellent piece which this section largely draws from. This section provides an even much more summarised version of his excellent paper for the purposes of this volume. Furthermore, his article "From Saucepan to Dish: Radio and TV in Africa"[10] is another excellent read on the subject.

As noted earlier, radio is undoubtedly by far the dominant and most important mass medium in Africa. As Mytton notes, its low cost, flexibility, and oral character suit the African culture and situation naturally, but Mytton (2000) adds, "yet radio is less developed in Africa than it is anywhere else. There are relatively few radio stations in each of Africa's 53 nations and fewer radio sets per head of population than anywhere else in the world."

Apart from in South Africa (where TV and press are both strong) and the Maghreb/Arab North (where TV is now the dominant medium), radio outstrips both TV and newspapers in reaching most Africans. Radio reaches 50 percent of adults in poorer countries to virtually everyone in more developed African countries, and Mytton cites Tanzania, where nearly nine out of ten adults listen to radio in an average week. In this vein, radio is a major factor in daily life of Africans. Indeed powered by cheap battery-transistor radios, radio provides a means of political and cultural communication on the continent unlike anything that preceded it.

The first phase of radio in Africa—which started in South Africa in 1924—was primarily a medium to serve the settlers and the interest of the colonial powers. Later, radio services were introduced by

---

8   Dr. Mytton was head of audience research for the BBC World Service from 1982 until 1996 and later controller of marketing for the BBC World Service. He is an acknowledged authoritative radio historian.

9   Graham Mytton (2003), *A Brief History of Radio Broadcasting in Africa,* http://www.transculturalwriting.com/radiophonics/contents/usr/downloads/radiophonics/A_Brief_History.pdf (accessed September 2013).

10   Graham Mytton, "From Saucepan to Dish: Radio and TV in Africa," in *African Broadcast Cultures,* edited by Richard Fardon and Graham Furniss, Oxford: James Currey, 2000.

and for indigenous people. The South African's success with radio (after some failures) came with the help of the British. Specifically it happened through the help of the first director general of the BBC, John Reith, who helped create the South African Broadcasting Corporation (SABC) in 1936. SABC Radio broadcasted mostly in Afrikaans and English up until 1943, serving the white audiences and European colonial interests. The same was true elsewhere where radio started: Kenya (1932), today's Zimbabwe (1932), Mozambique (1933), and French Congo (1935). The British set up radio in Sierra Leone, Nigeria, Ghana, and other British African colonies for indigenous people in 1936, followed by countries like Zambia. The French set up shortwave radio stations in Cameroon and French Congo, as well as Senegal during the Second World War years. This first phase of radio in Africa continued post 1945. After the war, the British developed an official policy which promoted broadcasting in most of its African colonies. BBC experts advised on establishing broadcasting in most, if not all, of British colonies, with some of these experts even becoming the first director generals of these nascent African broadcasters, as was the case in Tangayika (today's Tanzania) with Torn Chalmers.

So it became that Ghana, Nigeria, Malawi, Zambia, Uganda, Tanzania, etc., all aped the BBC model, though unlike the BBC, they were (and still are) mostly government controlled. French policy was rather different from the British. Where the British promoted African languages, the French centralised radio across its colonies and broadcasted mainly in French. This happened until independence, when separate radio stations were established in Mali, Senegal, Ivory Coast, Niger, Chad, Gabon, and other locations.

The first indigenous broadcast was set up by British broadcasting pioneer Harry Franklin, who was director of information in the Colonial Administration. He set up a tiny radio station in his spare time in Lusaka (capital of Zambia) in 1942 to broadcast news about the progress of the war to families of Africans serving in the Northern Rhodesian Regiment, who fought in Somaliland. Though there were hardly any sets available at the time—those that existed used valves or tubes and had to be connected to electricity, so some chiefs in Northern

Rhodesia were supplied with radio sets with large batteries (since they had no electricity) so they could relay the news to their subjects.

In the second phase of African radio broadcasting, which lasted until 2000, Mytton notes that, without exception, all fifty-three nations of Africa had national broadcasting services dominated by radio, and also in all cases, the governments maintained the monopoly of radio broadcasting for more than thirty years. Much radio broadcasting in Africa still relies on AM shortwave radio—using frequencies between 1.8 MHz to 30 MHz (i.e., some MF and HF frequencies). Remember why? The reason is because these low frequencies reach a widely scattered population over large areas. However, these frequencies are subject to fading and distortion, hence the cracking noises heard many a time. Africa has the world's largest audiences for international shortwave radio broadcasts, particularly BBC World Service, Voice of America, and Radio France Internationale. However, shortwave radio coverage by African broadcasters is rather poor, beset by inadequate resourcing, power breakdowns, and so on. Radio pluralism came late to Africa: there were only five to six privately owned radio stations in all Africa by 1987.

The third phase was heralded by some limited deregulation and liberalisation of radio, which ushered in competition, and many new radio stations arrived, mostly transmitting using a mix of methods—FM, AM, medium wave, and short wave. These stations compete for audiences. By 2000, Mytton notes there were more than 450 independent radio stations in Africa, from commercial, religious, community radio stations, "factional" radio stations (which promote a particular faction in a conflict, including the detested, hated ones), and humanitarian radio stations (which evolved to counter the factional ones, promoting peace and harmony). The key difference between state radio and independent radio on the continent is that the former are mostly national in both reach and objective, whilst the latter (i.e., independent radio stations) are mostly based in cities, with their coverage restricted to the urban areas. However, some African state radio was also very creative in places, broadcasting ad-libbed/unscripted drama (Ghana, Nigeria, and Zambia), poetry, music, oral literature, etc. Many well-known musicians on the continent today promoted themselves via state radio stations. By 2000, there were more than seventy community radio stations in South Africa and one hundred in west Africa, mostly in rural areas. Such radio genres promote local languages, women empowerment as well as local democracy.

As regards programming, governments' hands were heavy on them, and broadcasting professionals were essentially civil servants, with "uninteresting speeches" from presidents carried in full or other dull announcements from ministers.

As regards law, regulation and private radio stations—though independent newspapers have been permitted to operate in most African countries—many governments have been much warier of radio and been reluctant to change laws and allow private broadcasting stations. They fear the power of the medium, particularly if rival political or ethnic factions control key private radio stations in shaky political setups. In some countries, commercial and private radio stations are very successful. In Ghana, new commercial radio stations are so successful that they have pushed the state Ghana Broadcasting Corporation out of its place as one of the top eight stations in the country in audience reach and share. A similar story applies to both Uganda and Nigeria and demonstrates, powerfully, the benefit of liberalisation and deregulation of the radio sector. This is what happens when competition comes: lazy civil servant producers who never worried about attracting audiences or advertisers suddenly faced up to new competitors who did. The problem then is that important state radio programmes on health, education, and development are getting marginalised in favour of new commercial radio stations pumping out music and popular entertainment.

A new phase (Phase 4) is emerging on the continent with the arrival of other new platforms for radio:

- Internet Radio: There are literally thousands of African radio stations now online, partly driven by a much less regulated environment on the Internet. The Internet is growing relatively fast, but mainly in urban areas.
- Mobile Radio: In some cases, particularly with the young, the old radio set is being gradually replaced for listening to radio stations by mobile phones with built-in FM radio tuners.

- Satellite Radio: Direct broadcasting via satellite also emerged on the continent. An Ethiopian, Noah Samara, launched the first digital radio service by satellite in 1999, and the satellite platform makes eminent sense given the costs involved in maintaining and running FM relays, along with their security. Worldspace launched its first satellite—Afristar—over Africa in geostationary orbit in order to provide radio services for the whole of Africa and the Middle East. This platform requires special receivers that are currently not affordable for many Africans. However, the company became insolvent and was liquidated in 2008/9, but satellite radio may well return.
- TV: With the new digital terrestrial platforms (DTT) emerging through the switch off of analogue TV, radio channels would also be consumed on DTT platforms.
- Digital Shortwave with DRM: This is another emerging platform, in contrast to analogue shortwave discussed earlier. The BBC, VOA, and others have joined the Digital Radio Mondiale (DRM) Consortium to develop this new platform that improves vastly on reception, yielding high-quality reception.

With all these plurality of platforms, the Africa radio supply side (i.e., producers, entrepreneurs, NGOs, etc.) has many choices, and African consumers and citizens should benefit greatly over the next decade.

To summarise, some of the main messages of this radio overview include the following:

- Radio remains the key dominant medium in Africa and will remain so for some time to come apart from the Maghreb countries and South Africa. Yet radio is not as widespread: there are fewer radio sets per head of population than anywhere else in the world.
- Part deregulation and liberalisation of the sector in Phase 3 ushered in hundreds of independent stations. There are between six hundred to one thousand radio stations on the continent today. Much African radio is on FM, with the rest on AM.

- Some radio stations are being listened to on the continent on cell phones that double up as portable radio, as in Mozambique (Machado, 2009),[11] and some radio channels are distributed on TV sets, like in the case of DStv in South Africa. These trends will grow on the continent over the next decade or two.
- The radio model on the continent emanates from the colonialists, with the biggest influence on the continent arguably being from Great Britain, but also from France.
- Mytton (2000) notes that all African countries have national radio stations belonging to the state with the objective of reaching the whole country. He also notes that "generally speaking, the fewer local sources to choose from, the greater the degree of state monopoly, the more likely it is that people will seek out alternative sources of information and entertainment coming from outside the country."

   African policy and decision makers should understand the lesson from this, as this explains why services like the BBC World service are listened to more in Africa than anywhere else. Good, objective radio content will be sought after.
- The three phases of radio on the continent have yielded many state radio broadcasters who truly *cannot* be referred to as "public service broadcast*ers*" though many of them do some good public service broadcast*ing*.
- Most radio stations' finances on the continent are in a parlous state, which reflects in the poor programming they put out.
- There are many platforms now emerging on the continent, including Internet, mobile, satellite, DTT TV, DAB, and digital short-wave (DRM), but the digital ones hardly have any traction today.
- Governments remain wary of full liberalisation of the radio sector, particularly for private radio stations, as they fear the emergence of factional radio stations like the notorious Radio des Mille Collines (Radio of a Thousand Hills) in Rwanda that

11   Z. Machado, "Mozambique—progress by many players," in Guy Berger's (2010) (with contributions from Fackson Banda, Jane Duncan, Rashweat Mukundu, and Zeineida Machado) *Beyond Broadcasting: the future of state-owned broadcasters in Southern Africa*, Windhoek, Namibia: Fesmedia Africa Series, pp. 35–44.

was widely held responsible for promoting ethnic hatred and killings during the 1994 genocide.

- I am clear that community radio clearly drives broader social value as people can hear local voices, hear their own locally-produced music/programmes, etc. However, there is no doubt that many governments fear licensing community radio stations for fear that they become "vernacular" radio – which are largely perceived on the continent as divisive.

- Digital radio is far too unaffordable in Africa and other emerging market countries to worry about in the short to medium term. With receivers in the US $200 to $300 range, they are just astronomically expensive for most Africans. I assert they need to be in the range US $5 to $10.

- It is unlikely radio wholesale migration from analogue radio to digital radio will happen anytime over the next two decades and more on the continent, like is happening with TV. There is no real spectrum dividend to be had switching off analogue radio.

- Radio has not (and will not be) humbled by al the digital TV being rolled out across Africa.

- Lastly, Mytton (2000) summarises: "radio plays a pivotal role in situations of conflict and crisis in Africa. Local radio stations, as much as international broadcasters, are the barometers and agents of change and development. No other medium of communication matches radio in terms of audience, political power or cultural influence.".

After the previous bullet relating to Rwanda, who can argue with this summary?

8.3.2 TV Broadcasting in Africa

TV broadcasting in Africa is not that dissimilar to radio in its evolution on the continent of Africa, with the key difference that TV came much later in most countries. Interestingly, the first TV broadcasts neither happened on the continent in South Africa as happened for radio (its TV happened in 1976) nor in any of the Maghreb countries. Rather, TV first happened in Nigeria. And its emergence was not planned either—indeed it emerged prematurely out of a spat. In the 1950s, Nigeria had three regional governments—Western Region, Eastern Region, and Northern Region—as well as a federal government at the centre. The regions were led by Nigerians, whilst the federal government was British led. Radio was the major broadcast means of the day, then known as the Empire Service. Egbon (1982)[12] explains TV transmission began on the continent in Western Nigeria on October 31, 1959 in Ibadan (capital city of Western Nigeria) as a result of the opposition leader Chief Obafemi Awolowo and his party colleagues walking out of Parliament in protest against a constitutional debate on the eve of Nigeria's independence. Whilst the ruling federal (British-controlled) government could get all over the federal all-Nigeria Radio Broadcasting Service and condemn the opposition, the opposition leader was denied any right of reply. Off in a huff, instead of establishing just another radio station to offer voice redress, the Western Region (which Chief Awolowo represented) commenced television transmissions too. So was born the Western Nigeria Television Service (WNTS). This was the first terrestrial TV in Africa. Therefore, Egbon concludes that TV started on the continent thanks to "regional pride" and "prestige."

Egypt was the second country to start TV broadcasting on the continent on Thursday, July 21, 1960 (Nwulu *et al.*, 2010).[13] Nwulu and colleagues also note that the first colour television in Africa was introduced by Television Zanzibar (today called Tanzania) on March 9, 1973.

---

12 I. M. Egbon (1982), "Origin and Development of Television Broadcasting in Nigeria," *Television Journal*, December, 4:4, pp. 27–28.

13 I. N. Nwulu, Adekanbi, A., Oranugo, T., and Adewale, Y. (2000), "Television Broadcasting in Africa: Pioneering Milestones," Telecommunications Conference (HISTELCON), *2nd IEEE Region 8 Conference on the History of Telecommunications*, Madrid, Spain. November 2010.

8.3.2.1 TV Phase 1—Terrestrial TV Only

In any case, TV in much of Africa—as likened earlier to radio—started as terrestrial TV and stems largely from the British (colonial) model where there is a state-owned broadcaster funded by the public. The British Broadcasting Corporation (BBC) still is today in the United Kingdom. So was born SABC is South Africa, GBC in Ghana, NTA[14] in Nigeria, ZBC in Zimbabwe, ZNBC in Zambia, CRTV in Cameroon, and so on. Again for the BBC in the United Kingdom, the ethos is truly one of "public service broadcasting," where the "public" refers (and has always referred) to "all Brits" or "virtually all Brits," not the few. The BBC is truly owned by all Brits who pay for it, and it is fully publicly financed (though it has a commercial arm called BBC Worldwide).

Under colonial Africa, "public" TV clearly could not, and did not, have such a grand ambition like the BBC's. It referred to a tiny minority of the colonials and largely civil servants. Post colonialism in Africa, and with zero true public funding for TV, other sources of financing from advertising had to be sought. This consequent departure from the true BBC ethos is important. Professor Guy Berger's (of Rhodes University in South Africa) fine work[15] concludes that "public service" came to mean "service to the government"—very few of us Africans, if any, will dispute this still in 2013/14.

So the notion of state-owned broadcasters in Africa is different from the BBC. Commercial financing and donor sponsorships also complement direct government contributions. State broadcasters put out mainly government-service content though these venerable institutions have public service names/acronyms like GBC, SABC, ZBC, ZNBC, etc. They continue to remain the biggest names in broadcasting on the continent too. These organisations have been (and still are) used and abused to varying degrees by their politicians who—without

---

14 Nigerian Television Authority, formerly known as Nigerian Television (NTV).

15 Guy Berger (2010) with contributions from Fackson Banda, Jane Duncan, Rashweat Mukundu, and Zeineida Machado, *Beyond Broadcasting: the future of state-owned broadcasters in Southern Africa*, Windhoek, Namibia: Fesmedia Africa Series.

the clear link of funding from individual public citizens like with the BBC—arguably have an easier path to abuse these organisations than politicians in the United Kingdom could ever dream of doing. As Berger (2010) notes, "they[16] are formidable forces in contributing to—or at the other extreme, working to counter—progress in democracy and development."

These organisations also mostly have a monopoly on national transmission and typically own/control all the towers and distribution networks from which programme transmissions happen. They are allegedly custodians of public service broadcasting with a duty to inform, educate, and entertain.

Therefore Africa's Phase 1 of TV refers to the years after the colonials left, where there tended to be just the one state terrestrial broadcaster in every country, assuming the country started TV transmission anyway.[17] Typically, these state broadcasters broadcasted on just one platform, on *analogue free to air (FTA) terrestrial platform* (i.e., the consumers do not pay to receive it via their TV aerials) and usually also just one channel or at most two to three channels. The coverage areas of these analogue TV networks outside countries like South Africa and Nigeria could hardly be referred to as widespread. The percentage of Tanzania's population that was covered by analogue TV was 24 percent.[18] Given not all in coverage could afford TVs, you can see why "public" in public service broadcasting referred to a tiny minority of Africans. This position really has not changed much for most African countries, and it is partly in this sense that the colonial old media description still feels apt.

In this first phase of TV in Africa too, some federated countries (like Nigeria who split the country into twelve states in 1967, nineteen states in 1975, etc.) had to constitutionally allow each new state to

---

16 Read: state TV corporations.

17 Many countries, including South Africa (1976), Cameroon (1985), Tanzania (1994), etc., started their TV projects decades after the colonials left.

18 R. Schumann, (2013), "Case Study of Digital TV Switchover in Tanzania," http://www.analysysmason.com/About-Us/News/Insight/Case-study-of-digital-TV-switchover-in-Tanzania/#.UjhvE8bWR5I (accessed September 2013).

have its own state TV station (Umeh, 1989).[19] This resulted in Bendel State establishing Bendel State TV in 1973 or Nigerian TV Benin, etc. Then in 1976, the then military government decided to establish the National Television Authority (NTA) which merged ten of these state regional TV stations and upgraded the stations to colour. NTA also set up TV stations in states that did not have any TV, and Nigeria has become the largest single terrestrial network in Africa with NTA, boasting of about ninety-four TV stations in Nigeria.[20]

It can thus be concluded that at the beginning (and frankly till this day), establishing mass communication was politically necessary, demonstrating African and other sovereignty, as well as creating a sense of national unity and identity.

8.3.2.2 TV Phase 2—The Emergence of Nonstate Terrestrial TV, Digital Satellite TV and Community TV

In the next phase (Phase 2) of the TV evolution—partly driven by the poor coverage of the state broadcasters leaving majority of their populations unserved, and not much good content either—most countries saw the emergence of either private nonstate terrestrial broadcasters or satellite direct-to-home (DTH) TV or both.

Some nonstate terrestrial stations are licensed to carry public service programming with specified weekly news quotas, local language quotas, etc. Then in some countries like South Africa, there are community service (radio or TV) broadcasters who are licensed to deliver public service to their local business and communities. Community radio/TV is traditionally intended to give ordinary people access to the airwaves to broadcast radio and TV programmes for the benefit of the communities concerned.

Berger rightly notes that one therefore has to distinguish

---

19 C. C. Umeh (1989), "The Advent and Growth of Television Broadcasting in Nigeria: Its Political and Educational Overtones," *Africa Media Review*, vol. 3: no. 2., pp. 54–66.

20 Nigerian Television Authority, http://nta.com.ng/ index.php (accessed October 2013).

between Public Service BroadcastERS (actual, partial or ought-to-be), and public service broadcastING. The institutions and the practice can be de-linked. Indeed, some state-owned broadcasters across the continent are actually poor at public service broadcasting of news and current affairs (where their service is really to government rather than public). Some private broadcasters on the other hand do meet public service broadcasting standards in providing impartial news and current affairs (Berger, 2010).

Satellite TV is now the second most common form of broadcasting on the continent of Africa. The first commercial satellite TV broadcaster is South Africa's Multichoice Digital Satellite Television (DStv) in 1995[21] preceded by M-Net[22], both owned by Naspers. DStv is currently in 2013 the biggest satellite service on the continent broadcasting in both Ku and C bands, with both audio and video channels. For Francophone Africa, French-owned Canal Horizon is the favoured satellite direct-to-home (DTH) TV service. Satellite TV is generally digital too these days, using DVB-S or DVB-S2 transmission standards. In terms of viewership, the biggest satellite provider on the continent, DStv, is known to offer a full range of channels for upper income earners and a "compact" service for middle income earners. Clearly, this is not a widespread TV service from DStv.

To summarise, some of the main messages of this TV overview include the following:

- One would not expect TV in relatively poor and/or developing countries to be ahead of radio. However, Mytton (2000) reported on evidence that this was exactly the case in India. This is partly because satellite TV is deregulated in India whilst the state holds the monopoly on radio and TV for

21 Multichoice South Africa, http://www.multichoice.co.za/multichoice/view/multichoice/en/page44122 (accessed October 2013).

22 The Electronic Media Network Limited (M-Net) was founded in 1985 as South Africa's first private subscription television service.

terrestrial broadcasting. At very low cost, Indians are getting access to many satellite services on cable services. This lesson is salutary to Africa and some emerging economies. If governments—as they are wont to—liberalise satellite services but hang on to terrestrial services, consumers will migrate to satellite platforms.

- TV is an emerging dominant medium in Africa but is no way widespread: there are even fewer TV sets than radio sets per head of population in Africa than anywhere else in the world. There are two key TV platforms on the continent: terrestrial TV and satellite TV. There is very little cable TV on the continent. Community TV is also far less evolved on the continent. However, community radio could really work on the continent. In Uganda, state-owned radio is dwarfed by private and community stations. There is a popular format in Uganda called *Ibimeeza*, wherein live broadcasts of heated debates amongst citizens in drinking bars are broadcasted. One can debate the quality of such programming, given it may not be that informed and impartial at all times, but it is evidently very engaging in Uganda.

- There is hardly any mobile broadcast TV (e.g., using DVB-H) of note on the continent today, though 3G MBMS[23] may offer more promise.

- However, Africa could (as of 2000) boast of circa six hundred TV stations (Nwulu *et al.*, 2010). There is less choice in African TV, whilst radio is more varied and provides more choice.

- There are many satellite TV channels on air on the continent, but the only real satellite player of note (i.e., with more than a million subscribers) is South Africa's Multichoice DStv, owned by Naspers. Canal Horizon and MNet are much smaller. Clearly satellite TV is not widespread, not least because it is not that affordable. Current offerings explicitly target middle- and upper-income earners. Indeed, Multichoice's

---

23 MBMS (Multimedia Broadcast Multicast Service) is a 3G broadcast standard which has not really caught on in Europe. It is allegedly currently in use in several African countries.

model is built on 2 to 3 million people paying about $60 per month as per late 2013. It is patently obvious that, though very profitable, it is hardly affordable across the billion plus African population.

- The terrestrial TV model on the continent emanates from the colonialists, with the biggest influence on the continent arguably being from Great Britain.
- The two phases of TV on the continent have yielded many state TV broadcasters (six hundred, as we now know). Like in the case of radio too, they truly *cannot* be referred to as "public service broadcast*ers*" though many of them do some good public service broadcast*ing.*
- Generally, TV in Africa also suffers from lack of adequate financing. Indeed, the economics of most broadcasters on the continent are quite fragile.
- Like radio, governments remain wary of full liberalisation of the TV sector.
- Thanks to the benefit of the impending UHF spectrum digital dividend, and to international ITU regulations, many countries are planning and/or have already achieved switching off their analogue TV and switching over to digital TV. In most cases in Africa, DVB-T and DVB-T2 will be the transmission standards adopted with MPEG-2 or MPEG-4 as the choice encoding standards. When the analogue transmissions get switched off, most TV sets on the continent will be rendered redundant unless they are capable of working with a set-top box which converts the content from digital back to analogue for consumption on the analogue TV.
- There is hardly any widespread use of social networking media platforms such as YouTube, Twitter, and Facebook.

8.3.3 Newspapers/Press and Magazines in Africa

Newspapers are clearly the oldest mass media anywhere in the world, and by definition, in Africa too. It will clearly continue to play a major role on the continent over the next decade and more. Africa today has between circa 650 to 700 newspapers.[24] A good significant number of newspapers are state owned and effectively mouthpieces of their governments, whilst there is a majority of privately owned newspapers on the continent.

The history of newspapers dates back on the continent back to 1800, arguably in South Africa. The state of newspapers on the continent depends on the individual country concerned. For example, Duncan (2009)[25] reports that newspapers reach just under half of South Africans: with the *Daily Sun* having the highest penetration. In Namibia, *The Namibian* newspaper is published five days a week and is the leading privately owned newspaper in Namibia, with a print run of just thirty thousand (Mukundu, 2009).[26] The newspaper claims it reaches at least one hundred thousand daily through copy sharing. What is the point of these examples? Newspapers and press are hardly widespread and (as for daily reading) also mostly unaffordable.

8.4 Core Drivers for Media in Africa and Where Media Is Going

The core drivers for what is happening to the media sector on the African continent as well as other emerging economies are not that different from the key drivers of the TMT sector outlined in chapter 3. They are technological changes, economics, consumer behaviour, industry, regulation, and the wider environment (or macroeconomy).

8.4.1 TV Broadcasting in Africa

---

24 Source: http://www.kidon.com/media-link/africa.php (accessed October 2013).

25 J. Duncan (2010), "South Africa—Migration Underway," in Guy Berger (2010) with contributions from Fackson Banda, Jane Duncan, Rashweat Mukundu, and Zeineida Machado, *Beyond Broadcasting: the future of state-owned broadcasters in Southern Africa*, Windhoek, Namibia: Fesmedia Africa Series, pp. 69–84.

26 R. Mukundu (2010), "Namibia—moving amidst uncertainties," in Guy Berger (2010) with contributions from Fackson Banda, Jane Duncan, Rashweat Mukundu, and Zeineida Machado, *Beyond Broadcasting: the future of state-owned broadcasters in Southern Africa*, Windhoek, Namibia: Fesmedia Africa Series, pp. 20–34.

We do not elaborate greatly on them anymore here, but we do summarise some of the key messages behind some of these drivers.

- *Technological changes:* So much is happening to the media sector technologically. It is not only core technical changes from analogue TV to digital TV, or FM radio being received on mobile phones, or radio being consumed on TV platforms, or TV with a return path to enable interactive TV. It's not only TV voting via SMS, Internet magazines and news sites, newspapers going online, smartphones/tablets providing good reading experience rather than buying paper newspapers, on-demand viewing, the emergence of the e-based newsroom, etc. It is the fact that social media is now becoming a key reality via Facebook, Twitter, and YouTube. Technology is clearly and unarguably a game changer.

- *Economics*: Economics will ultimately determine the number of players who can participate in the media sector in Africa. As explained earlier in the book, advertising will follow the audience capable of being monetized. This is a simple law of advertising. Audiences are fragmenting from original mass audiences into many small subaudiences (along lines of age, income, ethnic tribes, language, region/province, etc.). When government-owned broadcasters lose most of their audience to Facebook, YouTube, Nollywood, etc., which will happen when broadband catches on in Africa, they will have to reinvent themselves or collapse fully. The mobile operators are building advertising business models or services based on advertising revenues. Mobile operators know more about their subscribers than broadcasters will ever know about their viewers. Furthermore, Google, Facebook, and Yahoo are positioning themselves to have the African broadcasters' lunches and dinners in just the same way they have done in Europe and North America. All the venerable broadcasting organisations on the continent today must realize that they are "on notice" from their audiences. Even Nollywood must be worrying about how it would adapt to the new media world in Africa.

- *Industry:* The industry itself is changing. For example, news-papers are using opportunities afforded by technology—and in order to manage their cost bases—to expand their reach and interaction with users. Mukundu (2009) provide an example of how *The Namibian* newspaper publishes a page or two dai-ly devoted to SMS messages sent by readers discussing and commenting on topical issues. This has even managed to rile the Government and ruling party who have accused the paper of trying to denigrate the leadership. This is a newspaper just keeping with the times whilst authorities want to keep it back 'in its box' where it will certainly ossify and die. Newspapers have to embrace other media, TV has to embrace other media, ditto for radio—this is the law of convergence.

- *Consumer Behaviour:* thanks to technology above, the con-sumer has so much more choice and options on their time and what media they consume. Indeed, consumers are now be-coming citizen-journalists themselves. Technology is becom-ing cheaper and cheaper by the day encouraging much citizen journalism which was clearly evident in the Arab Spring in the Maghreb countries. Interestingly, Mukundu (2009) also cites an IT manager on *The Namibian* who reports that 30 percent of its stories come from public "tip-offs" via SMS.

- *Regulation/Wider Environment:* Regulation clearly is an im-portant driver going forward, and regulators need to learn how to use this key tool to shape this vital TMT subsector of the media. Indeed, regulation holding back this sector is a major risk, as most African regulators I have met appear befuddled by the emerging new media sector. It does not help with many regulators on the continent not being converged regulators and with so-called broadcast regulators (where different from communications regulators) feeling "straitjacketed" by their current out-of-date statutes. An illustration of the folly of not looking at regulation in a converged manner follows below.

If an African broadcaster broadcasts a news item/bulletin on some national strike and/or adverts on its terrestrial plat-form, it is subject to broadcasting regulatory rules from the broadcasting regulator in terms of "taste and decency" measures, news quotas, adverts quotas, etc. However, if a newspaper organisation shot a similar news bulletin, probably of the same strike, and deployed its footage online, it is likely *not* going to be subject to the same regulatory constraints as its *paper* newspaper. Imagine the broadcaster owned the newspaper organisation then. The single "converged" terrestrial broadcaster, the paper newspaper and the online publisher, would be subject to two or three separate regulations because they are operating on three different platforms. This means costs for the organisation and, possibly, inconsistencies and confusion. Or should the online publisher "raise" its regulatory standards to that of its terrestrial broadcast division, or should the terrestrial broadcaster division "dumb down" its news bulletin standards to that of its online news bulletins? These are difficult areas for regulation to address. Berger (2010a)[27] could not illustrate the regulatory point here any better:

> As regards the *wider environment* that impacts on digitisation, there is a disconnect between policy, law and regulation. In Mozambique, things don't quite add up between two regulatory bodies; Zambia and Mozambique suffer from the lack of converged and autonomous regulation. Namibia has several policies in place but still not as yet an overall approach to Digital Migration. There, and in Mozambique and Zambia, radio operators are in the dark about whether migration applies to them... In the same country [South Africa] specification of public interest content on digital TV Multiplexes is vague and the issue is not yet even on the table in Mozambique, Namibia and Zambia.

---

27   G. Berger (2010a), "Conclusion: Looking Forward," in Guy Berger (2010) with contributions from Fackson Banda, Jane Duncan, Rashweat Mukundu, and Zeineida Machado, *Beyond Broadcasting: the future of state-owned broadcasters in Southern Africa*, Windhoek, Namibia: Fesmedia Africa Series, pp. 85–89.

Do you now believe regulation (or lack of) can hold the media sector back? There is a chapter on regulation later (chapter 11). However, more importantly, regulation would have to *proactively* preempt the growth and investment in the media sectors in most African countries.

8.4.2 Where Is Media Going in Africa?

As regards where media is going on the continent, Berger (2010b)[28] sums it up aptly: "more and interactive." And we have touched on many of the strands of "more media" and "interactive media" already.

More Media: Berger notes that every African now has a choice of media, albeit limited but which is more than what it was and will become even more still. He rightly argues this is due to the democratisation effect of technology as well as the technology growing cheaper. Satellite TV, as noted earlier, may not be that widespread as it is still largely for the elite—but they are highly influential alternatives to government-owned broadcasters. So more media means state-owned broadcasters have competition. Good. It also means "plurality" of voices on our airwaves. This is better—in the context of Africa. Analogue to digital terrestrial transition should also increase plurality as more channels will be unleashed by digital. It is also a fact of life that more media means more costs. Digital migration is expensive, as there would usually be a period of "dual illumination" when both the analogue and digital signals are still on air. Consumers have to purchase set-top boxes or even more expensive new, digital TV sets. Filling up two to thirty new digital channels with good content would be costly too, or would they be filled with imported, cheap, drivel content and even more religious programming? Then there is the web-based content on its way, thanks to all the submarine cable landings and new 3G/4G and fixed networks that would be deployed on the

---

28 G, Berger (2010b), "Introduction: Beyond Broadcasting," in Guy Berger (2010) with contributions from Fackson Banda, Jane Duncan, Rashweat Mukundu, and Zeineida Machado, *Beyond Broadcasting: the future of state-owned broadcasters in Southern Africa*, Windhoek, Namibia: Fesmedia Africa Series, pp. 7–19.

continent. YouTube, Facebook, Twitter, and other social media sites will grow to occupy Africans' media time.

Interactive Media: Interactivity is real. Recall *The Namibian*'s publishing of SMS messages in pages in its newspapers to generate "interaction" with its readers and how the SMSs provide 30 percent of the tip-offs for the stories in the newspaper. This is "delayed" (i.e., not instant) interactivity, but interactivity nonetheless. You also have more direct interactivity via talk radio call-ins, SMS contributions, and SMS votes on TV/radio programmes, particularly "reality" TV shows. The concept of "public service" moves away from just the delivery of content to also the provision of a platform where viewers can contribute to the context mix. So a news item would have around it blogs, citizen videos showing different perspectives of the same event (like different angles of the same goal in a football match), etc. Berger concludes that this means expanding beyond "public service broadcasters" doing "public service broadcasting" to a scenario where the latter is just part of a wider "public service media." Secondly, he also notes the idea of a one-way inform service to the audience will be increasingly challenged by an increasingly active audience. Government broadcasters have to learn to live with this emerging reality.

8.5 The Africa New Media Problem Statement and Recommendations

This section also answers the issue of "Where Africa Media Is Going and Some Lessons from the Rest of the World."

With respect to where African media is going, you are reminded of the futuristic four matrix scenario captured in figure 20 covering "traditional new media," "media buffet," "portal of me," and "tons of Twitter." This will not be that far away in countries like South Africa, where three million people access the Internet only via their mobile phones, five million on desktops (mainly at work), and two million on both—making 20 percent of the population that has some Internet access. Berger (2010b) notes that for this 20 percent, available to them is a mass of content of which local public interest news and other South

African state-broadcasted content is just a "miniscule" option. You can see how traditional African viewers would drift into one of the scenarios above pretty naturally, particularly given the poor programming in Africa in general. As broadband becomes more than just a declared indaba right on the continent—but a reality—these scenarios will commence to evolve.

Indeed, I instinctively believe this drift effect into these scenarios is likely to be more profound and faster in Africa. Why? This is because in Europe, TV and radio programming are relatively very good with much choice, and over many years viewers have become accustomed to their daily "diets" of traditionally linear broadcast. Indeed, all Ofcom studies on broadcasting in the United Kingdom continue to show the enduring nature linear broadcast TV/radio over nonlinear audio visual over the Internet. As humans, we instinctively do not like to change our habits. In Africa, we will literally just have vacuums of media time to fill as broadband evolves.

What these and some of the earlier narratives mean is that Africa media has some profound challenges which they have to confront. Below is not exhaustive, but it also attempts to draw from lessons from the developed world as well as from leading media thinkers in Africa in order to frame the challenges and some associated recommendations.

1. *The Future of Government-Owned/State-Owned Broadcasters Challenge:* This has to be problem number one for government- or state-owned broadcasters. With these frightening[29] scenarios before them ("media buffet," "tons of Twitter," and "portal of me"), they need to start positioning themselves to be relevant and viable in the new world. They have to embrace websites, more media, interactivity, MOBI-type sites, social media, user generated content (UGC), etc. However, these mean costs—and they are not exactly flushed with monies. There is no obvious answer to this challenge, and it would vary by country. However, some key decision makers would have to commission (or start thinking about commissioning) strategic

---

29 From traditional broadcasters' perspectives.

reviews about the future of state-owned broadcasters on the African continent.

2. *The Reinventing Public Service Broadcasting Challenge:* In tandem with "1" above, most current broadcasters on the continent have no alternative but to reinvent what they do— or more accurately, what they think they do. Many venerable broadcasting institutions on the continent currently have "bastardised" versions of the classic BBC public service broadcasting model (i.e., its purpose and characteristics). The classic BBC *purposes* are to educate, inform impartially, to entertain, to reflect national culture, to be inclusive of all minority segments of society, and to create a sense of being British to all in the United Kingdom. The BBC's *characteristics* cover adjectives/nouns like original, high quality, engaging, inclusive, challenging, widely available, informing, etc. By and large, the BBC achieves these purposes and characteristics.

It is arguable if any broadcasters on the African continent can measure up, not least as they are not "fully" funded like the BBC. Nevertheless, it is the case that concepts/precepts that define public service broadcasting are changing around the BBC, which I have firsthand experience of from my time at Ofcom. Berger (2010b) rightly defines this transition of this key phrase "public service broadcasting" as follows:

- Public is a concept referring to "of general interest of everyone." The concept is now transitioning to referring to a plural set of forming fragmented "publics," with the larger common public group shrinking into what he terms an evolving and dynamic "sphericals" of "micropublics." This is the transition lesson from Europe. Given the "larger common public group" in most of Africa amounts to a small elite and a bit more, there is the twin challenge of coalescing a true larger common public group which encompasses almost all living in the country in the first place, as well as serving the evolving "micro-publics."

Some countries would ask themselves whether they should bother about the former and just worry about the latter. I believe that broadcasting is *ipso facto* a mass medium and that the purposes of the BBC model above are valid to all African countries, arguably even more so as they tend to be fragile democracies. So countries have to address both challenges, despite the costs. Who ever said democracy is cheap? This is said with some trepidation because the finance challenge is truly nontrivial, and this is covered later in this section.

- Service means "provision of something to waiting recipients"—this is the classic passive model. Not anymore! The idea of broadcasters just serving daily diets of schedules to viewers is ebbing away, and it was never really there for the masses in most of Africa anyway. Service is now transitioning to mean more participation from viewers who are becoming active participants, who engage in user-generated content, and who vote and SMS, and it is also a key source of revenue to cash-strapped broadcasters.

- Broadcasting means mass-scale transmission of radio and TV typically via the airwaves. Broadcasting is now transitioning to be complemented by *narrow*casting to fragmented audiences or "micro-publics," and it is no longer just via broadcast airwaves but also via other wireless means, like 4G (e.g., WiMAX) or wired means (e.g., telephone lines, cable, and fibre-optic lines)

The last bullet above suggests public service broadcasting is now moving to be "technology neutral," alluding to the fact that whilst terrestrial broadcasting may be the default mass-scale transmission means on the continent today, other broadcasting and narrowcasting means must also complement terrestrial. To achieve wide-scale access to affordable TV and radio on the continent requires a technology neutral mindset wherein broadcast to mobile (e.g., via DVB-H), terrestrial broadcast via DTT, satellite broadcasts via DVB-S, and narrowcasting means (e.g., MBMS, on-demand via Internet, etc.) would all have to be considered as a whole. Ofcom in the United Kingdom has asserted:[30]

> Public service broadcasting will need to embrace these new digital platforms or risk declining relevance. Linear broadcasting is no longer the only way to achieve reach and impact amongst audiences, who expect content to be available whenever and wherever they choose. The needs and habits of different audiences should be taken into account to achieve this. An important conclusion from this review is that *public service content should be available across all digital media, not just linear broadcasting.*[31]

3. *The Public Service News Challenge:* It is already a challenge on the continent today, i.e., so-called public service broadcasters struggle to provide quality and impartial news. African countries are in good company with this challenge. An Ofcom 2007 report[32] provides a salutary warning that African countries must learn from: "Whilst no form of television news in the UK currently pays its own way, the economics are particularly stark for nations/regions news and it will require regulatory intervention if its long-term presence is deemed important on commercial PSB."

Public service broadcasters (PSBs) need to inform (impartially), educate, and entertain. A major part of the informing is news provision. In the United Kingdom, news does not pay its way, and Ofcom notes that in the regions (i.e., Scotland,

---

30 *Ofcom's Second Public Service Broadcasting Review: Putting Viewers First, Statement,* 21 January 2009, http://stakeholders.ofcom.org.uk/binaries/consultations/psb2_phase2/statement/psb2statement.pdf (accessed October 2013).

31 The italics is Ofcom's emphasis, not mine.

32 Ofcom, *New News, Future News: The Challenges for Television News after Digital Switch-over,* An Ofcom Discussion Document, June 26, 2007, http://stakeholders.ofcom.org.uk/binaries/research/tv-research/newnews.pdf (accessed October 2012).

Wales, Northern Ireland, and other sub regions), the situation is even direr than in London. So if news cannot pay for itself in Lagos, Cairo, Johannesburg, etc., what more of Sokoto and Yenegoa (Nigeria), Luxor (Egypt), or Durham (South Africa)? It is most likely that the advertising around news programmes in most of Africa will not cover production costs. State broadcasters may just have to swallow these costs, but we also need private service broadcasters putting out quality and impartial news programmes in order to have a *plurality* and *diversity* of new sources within the country. I believe the answer to this conundrum arguably partly lies in spectrum—specifically in the fact that most broadcasters on the continent have been "gifted" spectrum, and they almost see it as a free asset on their balance sheets (if they have or understand what balance sheets are). If this spectrum is rightly valued and tested for opportunity cost, both public service and commercial broadcasters would realise they do not get spectrum for free. This way, there is a clear rationale for commercial service broadcasters to either pay the full price for their frequency spectrum or agree to some public service obligations from the regulator (including having a daily/weekly news quota, say) in exchange for reduced frequency spectrum fees. This said, there may be another problem on the African continent—that of the opportunity cost (i.e., the value) of the spectrum not being that meaningful for such a model to work anyway. Nevertheless, if one looks out a decade or two, this is an important principled position to consider.

Other suggestions include the state-owned PSB (i) sharing news production infrastructure, particularly in regional towns and cities with commercial players, (ii) buying news from commercial players, (iii) co-selling of each other's content, (iv) sharing news content with newspapers, and (v) more linking to small players' sites, etc. So the PSB has a role to effectively promote the entire sector.

4. *The Regulatory Challenge:* Regulating the TMT sector, perhaps particularly the media subsector, is becoming ever more nontrivial. A quote from Berger in the previous section (section 8.4) truly demonstrates the gap (or is it lack of competence?) to regulate media on the continent anywhere near properly. Converged regulation just makes eminent sense here. Understanding the various scenarios of what is likely to happen to the media subsector is very important to preempting credible regulatory solutions.

5. *The Financing/Funding Challenge:* Some would argue that this is the biggest challenge to media on the continent. I would not disagree, for this is really a problem. It is not obvious where African governments turn to for funding for this key sector beyond their dwindling government subsidies or advertising revenues, which we know are being fragmented away. South Africa Broadcasting Corporation (SABC) is arguably the best-funded public service broadcaster on the continent. However, looking at SABC's 2011 Audited Accounts[33] clearly shows that 76 percent of its revenues came from advertising and sponsorship, at 67 percent and 9 percent, respectively. License fees made up only 17 percent of SABC's 2011 revenues. The government grant amounted to less than 3 percent, and it was down 53 percent from the previous year. The BBC is 100 percent license fee funded. In a revealing sentence in the chief financial officer's report in this 2010–11 Annual Report, Mr. Lerato Nage writes: "The SABC therefore has to achieve its public broadcasting mandate on a mainly commercial revenue base, which fluctuates year-on-year."

This is financial-speak for "this public service broadcasting mandate cannot be guaranteed." Given who pays the piper

---

33   South African Broadcasting Corporation 2010–11, Annual Report, http://www.sabc.co.za/wps/wcm/connect/8ebfc980487814c8bbe4bb12e7ad9f1e/AnnualReport+2010-11.pdf?MOD=AJPERES&CACHEID=8ebfc980487814c8bbe4bb12e7ad9f1e (accessed October 2013)

calls the tunes, in what real sense is SABC a government/state broadcaster like the BBC beyond holding a state license? On the other hand, I live in the real world[34] and do not believe the BBC model can or should be transposed to Africa.

By all accounts, SABC is doing well financially, but some like Libby Lloyd believe there is just a continued commercialization of SABC. In a downbeat but realistic assessment of a comparison of state-owned broadcasters compared to an almost-ideal like the BBC,[35] she is brutally frank that we are so far off the ideal that she almost throws in the towel for state broadcasters in the South African region and, by my extension, for the rest of Africa too. She is a key broadcasting authority with vast experience within SABC and at the regulator, and her views must be carefully considered. She asks with respect to the finance challenge:

> Are, for example, the existing public broadcasting models, given obstacles, the best means for ensuring viewers and listeners have access to meaningful information and programming? Or do we need to focus more broadly on other mechanisms for delivery of public content to citizens?...How can public broadcasting be funded in the region? The debates on funding for public broadcasting have to move beyond defining principles to developing practical, viable and affordable funding models. Any discussion on such funding has to explore ways to ensure that funds are dedicated to the production of content and not just institution building and be based

---

34 I believe, most of the time.

35 L. Lloyd (2010), "Appendix 1: Public Broadcasting in Southern Africa: Beyond Protocols and Rhetoric. A Review, in Berger, Guy (2010) with contributions from Fackson Banda, Jane Duncan, Rashweat Mukundu, and Zeineida Machado, *Beyond Broadcasting: the future of state-owned broadcasters in Southern Africa*, Windhoek, Namibia: Fesmedia Africa Series, pp. 90–101.

on thorough evaluation of the needs of broadcasters
in relation to their mandates.

Conferences galore have been held on the continent to address
this problem, but nothing concrete has emerged. Many countries are struggling to afford the analogue to digital migration
project, though they are proceeding with it because the spectrum could be deployed to much more beneficial use, i.e., there
is a real spectrum dividend to be had. Indeed, the spectrum
could be auctioned in some countries for more that the costs of
the switchover to digital. Collecting fees from consumers and
citizens is not really an option for many countries, as they do
not have the systems and processes to enforce it. Given much
finer brains (than my average one) at many conferences have
looked at this financing problem to no avail, who am I to be
able to "crack" it in this chapter? Therefore, my only suggestion is to revert to the proposal of chapter 1 of this volume—i.e.,
making the case for the entire TMT sector to be investable and
looking at the problem as one entire TMT sector. And if "cash-
rich" telecommunications has to "subsidise" "cash poor" media (who deliver significant broader social value), so be it.

6. *The Newspapers/Press Challenge:* Newspapers are dying on
their feet in Europe. Only South Africa on the continent can
claim its newspapers are reaching anywhere just under half
its population. In Africa, newspapers and the press tend to be
overpoliticised at the tabloid end, and their business models
are very fragile. There is much evidence that newspapers and
press only happen in urban areas on the continent—though
it is also the case for newspapers/press in general (including
in Europe and North America) that their influence/impact is
typically disproportionately larger than their circulation and
reach. The financing model for newspapers/press though is a
major challenge. There is still much scope for entrepreneurship on the continent to provide quality newspaper products,
and there may be a lesson to be learnt from Europe, where

mergers occur between newspaper groups and some local or community broadcasters, subject to politicization concerns and regulatory checks.

7. *The Widespread Availability (Reach) Challenge:* This chapter has established that whilst radio is dominant on the continent, TV and newspapers/press can hardly be said to be widespread on the continent, not least as the latter two are only urban phenomena in general. Recall Mytton noting that radio outstrips both TV and newspapers in reaching most Africans and that radio reaches 50 percent of adults in poorer countries to virtually everyone in more developed African countries. Even a rural-dominated population like Tanzania still manages 85 percent radio listenership versus only 41 percent of Tanzanians who watch TV every week.[36] However, Mytton also notes that there are fewer radio sets per head of population than anywhere else in the world. Mobile phones with FM/FM tuners may be the answer here for African countries to consider. The analogue to digital switchover process in most countries is trying to improve the reach of TV. However, I am still sceptical whether the economics of terrestrial broadcasting in our cash-strapped economies will deliver the widespread availability of quality TV across our countries. It appears self-evident that satellite direct-to-home (DTH) promises the broadest reach. On a country by country basis, reach figures for all media must be studied and optimized. DTH entrepreneurs must look at the TV reach problem in Africa as a real opportunity.

8. *The Affordability Challenge:* A key sister challenge to the prior reach problem is the affordability one. Reach without affordability is futile. Affordability without reach is sterile. Radio's reach is best on the continent, particularly for AM and FM, and its affordability seems moderate. TV is still a work

---

36 R. Schumann (2013), Case Study of Digital TV Switchover in Tanzania, http://www.analysysmason.com/About-Us/News/Insight/Case-study-of-digital-TV-switchover-in-Tanzania/#.UjhvE8bWR5I (accessed October 2013).

in progress as terrestrial TV networks get rolled out on the continent. However, some of the omens from countries like South Africa where there are spats between industry and government on prices of set-top boxes do not bode well. Unless Africa standardizes on the same compression (encoding) and transmission standards regionally (at least) and across the entire continent, economies of scale for set-top boxes will not be achieved, which would lower prices and increase affordability. Entrepreneurs have a key role to play here.

9. *The Quality Challenge:* This chapter is titled "Towards Widespread Availability of Affordable *High-Quality* Radio, TV, and Other Media." Most of the programming on the continent ranges from the mundane to the terrible, as noted earlier, a function of the finances, skills shortages, equipment shortages, etc., on the continent. The quality challenge is one of good regulation, competition, choice, and the market working well for African consumers and citizens. Clearly, there is also a financial/investment aspect to it. Seen over the next decade, the quality problem should be gradually addressable. Entrepreneurs who deliver quality will attract audiences who are monetisable.

10. *The Political Challenge:* Lloyd (2010) rightly points out the "absence of political will" challenge. She defines this as ruling parties inevitably being reluctant to hand over editorial control of national broadcasters. She notes:

> The political will to meet the spirit and not only the letter of international, continental and regional agreements is predictably absent as a critical and insightful media and informed citizenry could potentially threaten governments and/or individual political leaders.

These all contribute to subverting the independence of broadcasting. As countries democracies' mature over the next decade and two, I am optimistic that this political challenge will ebb slowly but surely away. Institutions in countries like Ghana, Kenya, and Senegal (amongst others) are firming up.

11. *The Institutional Challenge:* This is another Lloyd (2010) concern which I believe is more problematic than most of the other prior ten challenges, with the exception of perhaps a couple. Here, she observes people within broadcasters or other state institutions like regulators as being bluntly reluctant to transform. What point is there declaring a broadcaster or a regulator as "independent," yet their boards are packed with government appointees? And what's the point if the employees of this supposedly independent institutions act no differently from state civil servants or, even worse, they do the bidding of the political masters of the day? Every time I describe how independent I was as a senior regulator to many senior African government colleagues in Africa, I can see the incredulity written on all their faces. Institutional independence must begin from the board/CEO downwards. They must believe, and convince their political masters to believe too, that long-term true independence would translate to benefits to the sector.

12. *The Skills/Knowledge/Expertise Challenge:* This challenge has been covered in other chapters too, but the following areas stand out: governance, policy making within government (e.g., spectrum challenges, 4G auctions design), general management (e.g., leadership of important institutions like regulators or state broadcasters), financial management, regulation, programming, managing change, etc. The lack of these skills truly holds back our TMT sectors, and the faster these skills are developed, the better it will be for our economies.

13. *The Technology Challenge:* The pace of technology change is a problem in the Western world, let alone Africa. Convergence, new standards of transmission, new standards of encoding, new and cheaper equipment, etc., appear daily with salespeople

from these technology organisations calling in to sell their new, shiny kits. Managing technology change—and all the associated training, equipment processes, and systems—is quite time consuming, expensive, and hard.

You will agree that this is quite a complex and intertwined set of problems, which have (with some luck) been reasonably well articulated. The next section summarises some other recommendations on how to achieve widespread availability of quality radio, digital TV, and other media on the African continent.

8.6 Other Recommendations Towards Widespread Availability of Affordable High-Quality Radio, Digital TV, and other Media

The previous section has already made many important recommendations to address widespread availability of affordable high-quality radio, digital TV, and other media. There are many other things that government, regulators, entrepreneurs, and others across Africa and some emerging economies should start doing. Some key ones are the following:

14. *Understand and appreciate all the new media challenges above:* All these challenges are real. No decision/policy makers (e.g., ministers, senior civil servants, etc.) should be overseeing this area without understanding all these challenges which provide a truly spaghetti-like and nontrivial problem. You hopefully now understand how complex, technical, political, economic, cultural, uncertain, etc., these challenges are. To shape this sector, these challenges need to be understood and preempted, or else media anarchy is on its way across Africa.

15. *Legislation to begin shaping the new media sector Africans deserve must begin now:* This media subsector needs so much shaping, and you hopefully now agree. And the shaping must

commence now. Regulators and government must understand and legislate for the new media sector they want to see. They must deregulate and liberalise—albeit slowly if they so choose to and at the country's right pace—radio broadcasting, TV broadcasting, newspapers, and new media. Remember the fact that London has more working in the media subsector than for technology and telecommunications combined. Remember also how liberalized radio in Ghana, Uganda, and Nigeria are outnumbering their state radios. Legislation and new regulations must have a clear line of sight to innovation, investment, and the creation of jobs at the minimum. It must be entrepreneur friendly. This media subsector must have a business plan to encourage national and international investments into the sector.

16. *For widespread radio, let AM and FM radio in particular thrive—radio is the biggest information and communication technology (ICT) in Africa and will remain so for the next decade (affordability is key):* As Mytton notes, radio's low cost, flexibility, and oral character suit our African cultures and situation naturally. Those who cannot read and write can be communicated to on a mass basis via radio—and in their language of choice too. And there are thousands of languages/dialects on the continent. Uneducated women and the old are best communicated to via radio. No other medium of communication matches radio in terms of audience and political/cultural power. So policy in the least-developed African countries where radio access does not reach 100 percent of their populations must be to achieve widespread 100 percent population coverage. Furthermore, each African must really have a choice of at least a handful of national, local, and community radio stations in addition to the usual international ones, like Voice of America, BBC World Service, and Radio France Internationale. It really should not be that hard to use a combination of market-based incentives and some clever regulation/licensing of different radio formats to achieve this outcome.

The African diaspora abroad could be key entrepreneurs or funders or both Digital radio, in my view, is nowhere near a priority for the coming decade or two for reasons expounded earlier. AM and FM are still quite resilient on the continent. With FM tuners now built into many mobile phones, widespread access to 100 percent (population) available radio is within reach. If more countries on the continent and in other emerging economies prioritize radio on the continent, the prices of radio receivers and sets will drop even further. After all, the World Bank predicts Africa will be the most populous continent by 2050 at 2.2 billion. The more coordination amongst African countries there is on many recommendations in this volume, the cheaper the devices and equipment will be for Africans over the next decade. Quality will come from good competition, regulation, etc. The next recommendation below notes where government investment should come from.

17. *For widespread TV, DTT terrestrial TV makes nationalistic sense, but free satellite DTH could/would walk away with the prize:* The move to DTT is crucial, as there is an important digital dividend for mobile broadband to be had. Governments should look justifiably at the TMT sector as a whole (as recommended in chapter 1) in order to make the business case for DTT. This makes eminent sense because the broadcasters are vacating the UHF spectrum to make way for a higher-use alternative in mobile broadband. So from a national perspective, governments can look at broadcasting and mobile "in the round," as this spectrum would attract receipts at future auctions as well as tax revenues from future mobile services. Broadcasting has so much value to society in broader social value that good radio and TV broadcasting deserves this investment. The emergence of real and functional advertising sectors on the continent would also be another source of revenues to the sector, as can be seen with SABC in South Africa. Entrepreneurs should be incentivized to invest in key channels on the digital platform. Coordination and harmonization must

happen across the continent to get set-top boxes as low as possible so as to maximize affordability.

All these said for DTT, it is my considered view that, in the long term, satellite DTH with its large footprints and almost zero marginal incremental costs per subscriber could/should be the optimal mode for achieving widespread TV on the continent. The nationalistic boundaries, language, and regulation are clear barriers but not insurmountable ones for the creative entrepreneurs we have on the continent. As noted earlier, Indians are getting access to many satellite services at low costs. And for rural-dominated countries like Tanzania and Uganda, satellite DTH makes much sense. It is no wonder there is much significant use of satellite DTH in countries like Tanzania already. How affordable can you get than free? *Free-to-air satellite* DTH services based on advertising business models would evolve regionally in Africa, and regional markets eventually evolve into single markets. Consumers would still have to fork out for one-off payment for the satellite set-top box and their TVs, of course, with no recurring monthly payments. One such service, Sabido, launched in late 2013 in South Africa to offer free TV,[37] including fifteen channels.

18. *A plurality of platforms also helps enhance widespread radio and TV access, and competition between platforms is good for quality and choice:* It is important governments and regulators liberalise both the primary platforms of satellite and terrestrial TV and radio and also encourage other platforms to flourish, such as IPTV, cable, the Internet, and mobile, so as to ensure a plurality of platforms. Innovations like DVB-H/MBMS for mobile TV/radio should be supported by legislation as well as by regulators since most digital services would be introduced and consumed by Africans over the next decade on wireless

---

37 "New free satellite TV for South Africa," *Africa Telecom & IT*, vol. 4, no. 9, September 2013, p. 36.

devices. I was quite pleased to read about satellite provider DStv introducing a DVB-H mobile TV handset in Nigeria called "Walka," priced at circa US$108 and enabling DStv subscribers to be able to watch satellite TV on the move.[38] Though the price of the handset is still steep, and it is clearly another way for those few in Nigeria with satellite subscriptions to watch TV on the move, this is still a good initiative.

19. *More media, interactive media, and social media are the future—they should be embraced, otherwise they will overwhelm all:* Even the most authoritarian regimes will not be able to stem the tide of more media (interactive and social). Newspapers will only survive—if they do on the continent—via more media and via interactive and social media where (as we saw), storyline tips come from their readers. For community and FM radios to survive and thrive, they must go SMS, use Twitter, generate social networking around their content, set up websites accessible via mobiles, and truly engage their audiences and convert them to subscribers or buyers of content. Regulators and governments must encourage these (and more media, more interactive, and more social media) rather than try and contain the uncontainable. If anything, in them lies the basis of so much natural African creativity, jobs, and future tax revenues for governments. Entrepreneurs who understand this triumvirate of more interactive and social media within the African context stand to build some truly innovative companies out of Africa. These three attributes are so African anyway.

20. *Affordability is as important and widespread access—reach without affordability is futile; affordability without reach is sterile:* All policy makers must fully understand the implications of this simple statement. Why does Africa have fewer

---

38 "DStv Nigeria launches mobile TV device, 'Walka,'" *Africa Telecom & IT*, vol. 3, no. 2, February 2013, p. 37.

radio sets per head than any other continent? If DTT set-top boxes in Tanzania cost US$40–60 in a country with a GDP per capita of circa $500 (and this is just for the box, yet alone the TV set) along with a monthly TV basic package of $5.63,[39] how can this be affordable for the masses? Other packages come at $11.25 and $22.50 monthly. Just for the basic package, this means $68 per year for the basic package, which is 13 percent of GDP per capita on top of a set-top box of a minimum of circa 8 percent of GDP per capita. And power is yet another story. This said, it must be acknowledged that the costs of set top boxes are now down to US $30 as of February 2014 depending on the package[40]. Then some countries are thinking of TV to handsets using technologies like DVB-H. However, there is the small problem of pricing for DVB-H–enabled handsets for DTT at circa $300. Tanzania is chosen here because it is the leading country in Africa in switching off analogue TV in favour of digital terrestrial TV. Is it any surprise that Tanzania has attained only 22 percent terrestrial population penetration with digital terrestrial population even though the big population cities/towns are switched over, albeit the process is still ongoing?[41] What these radio and TV examples illuminate is the yawning affordability problem which the previous chapter on broadband also tried to address. What then are the solutions for radio, TV, and other media?

Firstly, the biggest answer to the affordability problem on the continent will come from cooperation and harmonization amongst countries. Nevertheless, having different transmission

---

39 R. Schumann (2013), Case Study of Digital TV Switchover in Tanzania, http:// www.analysysmason.com/About-Us/News/Insight/Case-study-of-digital-TV-switchover-in-Tanzania/#.UjhvE8bWR5I (accessed October 2013).

40 Source: personal visit to set to box retail outlets Tanzania in February 2014.

41 H. Gunze (2013), Tanzania Communications Regulatory Authority (TCRA), Country Status on Migration from Analogue to Digital Switchover, A Presentation to 8th CTO Digital Broadcasting Forum, February 12, 2013, Sandton, South Africa, http://www.cto.int/media/events/pst-ev/2013/DBSF-2013/Tanzania-Country-Status.pdf (accessed October 2013).

and compression standards across the continent is just a subop-timal idea. The Tanzanians, being part of EAC, have already standardized on DVB-T2. Leadership from regional inter-governmental and pan-African organisations is sorely need-ed now more than ever: the Southern African Development Community (SADC), the East African Community (EAC), the Economic Community of West African States (ECOWAS), the Economic Community of Central African States (ECCAS), and, of course, the African Union. All these economic organ-isations must understand that affordability comes from har-monization of standards. If all of these economic entities and their regulators cooperate and harmonise on the same stan-dards, set-top box pricing should drop another 50 percent to twenty US dollars. The current map of digital TV harmoniza-tion in Africa is not terrible, as is shown in figure 54. Most of sub-Saharan Africa as of October 2013 has opted for DVB-T2, whilst the rest have mostly chosen DVB-T, according to DVB. However, it can be seen that Botswana has decided to go with ISDB-T,[42] the Japanese-led standard for TV which has been adopted by most of South America, as can be seen in Figure 54 below. Botswana must believe that there are economies of scale in TV receivers and sets to be had with the southern American states. South Africa is also known to have seriously considered switching to ISDB-T when they instituted a review of their DVB choice in 2010. This has contributed to slowing down the DTT migration in South Africa.

---

42   ISDB-T—The International Services Digital Broadcasting-Television is a Japanese standard for digital television and digital radio used by Japan's TV and ra-dio networks. Most of Latin America has adopted this standard for their digital TV.

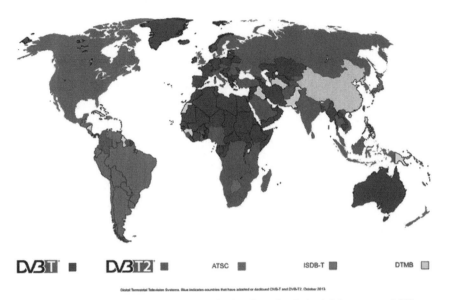

Figure 54—Choice of TV Transmission Standards in Africa as per 2013
(Source: Digital Video Broadcasting Project, October 2013)[43]

Then governments may subsidise for the poorest in society. Secondly—and yet again—taxing such equipment is folly with respect to affordability.

Thirdly, even FM/AM radio sets should not be taxed either, which some countries do, and if these economic communities procure together, these radio sets would be much cheaper. Fourthly, power is clearly an issue across the continent. Talking about TVs across many parts of the continent is academic when they have no access to power; at least for radio sets, batteries can be used. Countries must continue to improve on their power problems. Fifthly, the regulators would have to ensure some of the basic packages for TV, say, are affordable through price regulation. There are other things to do, but most importantly, decision makers must just make it their business to prioritise affordability. This has not truly been a priority in most parts of the continent in the past.

---

43   DVB-T and DVB-T2 Worldwide, Countries that have adopted DVB-T and DVB-T2 (including ITU RRC-06 Signatories), October 2013, http://www.dvb.org/resources/public/images/site/dvb-t_map.pdf (accessed October 2013).

CHAPTER 9

DIGITAL TV SWITCHOVER

The analogue to digital switchover of TV should not just be an exercise in technocracy—it should and must be exploited as an opportunity to light the burners of the new multichannel, multimedia, more interactive, and more social media sector.

This chapter on the analogue to digital switchover of television on the continent of Africa and other emerging market countries is arguably different from the chapter on the widespread availability of affordable high-quality radio, digital TV, and other media. However, it is arguably germane for three reasons. First, digital switchover is a significant technical task that all African countries have either undertaken by the end of 2013 (e.g., Tanzania, largely, and Mauritius), or are undertaking, or will be undertaking. I venture to assert that many countries are undertaking the project almost as a mechanical and technical exercise of switching off analogue signals and switching on digital. If your country falls in this category, then this chapter is for you.

This project should be more than that. Following on from the latter, the second reason why this chapter is germane to this book stems from the core reason the entire digital switchover process is happening in the first place, which many forget. The core reason it is happening is in order to deliver a spectrum digital dividend, i.e., freeing up some UHF frequencies that can be reused *not* only for digital TV but also for TV to mobiles (e.g., via DVB-H) or for mobile broadband (e.g., via LTE/4G) or license-exemption for TV white space–based rural broadband. So indeed, the digital switchover (DSO) project in digital terrestrial television (DTTV or DTT) presages, as night follows day, other projects, e.g., reassigning the rights to the released to mobile via a 4G auction, say, thinking about high definition TV too or rural TV white spaces–based rural broadband. In this chapter, I prefers DTT to DTTV because the former (i.e., DTT) is more authentic to what this chapter is about whilst the latter (DTTV) is more general. The reason is there are other means of digital TV, including digital satellite TV, digital cable TV, or Internet TV. Next, perhaps the third reason for having this chapter is most important. It is to ensure that any digital switchover over (DSO) project also preempts a new media sector in our countries—the sort of media sector described in chapter 1 that employs as many people as the technology and telecommunications subsectors combined. We also described in the previous chapter how more media, interactive media, and more social media are all *de facto* happening in our countries whether we like it or not. The question then is do we design for it, or do we let it develop haphazardly? You know by now where I stand on this question, and DSO provides a good opportunity to think about the new evolving media sector afresh, and with jobs and GDP growth top of mind. This is the real prize. Hence why this chapter begins with a clarion call to recognize such a worthwhile benefit and act accordingly and not to let technocracy reign with DSO across Africa and other emerging economies.

For those countries that have already completed the mechanical and technical exercise of switching off analogue signals and switching on the digital ones, there is still time for them to revisit chapter 8 (and chapter 1 at least too) and work towards widespread and affordable radio, digital TV (via both fixed TV sets and mobile devices), newspapers, and new interactive and social media. Hopefully, you would agree that this is also consistent with other parts and sections of the book which has made the same or similar arguments.

This chapter answers the following:

- What is this digital switchover (DSO) to digital terrestrial TV (DTT) all about? What are its attractions? What are some of the myths and misunderstandings about DSO in Africa and other emerging market countries?

- What technically does DSO entail? (This chapter does not get too technical at all.)
- What is the structure of the analogue TV market and industry, and how does it change through going digital? What are the implications of this change?
- What is the cost benefit analysis and business case for digital switchover? Who are the real beneficiaries of DSO? What are the costs?
- What are some of the regulatory implications of DSO to DTT, and how should they be dealt with? What are some of the other policy issues around DTT that should be addressed?
- What then are some key recommendations to improve your chances of a successful end-to-end DSO project and programme?

9.1 What DSO Is: Its Attractions and Some Myths

Recalling from faraway chapter 1, all countries in ITU Region 1 (i.e., practically all African and European countries and more) undertook in a Geneva 2006 agreement to complete the transition from analogue to digital terrestrial TV broadcasting by June 2015 for southern African countries, and 2020 for the rest of Africa. The countries with the 2020 deadline number up to thirty countries. The 2020 Africa countries are noted in a footnote in chapter 1 and therefore for completeness they are listed following: Algeria, Benin, Burkina Faso, Cameroon, Central African Republic, Chad, Congo, Democratic Republic of Congo, Egypt, Equatorial Guinea, Eritrea, Ethiopia, Gabon, Ghana, Guinea, Guinea-Bissau, Ivory Coast, Liberia, Madagascar, Mali, Morocco, Mauritania, Niger, Nigeria, Sao Tome and Principe, Sierra Leone, Somalia, Sudan, Togo, and Tunisia. The remaining African countries are in the 2015 camp, i.e., only the southern African countries are committed to the June 17, 2015 ITU deadline. The rest of ITU Region 1 (i.e., European nations, the former Soviet Union, etc.) are all subject to the 2015 deadline. Recall from chapter 1 too that the ITU splits all the nations of the world in three different geographical regions. Region 1 comprises Europe, Africa, the Middle East west of the Persian Gulf but including Iraq, the former Soviet Union, and Mongolia. Almost all of the emerging countries in Latin America, part of ITU Region 2, have also committed to a switch off date circa 2020; Region 2 covers North and South America, Greenland, and some of the eastern Pacific Islands.

Now let us return to why there is this "forced" ITU migration to digital from analogue. We have covered many already throughout this volume, but we summarise the reasons here again for completeness.

- *The spectrum digital dividend:* By far the most important driver behind the digital migration (or DSO) is the need to free up bandwidth-greedy analogue TV for digital TV. The digital dividend is the set of frequencies that is freed up when the bandwidth-hungry analogue signals are switched off in favour of more efficient digital signals. For the same amount of frequency as one of the analogue channels mentioned above in all these countries, at least eight typically new digital and better quality standard definition (SD) channels can be delivered. This way, more valuable spectrum can be freed up for other uses on the continent. The better the transmission standard (e.g., DVB-T2 over DVB-T) and/or the encoding/compression standards (e.g., MPEG-4 over MPEG-2), the more efficient you use the spectrum airwaves.

- *Better quality sound and images:* Digital signals being a series of zeroes and ones leads to good sound quality, no *sshhh* sounds due to interference typical with analogue signals, and much clearer and higher quality pictures. The downside is that—unlike with analogue where one gets a graceful degradation of pictures (e.g., fuzzy images) with weaker or distorted signals—with digital signals one is more likely to have brilliant images/sound or none at all. Failure with digital is most unforgiving.

- *Much production, archives, and live shooting have already gone digital:* Most of the equipment being used in Africa and emerging markets today to shoot live TV and other production are already using digital equipment. Even today, a significant number of radio stations in Africa and emerging economies too use digital equipment for producing their radio programmes. So paradoxically, much content being transmitted across the airwaves is generated digitally and then reconverted into analogue for transmission as analogue signals. This clearly makes less sense bar for the fact that most African customers have analogue receiving TV sets/devices; but once production is digital and transmission goes digital, the reception would have to follow suit, and this is one of the real challenges of DSO. The point of DTT is to digitise this entire process from content generation to consumption by the customer whilst yielding a considerable digital dividend. Why has much production gone digital, you may ask? Simple: because it is less costly, and, frankly, we have to move with the times. Analogue vinyl records are long gone. Even old archive footages are also being increasingly digitised for both easier reusability and longevity of the archive. Analogue tapes clearly degrade over time. With audio voice, pictures, music, and data all represented as zeroes and ones, so much of it can be put together and edited in different ways, etc. Of course, piracy has increased exponentially due to the ease of manipulating digital information. With digital content, it is so trivial to copy, save, alter it, mix it, edit, and even e-mail, MMS, or Tweet to others.

- *The Internet is digital:* The Internet is the biggest platform in the world and is all digitally built on the Internet protocol (IP), and this also drives the economies of scale for digital. A key difference with IP technology in addition to its connectivity is that it relies on "package switching" technology. Packets of data, addressed according to the Internet protocol TCP/IP,[1] are sent to the destination in any order, along multiple network routes. Upon arrival the recipient computer recompiles the data

---

1 Transmission control protocol/Internet protocol—the communications protocol developed to enable computers of all kinds to share services and communicate directly as if part of a seamless network.

into the intended order. Networks are designed in such a manner that there are multiple routes available to the data, thereby ensuring there are no single points of failure. The packets are "routed" round the network until the destination is reached. As a packet-switched network does not rely on the establishment and maintenance of a continuous circuit connection from origin to destination (as is the case with old and traditional [circuit switched] telecommunications networks), the volume of data that can be transferred simultaneously through one line is far greater than by traditional means. What has this got to do with DTT? The answer is that one can do digital broadcasting too on the Internet. It is not the same scale of mass broadcasting as with DTT and satellite, but the typical "unicasting" (one-to-one transmission) used to view videos on YouTube on the Internet has been extended into "multicasting" (i.e., a one-to-many protocol) that allows one video or audio stream to be sent to multiple receivers. This is why Internet protocol TV (IPTV) is increasingly a substitute for many to satellite/DTT broadcasting in Western countries. Digital is here to stay. The only thing to debate are the variants of digital in use.

So given the above main drivers to DSO, what are some of the myths that have accrued on the continent? There are many, and they include the following nonexhaustive list (ill-informed journalists and commentators have sadly fanned some of these myths).

- *Myth 1—June 17, 2015, is a drop-dead date for analogue TV in Africa and most emerging economies*: As we saw earlier, this is not true, but it surprises me to no end how many people in multiple countries who should really know that thirty African countries have June 17, 2020, as their agreed cut-off date, i.e., there is an additional five-year extension for the countries using VHF Band III (174–230 MHz) for their digital TV over UHF. Yet many do not seem to realise this. As noted earlier too, most emerging countries in Latin America have also agreed to a 2020 switch off date. There are two key reasons why this myth has caught on. First, because many African and emerging economies' leaders and policy makers travel to Europe typically on conferences like annual IBC conference[2] in Amsterdam or the DVB conferences and get "fed" the European switch off dates in presentations with no caveats or carve outs for the 2020 countries. Second, this "feeding" also typically comes from suppliers of digital transmission and encoding equipment, as well as digital set-top boxes and other receiving equipment. It suits these suppliers to have an earlier date and drive up new equipment sales, be they transmission or TV receivers. TV manufacturers obviously want to sell more shiny, new digital TV sets which would require no set-top boxes, enabling a total digital end-to-end process. It reminds me of the onset of 3G in Europe, where the equipment suppliers' side of the industry talked up 3G to such an extent that operators ended up bidding astronomical amounts at 3G auctions, only for the 3G equipment not to appear in volume for almost half a dozen years later. Never has the tail of the telecommunications industry wagged the dog so violently.

- *Myth 2—After June 17, 2015 or 2020, something terrible will happen to all TV programming in Africa and elsewhere:* Yet another dose of nonsense. As noted in chapter 1, these dates have a simple and clear aim or intention. Beyond these dates, the ITU will no longer guarantee the protection from interference of these analogue signals. Note that the ITU—as a UN body— is responsible for orderliness in spectrum use wherein Nigeria is not using the same frequencies for its TV that its neighbour Cameroon is using, particularly around the borders. This will result in a scenario where Nigerian and Cameroonian TV will interfere with one another, and everyone loses—chaos sets in. This is sometimes referred to as the tragedy of the commons. If there are lots of analogue TV channels in the air, densely packed, across both Cameroon and Nigeria, then this will be a

---

2 This is the International Broadcasting Convention (IBC) conference that meets every September in Amsterdam.

problem. However, as is noted in the previous chapter (and can be seen in figure 39 for Malawi in chapter 6), we do not have this "rich man's" problem in Africa. There is hardly that much analogue TV on air in both Cameroon and Nigeria. So frankly, these dates do not amount to much for most of Africa, as there is not that much analogue TV on air to "protect" by the ITU anyway. On the contrary and if anything, Cameroonians will be quite pleased to pick up any channels from across the border in Nigeria and vice versa. Analogue TV "spillover" (or interference into used channels across the border) in most of Africa is indeed perceived as a positive externality—in plainer English: a good thing. So the sky will not crash in past these dates at all on the continent. A small minority of Africans watch or ever watched analogue TV anyway. These dates are more meaningful in Europe, where there was a lot of analogue TV on air across a much smaller geographical Europe. No terrible things will happen in Africa, neither after June 17, 2015, nor after 2020. This said, you would know by now that this volume has argued for countries to commit to switch off earlier and the reasons why.

- *Myth 3—One must go digital now because it is cheaper, and analogue TV equipment is going obsolete:* Another nonsense line pushed by suppliers. If well planned end to end with a clear business case, it may indeed be the right thing to go digital sooner, as it offers other clear advantages over analogue. However, digital in itself is not by definition cheaper, any more than replacing your analogue VHS tape recorder with a CD player is cheaper. Indeed, many people end up purchasing the same old movies all over again in digital format—this is not cheap. Indeed in practice, there usually is a prolonged period of "dual illumination" in the case of DTT wherein both analogue signals and digital signals of the same channels are broadcasted, meaning the broadcasters are running both analogue and digital infrastructures in parallel. This is to ensure that the migration has happened properly and to give citizens more time to change over to digital receiving equipment. This is certainly not cheap for both broadcasters and consumers—but it is certainly good for the suppliers industry. As to the obsolescence issue, there is so much second-hand spare equipment being switched off in Europe that this is a nonissue.

- *Myth 4—More TV channels will be shown in Africa on digital channels:* Well, I desperately wants this to be true, particularly to see widespread access and affordability to digital TV (news, drama, comedy, entertainment, and other formats). However, as is explained in the previous chapter, this is nontrivial to be achieved. There is already much evidence and squabbles from some of the avant-garde DTT countries in Africa, like South Africa and Kenya, that they are struggling to fill up their new digital channels with bona fide content. Indeed, the current state broadcasters in these countries abhor the fact that the same amount of advertising dollars on the continent is being divided up amongst an increasing number of digital TV channels, leading to decreasing revenues and increasing costs (to compete with these new channels). They hate competition. For clarity, I want this myth to be true eventually as per the previous chapter, but it would not happen without the prescriptions therein.

What all these myths amount to in Africa is that, strictly speaking, there should be no rush to DTT really. However, I have made different, and hopefully cogent, arguments all through this volume as to why an early date DTT in most countries would be preferred. However, more important is the alignment of DTT, submarine capacity distribution via national fibre backbones, 4G spectrum releases or broadband, TV white spaces for rural broadband, and prioritizing affordability and accessibility. Whether these aligned projects commence early (as in circa 2015) or later (circa 2020) is a secondary issue. It stands to reason that an earlier beginning to these projects is preferred, subject of course to adequate financing, which is more likely to happen by taking a TMT business plan approach à la chapter 1.

TYPES OF MOBILE FINANCIAL SERVICES
SOURCE: INTERNATIONAL TELECOMMUNICATION UNION (ITU-T, 2013A)

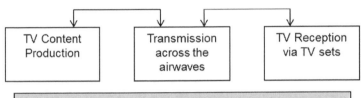

Figure 55—The Broadcast Value Chain
(Revisit figure 51 for analogue vs. digital TV transmission)

9.2 What DTT Entails Technically and the Structure of the Analogue and Digital TV Value Chains

Having read the previous section, you would be able to surmise what DTT is all about. Figure 55 provides the idiot's definition of what it entails.

As figure 55 notes, DTT is a journey of migrating this entire chain of TV content: production (mostly already digital these days), transmission across the airwaves in digital rather than analogue, and eventually reception digitally too. As figure 52 depicts, many receiving equipment (most TV sets) on the continent in 2013/14 are analogue, and hence a device called a set-top box will be needed to reconvert the digital signals back into analogue for viewing on the analogue TV sets.

Much of the fuss about what DTT entails is all about the engineering involved in taking the digital-generated content and instead of transmitting as analogue (see figure 51), transmitting as a series of zeroes and ones. Of course, there are several technologies involved at the new digital transmission site, including drives, power ampli-fiers, main and/or reserve combining units to multiplex channels, and antennas to do the digital transmission on air. However, we skip these details here as they are unnecessary for the rest of this chapter. Suffice to reemphasise that the focus of DTT is the digitisation of the signal transmission across the airwaves though most receivers on the conti-nent remain analogue, necessitating the use of set-top boxes.

The analogue broadcast TV broadcast value chain is essentially as per figure 55 above: TV content production, transmission across the airwaves, and reception via TV aerials into the back of the TV. In con-trast, the DTT value chain looks more like figure 56 as shown below: content production, multiplexing (or content aggregation), transmis-sion, and then reception. The bandwidth allocated for television trans-mission is 7 MHz or 8 MHz in the VHF (very high frequency) and UHF (ultra high frequency) bands, respectively. Analogue TV trans-mission, as described earlier, is wasteful of bandwidth, as the entire bandwidth is used to transmit just one programme (station/channel). Digital TV transmission, on the other hand, makes good use of the bandwidth by transmitting six, seven, eight, or more programs aggre-gated (or multiplexed together), depending on the encoding/compres-sion standard and the television format used.

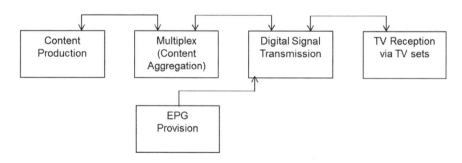

Figure 56—The DTT Digital Broadcast Chain

A key difference between the analogue and digital value chains is the multiplex stage. In digital broadcasting, several programmes are all bun-dled together on the same multiplex, resulting in identical coverage and quality of service for all the services throughout some service area. This is in contrast to analogue broadcasting, where each channel has unique coverage areas and associated quality of service for the separate stations broadcasted on separate frequencies. The other main difference of figure 56 from figure 55 is the existence of the electronic programme guide (EPG) provision. DTT introduction ushers in an era of multichannel TV. Since a single DTT multiplex carries many individual programmes, there must be an easy way for viewers to navigate these programmes. Hence, DTT multiplexes can also carry data which describes what programmes are available. This information is known as the electronic programme guide (EPG). An entity independent of all the service providers may have to be licensed to compile and provide the EPG. Within an EPG, programmes are numbered to allow ease of access.

For completeness, we list the players in the DTT chain below, introducing some new terminology used later in this chapter:

- content creators/providers companies (ContentCos): these make the programmes.
- multiplex operators (MuxCos): these are content aggregators who collect bouquets of programmes of similar or various genre from various content providers
- service companies (ServiceCos): these market bouquets of programmes and operate pricing systems for the programmes in the case of pay TV. Others sell advertisements to accompany the broadcast of programmes, etc. Key service companies include public service broadcasters (PSBs) or commercial service broadcasters.
- EPG company (EPGCo): the EPGCo allows easy navigation of programmes by viewers. An entity independent from all the service providers typically has had to be licensed to compile and provide the electronic programme guide (EPG) to the MuxCos. Typically the programmes at the beginning of the EPG numbering system are either the most watched programmes/channels or those licensed as public service broadcasters. The regulator therefore has to establish rules via which programmes get the top EPG positions. Issues to consider in

such rules include public service broadcasting versus commercial broadcasting, proportion of homemade content versus foreign syndicated content, popularity of content in terms of audience share, etc.

- network operator companies (NetCos): these operate the digital multiplexes and deploy and manage the physical broadcast network transmission infrastructure. Network operators can either be the multiplex operators (MuxCo) and/or the transmission companies (TransCo). The TransCo typically owns and runs the network of transmitter sites that form the last link in the broadcast chain.

The level of capital expenditure (capex) required to setup a TransCo means that most countries (particularly in Africa and other emerging countries) can only afford one national TransCo, or there is likely to be only one TransCo and therefore must be regulated. The TransCo is heavily price regulated and required to give fair, objective, and reasonable access to their sites to all duly licensed MuxCos. The MuxCos are customers to the TransCo. MuxCos own and operate the digital multiplexes for DTT, the playout centres[3] required to serve these multiplexes, and are responsible for delivering the multiplex streams of programmes to the TransCo for broadcast. The MuxCos have ServiceCos as customers, and these pay for the *multiplex slots* on the multiplex that carry their programmes.

Punch-drunk with new acronyms? You are over the worst of it if it is any consolation.

9.3 Cost Benefit Analysis and Business Case for DTT

It is important for such an important project as DSO to have a clear cost benefit analysis and a business case, as well as a good

---

3 Playout is a term referring to the transmission of radio or TV channels from a broadcaster into broadcast networks that deliver the programme to the audience.

understanding of the capital and operational costs. It is even more important in the context of this volume to cost for access (i.e., widespread access to digital TV, or else why bother doing it?) and ensure affordability. This section covers this important aspect and is consistent with chapter 1. This section draws from the final report of the UK Digital TV Project (Starks, 2004)[4] which preceded the commencement of the core engineering project.

The capital and operational costs of building DTT networks are significant, and they depend upon the scale undertaken, e.g., to 50 percent population coverage, 60 percent, 70 percent, etc. Indeed, the operating costs are also significant and typically no less than the equivalent costs for the *status quo* analogue distribution networks. Aggregating multiple broadcast channels into single multiplexes can reduce costs incurred for transmitters and head-end infrastructure, but other new costs for linking channels to the common aggregation point will increase. Also not to be forgotten are the costs of operating both analogue and digital services together during the period of dual illumination. This will also strain operating costs budgets and place extra demands upon staff that may generate a requirement for more to be recruited. Whether capital funding to create DTT network(s) is sourced commercially or with the aid developmental finance (e.g., World Bank, IMF, etc.), related fund raising activities need to be planned, fully costed, and have a clear business case.

9.3.1 Cost Benefit Analysis

The cost benefit Analysis should be a continuation of the *status quo* of analogue broadcasting with the policy option of a planned digital switchover added on. The key exam question is whether as a whole the country has a business case for making the switch. It should quantify the benefits as far as possible through survey work (inevitably a very inexact science), estimating the costs (again imprecisely but with

---

4 Michael Starks (2004), *Report of the Digital Project, Version 6*, November 2004, http://www.kigeit.org.pl/FTP/kl/DICE/Report_of_the_Digital_Television_Project_UK.pdf (accessed October 2013).

fuller data available), and a select a license term of, say, fifteen to twenty years. Estimates of costs and benefits should be made for different dates for the completion of switchover for each year, making it possible to estimate the net present value of making the switch under various timing options. In many countries' cases, the date is fixed at 2015. However, in the case of a 2020 date, the country has more options on timing. This work should be done by economists that the government or the regulator appoints and then reviewed by independent economic auditors.

The central estimate showing the quantifiable benefits of switchover for the country should be expressed in net present value (NPV) terms. The benefits do not materialise, of course, until after switchover has been completed. The principal beneficiaries, in order, are:

- households in areas which *cannot* receive analogue TV now but which will in future receive digital terrestrial television when analogue ceases (this clearly has to be the case since the government—surely—would want widespread access to digital TV)
- incremental consumer benefits accruing to old/former analogue households from more channels/multiplexes and the consumer benefits to new households which have come into coverage after DTT
- consumers of whatever new services make use of the capacity provided by the released spectrum and the new multiplex(es)
- growth in the country's content production and media sector, including TV content production and the marketing both locally and overseas (e.g., if Nigerian channels are marketed and sold to Nigerian diaspora abroad amongst others)
- receiver and recorder manufacturers (if any in the country) and retailers can also expect some benefit

There might be some policy benefits for government, who could make use of the new capacity for public services such as health and education.

Costs, which need to be *incurred before switchover*, fall primarily on consumers, not all of whom would individually benefit, and on broadcasters investing in additional digital transmission infrastructure. Receivers are also required.

Benefits	$
Consumer benefit (incremental) in current analogue areas from going digital	
Consumer benefit from new households covered by digital	
Consumer benefit from additional services in retailed spectrum	
Consumer benefit from reuse of released spectrum	
Imputed consumer benefit of compulsory migration	
Economic benefits accruing from media production	
Total Benefits	
Costs	
Compulsory consumer investment in reception (set-top boxes and new TV sets)	
Broadcaster investment in digital transmission infrastructure	
Marketing and practical support costs (excluding any targeted assistance)	
Planning and implementation costs	
Total Costs	
Total NPV	

Figure 57—DTT Cost Benefits Analysis Table

(this is illustrative and not exhaustive)

An illustrative summary of the main cost and benefit headings can be set out in a table as in figure 57. The figures will continue to be subject to revision, and any single figure should be seen as subject to sensitivity analysis. The alternative to switchover—the "no nothing" option—is not really an option.

What the table above also illustrates is the art of looking at TMT as a whole, as argued for in chapter 1. You can see the inclusion of benefits from spectrum release, presumably the estimated value from the auction of the spectrum vacated. Recall that this is the most important driver for DTT. Benefits accruing from the increase in new media content production, particularly driven by easier digital manipulation, must also be estimated.

9.3.2 Cost Categories

The level of infrastructure change in the said country that would create a DTT network for the desired percentage population coverage would have to cover costs such as the following:

- costs to create a single DTT network (and any local networks if required by policy)
- costs for upgrading existing towers or masts and costs for new tower/masts
- costs for purchasing and installing new transmitting antenna for masts to be upgraded so that existing analogue television services would not be interrupted (and costs for mast strengthening if needed)
- costs to upgrade existing building facilities
- costs to upgrade protection power supplies
- costs to purchase and install new redundant DVB-T transmitter system
- costs to purchase and install a suitably dimensioned DTT head-end system
- costs to purchase and install dedicated fibre optic cable in the ground between whichever broadcaster(s) or ServiceCos

linking their channel(s)/programme(s) to the MuxCo and then on to the NetCo's transmitter site

- costs to interface existing analogue production systems to the new DTT head-end and/or contribution link(s)
- costs to commission and test all systems
- costs to train local staff to operate and maintain all systems
- costs to source hundreds of thousands or millions of DTT receivers for the country's households with television, which consumers will have to buy
- contingency costs

9.3.3 Illustrating a Costs Benefits Case: The UK DTT Example

To illustrate the above table using a real example, below are the final costs and benefits that were *predicted in 2004* for the UK DTT project which concluded in 2012. It predicted an estimated £2.3 billion NPV benefits of full digital switchover (Starks, 2004)—the following text in bold is verbatim from the 2004 report:

- **it improves spectrum efficiency—and, more specifically, that it will enable the 20-25% without digital terrestrial coverage to have this option (likely to be of special appeal to those not wishing to subscribe to pay TV)**
- **it will enhance reception in areas of existing coverage**
- **it will enable the broadcasters to make savings on their transmission costs and, in particular, avoid the need for whole-scale reinvestment in the present analogue transmitters during the period 2010-2015**
- **14 frequency channels can be freed for re-use, whether for new broadcasting purposes or, subject to international agreement, more flexibly**
- **there will also be scope for additional new broadcasting services within the spectrum retained for digital terrestrial television (e.g. on one or two further multiplexes and/or for local television).**

However, full switchover also carries some compulsory costs in that:

- those who do not want digital television at all, but do want their familiar services, will be required to acquire it
- those who are content to have it for one TV set only will be required to adapt all the TV sets which they wish to continue using after analogue switch-off
- those who wish to be able to record a different channel from the one to which their TV receiver is tuned, will need to replace their VCR—and re-plugging will be required in many other VCR households (Starks, 2004).

The final NPV analysis from the business case is shown in Figure 58.

Benefits	£m
Consumer benefit in current non-DTT areas	2725
Consumer benefit from additional services in retailed spectrum	659
Consumer benefit from re-use of released spectrum	1011
Imputed consumer benefit of compulsory migration	657
Broadcaster benefit from savings on analogue transmission	1233
Total benefits	**6285**
Costs	
Compulsory consumer investment in reception	3195
Broadcaster investment in digital infrastructure	619
Marketing & practical support costs (excluding any targeted assistance)	163
Total costs	**3977**
Total NPV	**2308**

Figure 58—The UK 2004 DTT Costs-Benefits and NPV Analysis

With such a significant positive NPV of the cost benefit analysis, naturally the ministers at the time approved and gave the go-ahead for the project. I observe at this junction that the benefits turned out to have been understated. Indeed, as you would know by now, just the sale of 800 MHz band generated auction receipts of £2.34 billion, which I led, but this was in 2013!

9.3.4 What to Do with the DTT Cost Benefit Analysis and Business Case

It is important to reemphasise how the illustrative cost benefit analysis above shows yet again the case for looking at TMT as a singular sector and to look at all the projects within the TMT sector "in the round," including 4G auctions or sale of release analogue spectrum, the benefits accruing from new productions and new media sector, etc.

The costs benefits analysis accordingly is also important because

- it enables ministers to decide *how and when* to proceed with DSO;
- it helps prepare for the proceeding project and programme to effect DTT switchover; and
- the business case and NPV can also be used to attract international or national investment to finance the project.

Al in all, it is highly recommended that such projects have clearly identified costs benefit analyses and business cases. If it is good enough for the United Kingdom, it surely must be good enough for Africa and emerging economies.

9.4 Regulatory and Policy Implications of DTT

Once the decision is taken after a cost benefit analysis and a positive (or not) business case, there are whole hosts of regulatory and policy formulations that must ensue. We review some of them, but they are not exhaustive. Rather, the following are discussed briefly, with the aim of the reader appreciating the depth and range of regulatory and policy issues that come with DTT. Policy makers, regulators, and decision makers are recommended to seek further expert advice on the issues such as these below and more. The lack of appropriate policy and regulation can hold back the DTT project no end. Nevertheless, the following are important considerations of note:

- *EPGCo policy formulation and regulation*: You would have noted earlier that an EPGCo needs to be set up in order to formulate and implement the rules for how the electronic programme guide (EPG) will be set up. An EPG is defined as a programme schedule, typically broadcast alongside digital television or radio services, in order to provide information on the content and scheduling of current and future programmes. Who wins top spot on the first page of the EPG, and which channels do not even make the first page, and why? Those on the first page of the EPG clearly have some sort of a competitive advantage with respect to those on page two. It would likely be the case that no piece of current legislation even mentions an EPG or an EPGCo, and who would be empowered to set it up? This is clearly an area of policy formulation and regulation which analogue TV without an EPGCo did not have to worry about, so no legislation and regulation was clearly needed in this area to address this issue of a fair, reasonable, and nondiscriminatory display of competing channels from different ServiceCos. Would the regulator be asked by statute to oversee the EPGCo, or can the MuxCos and broadcasters work together themselves to make EPGCo work? Either way, there must some policy formulation for EPGCo to emerge and some statutory or nonstatutory set of regulations to make it work. Access to EPGs would/may have to be legislated for in the communication acts across the continent, empowering the regulator preferably to consult and formulate a bona fide fair, reasonable, and nondiscriminatory EPG code that all MuxCos and ServiceCos/broadcasters would have to abide by.
- *Conditional access policy and regulation:* Closely associated with the EPG issue above too is the problem of "conditional access" services. Conditional access services (CAS) encrypt (or scramble) broadcast signals so that only those who are entitled to receive them can do so. This way, the broadcaster controls the subscriber's access to digital and interactive TV services. Governments have a clear stake in CAS systems, as the systems help ensure certain channels are blocked, as may

be the case with adult content not being suitable for children. The challenge is this must be blocked at the EPG. PayTV players would also want to be able to disable set-top boxes of owners who have not paid their monthly subscription dues (fees) or in cases where the boxes have been stolen. Access-related conditions would need to be formulated that regulate the access control to set-top boxes and electronic programme guide (EPG) within some legislated acts. Content owners, such as the big movie studios, clearly have a vested interest in ensuring that the digital signal is not easy to copy and the content then pirated.

- *MuxCo policy formulation and regulation:* Similarly, you also saw earlier that a MuxCo or two also comes with DTT, as it is axiomatic with digital that several programmes (or channels) are combined into a single multiplex digital signal. This signal needs to be transmitted across the airwaves, so the MuxCo needs access to spectrum. A first and key decision concerns whether to have only one MuxCo or perhaps two or even more. This is an important policy decision. Legislation would have to be updated to recognize the emergence of a MuxCo or MuxCos. MuxCos will have to be licensed by the regulator to have access to the airwaves. However, even more fraught is deciding who will become the MuxCo. Is it a consortium ownership to the one MuxCo, or does one broadcaster emerge to become the MuxCo and hence become a gatekeeper to the valuable spectrum? For example, in Kenya the government decided the Kenya Broadcasting Corporation (KBC) will operate the country's digital multiplexes, and hence it is the MuxCo.
Conflicts of interests arise almost immediately about how KBC subleases any unused "slots" in the multiplex. So if the multiplex can have eight TV programmes and there are only four "slots" taken, how are the other four allocated? Regulation will decide which broadcasters get the slots on the multiplex and for what channels or programmes. What would be the news and current affairs quotas expected of the broadcasters in return for their slots? Government may even want the

legislative bodies' deliberations to be broadcasted via a parliamentary channel, for example, so voters can see democracy in action. How are the costs of this multiplex shared by all on the multiplex? How do the other broadcasters ensure that KBC is efficient and is not hiving off some of its costs into MuxCo for its competitors to pick them up? Policies to encourage competition and innovation around a multiplex will need to be formulated, and the regulator will be critical to these all.

- *DTT policy and strategy formulation:* DTT migration will not be taken seriously by several stakeholders in the country—broadcasters, manufacturers, NetCos, etc.—unless there is a clear and unambiguous policy that this is what the government wants to do and that it is a priority. The policy will need to show a clear business case and costs benefit analysis for the migration and be crystal clear on the timetable, the benefits promised, and the resources government is making available. The policy would need to be translated into specific legislation with clear directions on how the government expects the policy to be implemented and by whom. The strategy needs to be a multistakeholder developed one but with the full weight of government behind it. The strategy would cover issues including:

  - How long will the period of dual illumination of analogue and digital signals last for?
  - What transmission standard has the government endorsed, e.g., DVB-T2, DVB-T, ISDB-T?
  - What population coverage will DTT cover and why?
  - What content should go on digital as soon as possible in order to entice citizens to adopt digital transmissions in their numbers?
  - How much would set-top boxes (STBs) costs to be affordable?
  - How many STBs would be ordered, and would the government underwrite the order—at least the initial one?

- How many STBs would be subsidized, and how would they be distributed? (In Kenya, set-top boxes appear to be in the range of five to six thousand Kenyan shillings using 2013 prices, which is very expensive for the average Kenyan. This has partly slowed down switchover in Kenya.)_
- Will there be a "return path" to the Internet in the STBs to allow for interactivity where consumers can watch an advert and make an order from their TV sets or vote?
- How would DTT consumer awareness be done?
- What dates have been agreed by government for DTT?
- Will incentives be given to those ContentCos participating in dual illumination of their channels, e.g., by offering them extra channels on the multiplexes?
- Would radio channels be carried on the DTT multiplex(es)?
- Does the government want local manufacturing of STBs?

There are clearly many questions for the strategy to answer. A clear road map, strategy, and communication strategy must be defined which is both credible and has the support of all the stakeholders.

- *Frequency spectrum planning for DTT:* DTT cannot proceed seamlessly without thoughtful spectrum planning. The new MuxCos would need to be licensed on new frequencies, and during dual illumination, there is clearly more demand for the spectrum airwaves. If the spectrum regulator does not issue a timely and comprehensive spectrum plan, there is almost certainly going to be a delay to the entire DTT migration programme.
- *Financing, incentives, and costs:* This triumvirate would have to be thought through to arrive at a clear policies and regulations to address them in the context of the DTT migration. Would the government pay for DTT up front, or would it get the broadcasters to pay in exchange for guaranteed twenty-year-plus broadcasting licenses, as partly happened in the United Kingdom? Would it be a public private partnership,

as happened in Tanzania? The public broadcaster (Tanzania Broadcasting Corporation) formed a joint venture (Star Media) with a foreign company (China StarTimes) to build out the DTT network in Tanzania. What incentives will be given to some recalcitrant broadcasters to migrate to digital, particularly if the commercial broadcasters argue—very cogently—that they will get absolutely no commercial benefit from the switch to digital through higher advertising revenues? Do you offer these sort of players extra channel slots? What incentives do you give broadcasters to dual illuminate? Remember that dual illumination essentially amounts to coercing the broadcasters to simultaneously run both the analogue and digital infrastructures at the same time. As noted in the previous chapter, the finances of most African broadcasters are already quite fragile. DTT may just tip many of the over the edge. This will be an unwanted outcome for the sector. What incentives will be put in place to encourage the public to go out and buy set-top boxes, particularly if they are not quite affordable?

- *Access (population and content) and affordability (set-top box policy) policy formulation and the role of state-owned public service broadcasters in a DTT world:* Universal access policy refers to the implementation of the policy for the benefit of every person in society, including those in rural areas. Universal service refers to the specific service that is delivered to all in society. Would DTT be a universal service? This is quite an onerous position for most African countries to take on. Even the United Kingdom does not go to 100 percent of the population for DTT. The BBC MuxCo carrying public service channels reaches an amazing 98.5 percent of the population, whilst the commercial UK MuxCos have an obligation to reach only circa 90 percent, up from 73 percent for their analogue coverage. Nevertheless, for both the BBC and ITV plc (the United Kingdom's biggest commercial broadcaster), it was felt that in order to provide more widespread coverage and a larger bouquet of channels, a digital satellite alternative was also necessary. Hence the Freesat[5] was launched. The remaining 1.5 percent out of reach of the BBC's multiplexes and the 10 percent out of reach of the commercial MuxCos have an option of going digital satellite. However, these sorts of ranges of population access numbers (i.e., 98.5 and 90 percent) are completely unreachable in most African countries as well as other emerging market countries too.

For South Africa, Africa's biggest economy, main public service analogue TV channels (SABC 1 and 2) reach 90 percent, whilst SAB-3 is just under this. Digital would have to match and/or better this. However, Tanzania at the beginning of 2013 had only attained 22 percent DTT penetration, compared to 24 percent for analogue, and the inability of the Tanzanian MuxCo to roll out countrywide has been publicly acknowledged (Gunze, 2013). Even after a well-trumpeted and successful DSO in Tanzania, huge trunks of the country (> 60 percent) are still not covered by digital TV transmissions as per February 2014. Countries would have to consider access questions carefully and decide on how widespread their DTT can truly be and over what timescales. Affordability policy decisions would have to be taken too.

Mauritius was the first African nation to get off the blocks in Africa with its DTT migration, but the experiences are mixed: 40 percent were reported not to be able to afford STBs, along with an open market of STBs leading to very poor quality of experience. South Africa's government decided that set-top boxes will be subsidised for the poorest in society to the tune of about 70 percent of the cost of the box, and there are an estimated five million households in this group, making this quite an expensive policy for government.

And how does the government decide who is poor in most other African countries outside South Africa? Hopefully,

---

5 Freesat is a contract-free satellite service owned by the BBC and UK commercial broadcaster ITV, launched on May 6, 2008. It offers the same bouquet of services as the digital terrestrial TV network in the United Kingdom but on a free basis after the subscriber purchases a Freesat receiver or set-top box.

these boxes do not attract taxes either to encourage affordability. Access also extends to access to the new digital content. African state-owned broadcasters truly find themselves in a bind with DTT. As "public service broadcasters," they are usually called upon to lead the DTT migration process, though they would typically have severe reservations. To them, justifiably, the government is not necessarily committing to increased funding to them in perpetuity, yet they are taking on more costs (dual illumination, "must carry"[6] obligations, marketing costs to compete with new digital competitors), etc. In most cases, state broadcasters would be aiding and abetting the fragmentation of their audiences, driving down their advertising rates. They clearly do not like this. Unless they get new funding, what incentives does government have to incentivize these state broadcasters? Governments need to realise these organisations have to change to survive and be viable in a DTT world, and their public service policy mandates have to be modulated to suit. On the other hand, even if the government could fund the state broadcaster (e.g., using oil monies, say), there is a key policy question then as to whether true competition can happen in the sector if public funds are going into one player whilst the others have to compete in the marketplace. These are all key issues that a good independent regulator should worry about. Generally, access and affordability questions abound in all emerging economies.

- *Competition (pluralism), content (including content diversity) and choice policies for DTT:* Much of what the previous bullets have left unsaid is the government would have to be clear on the competition and choice landscape it wants as an outcome in their country. Ideally, competition would love to see a pluralism of broadcasting players providing a diversity of broadcast content in many different languages. How many languages would

---

6 Must carry conditions oblige these state broadcasters, for example, to ensure their public service channels are carried on other digital competing platforms, e.g., satellite or cable. These state broadcasters usually are expected to pick up the costs of these as well.

the government want to hear on air covering news, drama, entertainment, etc.? These are all important but costly considerations. In Africa, it is easy for new players to come in and win broadcasting licenses, and in many cases they are just not up to the task of being broadcasters. A good independent regulator is arguably best placed to make decisions on those who deserve broadcasting licenses. The government clearly needs to have a proactive set of policies to promote a digital content industry.

We digress slightly to emphasise pluralism and Africa. Africa has fifty-four countries, over a billion people, and hundreds of ethnic groups, cultures, languages, and dialects. Africa has lots of complexities in its huge diversity of peoples, languages, and cultures, within and across national boundaries. One of its intrinsic beauties comes from Africa being so highly diverse. The most populous state of over 170 million people, Nigeria, alone has nearly four hundred native languages. Ethiopia has seventy unique languages, with two hundred different dialects. Nevertheless, size of population is not fully correlated to the number of languages. Burkina Faso has a population of over sixteen million people, yet there sixty ethnic groups. A digital content industry which promotes such pluralism within and without national boundaries offers significant opportunities, as Nigeria's Nollywood is already proving.

9.4.1 The Tanzania DTT Example

To emphasise and illustrate some of the above policy points in general, it is illustrative to review the successes and the challenges of the Tanzanian DTT switchover. Tanzania concluded part of the first phase of the analogue to digital switchover on December 31, 2012, starting with the capital Dar es Salaam with the switching off of fourteen transmission sites. They continued switching off through 2013 and will have fully completed the process by the end of 2014. Nevertheless, reviews of the Dar Es Salaam switch-off by the Tanzanian regulator TCRA (Gunze, 2013) and by consultancy Analysys Mason (Schuman, 2013) illustrates many of the points articulated above.

Gunze (2013) acknowledges that only 24 percent of Tanzanians had access to analogue TV before switchover, so the challenge was arguably easier than for many other countries.

Both reviews[7] by TCRA and Analysys Mason[8] acknowledge the following success factors (there are key messages herein for other countries to learn from):

- DTT was "policy driven rather than market driven" (Gunze, 2013). He acknowledges clear and unequivocal political will from the cabinet (2008) on the digital migration roadmap, digital migration strategy, and the communication strategy followed by endorsement by the president of Tanzania. The government put in place the necessary legislation that put the legal framework in place via the Electronic and Postal Communications Act (EPOCA) of 2010. The EPOCA Digital and other Broadcasting Networks Regulations 2011 provided the legal basis for the analogue switch-off. These are all as recommended above under "DTT policy and strategy formulation."
- The regulator (Tanzania Communications Regulatory Agency—TCRA) drew up and consulted on the roadmap. Next, TCRA put in place a clear regulatory framework for DTT, including the separation of content from transmission (NetCo), which lead to licensing of MuxCos as separate from channels (ServiceCos). Regulations were put in place for the licensing of set-top boxes and TV sets. TCRA also clearly decided against mobile TV or high-definition TV services and designated the four then existing free-to-air channels as "must carry" channels. TCRA concluded on three MuxCo licenses, one public

---

7 H. Gunze (2013), Tanzania Communications Regulatory Authority (TCRA), Country Status on Migration from Analogue to Digital Switchover, A Presentation to 8th CTO Digital Broadcasting Forum, February 12, 2013, Sandton, South Africa, http://www.cto.int/media/events/pst-ev/2013/DBSF-2013/Tanzania-Country-Status.pdf (accessed October 2013).

8 R. Schumann (2013), Case Study of Digital TV Switchover in Tanzania, http://www.analysysmason.com/About-Us/News/Insight/Case-study-of-digital-TV-switchover-in-Tanzania/#.UjhvE8bWR5I (accessed October 2013).

and two commercial, and it also decided on a twenty-five-year duration for the MuxCo licenses with an upfront fee of four hundred thousand US dollars and an annual fee of 0.8 percent of revenue. These are all questions posed above.

- TCRA also decided wisely that the state broadcaster, the Tanzanian Broadcasting Corporation (TBC), should be split into a signal distributor, TransCo, and a content provider (ContentCo/ServiceCo). However, TCRA decided on multiple TransCos, rather than a single one.

- TCRA began a public education road show in April 2011, where the president of Tanzania launched the Digital Tanzania campaign along with the digital logo. This is good and symbolic leadership for a totemic project. This was followed by another clear communications strategy prepared by TCRA and approved by government for all communication outlets, including print, newspapers, TV, radio, road shows, talk shows, meetings, seminars, jingles, and songs, both audio and visual, from local (ward) to national levels. These communications were tailor-made for the various age groups and audiences.

- Financing was also agreed, as noted earlier, via a PPP joint venture called Star Media between TBC (35 percent) and China StarTimes (65 percent) to build the DTT network. Two other private players won MuxCo licenses, Agape and Basic Transmissions, who are also bringing in private capital. The Tanzanian government, unlike previously in this volume, exempted all import duty and VAT on STBs up to the end of 2012 to improve affordability. These taxes were sadly restored, but common sense prevailed and both tax exemptions were reintroduced in July 2013.

Let us look too at the challenges beginning with those acknowledged by TCRA itself (Gunze, 2013):

- TCRA laments high costs of simulcast periods (i.e., dual illumination), including satellite capacity costs, utilities, and human resources.

- TCRA laments the inability of MuxCo to roll out countrywide and the existence signal coverage black spots due to uneven terrain. They lament only 22 percent population of DTT penetration thus far (as of February 2013), compared to 24 percent analogue penetration.
- They lament poor initial distribution of set-top boxes (STBs) and a lack of consumer understanding of STB/antenna installation, as well as lack of training in the use of remote control functionalities. There have also been issues about the importation of poor quality STBs and STB inter-operability/compatibility issues, as there are both DVB-T and DVB-T2 boxes in Tanzania.
- TCRA has already been called in to adjudicate on disagreements between MuxCos and ContentCos/ServiceCos, as discussed earlier under "MuxCo policy formulation and regulation." TCRA has been called in to referee disagreements on service level agreements (SLAs) between MuxCos and ContentCos (or channels). High transmission fees imposed by MuxCos to ContentCos/ServiceCos have had to be revised by TCRA who ensured the fees were truly costs oriented.
- There is already what TCRA calls "local content thirst," regulatory-speak or code for they do not have enough Tanzanian content and that they perhaps did not have enough policies to stimulate local content production. There is general lack of local content across all the East African countries that have already migrated to digital – an important lesson for other countries to learn from. In Mauritius, twelve additional channels were introduced, but content has been secured only to fill six! From my experience with some other countries across the world, I will counsel countries to beware of setting up well-intentioned local content regulations because of the law of unintended consequences. A case in point is as follows: if a regulator mandates that 60% of the content on the new digital muxes must be produced locally when it costs US $8000 to 10,000 to produce an hour of content (vs. US 300 to 1,500) to buy. Such economics clearly does not work and inextricably leads to very poor quality

being produced and aired locally. The balance here is very fine. Furthermore, any country that rightly pushes for more local content must also be prepared to take on the rampant pirates across all the streets on the African continent and elsewhere.

- At another conference[9], Gunze lamented their decision on multiple signal distributors or TransCos, noting that this has created conflicts with co-location on the same sites and masts and duplication of effort. He recommends starting with one (which is clearly regulated) and evaluating the market structure later. I agree. In the United Kingdom, there used to be two, but later they merged to form one called Arqiva[10]. I was a Managing Director at Arqiva for 4 years.
- Lastly, TCRA laments issues with regional and rural insertion to MuxCo's networks.

Analysys Mason's Schuman (2013) highlights some key challenges too:

- The two other MuxCos, Agape and Basic Transmissions, launched in six and three localities, respectively, only after the December 31, 2012, switchover date in the first half of 2013. This shows some lack of coordination in project plan between public and commercial MuxCos.
- The pricing of STBs is clearly challenging. It started off at sixty US dollars to buy it outright in a country with GDP per capita of five hundred dollars, with a lowest "rent" price of twenty-five dollars, provided the subscriber subscribes to a monthly package of $5.63 a month. This is frankly unaffordable and not inclusive. Reach without affordability is futile. TCRA has promised to develop a scheme for low-income users, but it appears the government did not have a clear access and affordability set of policies.

---

9 Digital Broadcasting Switchover Forum Africa, 11 – 14 February 2014, Arusha, Tanzania.

10 www.arqiva.com

- There have been issues with the STB supply chain, including distributors being slow in getting STBs into stores. Schuman notes that viewers they spoke to reported that suppliers in Dar es Salaam ran out of STBs during the final month before digital switchover, and there were reports of unscrupulous vendors selling fake STBs. Analysys Mason's study also report of a perception that vendors were incorrectly advising consumers to buy analogue equipment, thereby confusing citizens whether analogue equipment would still be usable post switchover. An analogue TV set is obviously usable along with a STB; it is understandable how consumers could miss this subtlety.

- Another salutary lesson from Tanzania's early experience is that an incredible 80 percent of the STBs purchased by consumers were returned to outlets, but 70 percent were diagnosed as users either ignoring instructions from customer care or having never gotten those instructions in the first place due to long queues at distribution centres. In other cases, consumers had to purchase a new antenna, which is not cheap. Nevertheless, STB quality issues persist, as acknowledged by TCRA above.

- Tanzania started its switch off with its most populous and capital city, Dar es Salaam. In contrast, London was the last city to be switched off in the United Kingdom! It appears a significant number of people in the capital did not have their STBs before the switch-off, leading to long queues in the first five days of the New Year after the December 31, 2012, switch off. Estimates of 20 to 50 percent of those in the capital having no access to TV after switch off shows there were real problems with the project preparations, planning, and implementation in the capital. These issues could have been ironed out, switching off smaller and border towns first before doing the capital last, as happened in the United Kingdom.

- Schuman appears sceptical as to whether the two commercial MuxCos (Agape and Basic Transmission) can develop a sustainable business against the StarTimes public multiplex.

It must be emphasised that overall, Tanzania is a good news story for its DTT migration. However, these Tanzania lessons in particular and this section in general provide real insights on the principles and praxis of DTT migration. I knows them well from my experience of one of the biggest switchovers in the world, in the United Kingdom, where 1,154 sites and relay sites were switched off/on.

9.5 Some Other Key Recommendations Towards a Successful End-to-End DTT Migration Programme

We conclude this chapter with the following recommendations towards a successful end-to-end DTT migration programme. These recommendations should be read in conjunction with the rest of this chapter, as it summarises some of the key takeaways. These recommendations draw much from Ofcom's recommendations to the UK secretary of state on driving digital switchover before the government approved the project in the United Kingdom (SoS Report, 2004).[11] The recommendations have naturally been adapted for the African and emerging markets context. Given that these recommendations were largely followed by Ofcom and other UK stakeholders to achieve one of the largest and most successful DTT migrations in the world, they are definitely worth understanding. It was genuinely my honour to have played some role in it over the project's last and critical four years spanning 2009 to 2012. The recommendations follow under the categories: regulatory framework, timing issues, consumer information and advice, a move from planning to implementation, international issues, affordability, and technology choices and decisions.

---

11 Driving Digital Switchover: A Report to the Secretary of State, Office of Communications (Ofcom), April 5, 2004: http://stakeholders.ofcom.org.uk/binaries/research/tv-research/dsol.pdf (accessed October 2013).

Regulatory Framework

1. *A unified and independent telecommunications regulator is highly recommended to facilitate DTT and DSO:* It is strongly recommended that countries establish a unified telecommunications regulator in Cameroon. For those countries still to do so, it is never too late to get it right for the 2020s. Other countries, including Kenya (CCK), Tanzania (TCRA), and Namibia (CRAN), have already made this momentous step. It needs to be independent and play a significant role in managing the regulatory framework to encourage DTT adoption and removing obstacles. It will need to regulate (i) for innovation and new entrants into DTT and elsewhere, (ii) for competition, both national and international in a global world (iii), for a wide range of public service content and high-quality radio/ TV programmes like news, drama, regional (provincial) quota productions, etc., (iv) for investment in order to attract foreign direct investment into the country, (v) for spectrum efficiency and more beneficial use of the country's airwaves for their consumers and citizens, and (vi) for growth of the economy, etc.

New entities will have to be licensed in this new digital world:
- ContentCos
- ServicesCo: new broadcasting licensees (ServicesCo) who may or may not be the ContentCos
- MuxCos: new multiplex licensees (MuxCos) which are not needed in an analogue world but much needed in a digital one
- TransCo: a new transmission provider would need to be licensed by the (new) regulator who would own and operate the high-power digital masts infrastructure and relays across the country (Since it will almost certainly have significant market power [SMP] in "Network Access" and "Managed Transmission Services" [NA/MTS], the [new] converged regulator with competition powers will need to regulate its pricing and costs.)

- EPGCo: a new EPGCo, which is needed too in a digital world and needs to be regulated in order to provide logical channel numbers (LCNs) on the new digital platform (The regulator will have to regulate for *prominence*, say, of the public service broadcasters over commercial ones.)
- content quota and news regulation: in order to regulate for a plurality of the voices (i.e., languages, cultures, etc.) on the new digital platform
- and much more

However, it is hoped the case for a converged regulator is clear, as it has been argued for several times already in this volume.

2. *SwitchCo—a not-for-profit organization to be set up to implement DTT migration:* It is important that a multistakeholder organization is set up to plan and implement DSO. Experience elsewhere suggests it is preferred the organization is created as a not-for-profit company or a company limited by guarantee. It may also be a separate government agency. It should be wound up after switchover completes and then its assets dissolved. This is what has happened in other countries. The state broadcaster and other broadcasters should play a role in this body. Broadcasters should not necessarily manage the process of implementing switchover themselves—as recommended, a not-for-profit SwitchCo should do that. However, it is reasonable to expect them to play a role in the switchover process, particularly by extending digital terrestrial coverage and availability nationwide as much as they can (not least as they are incentivized by advertising to as many "eyeballs" as possible. SwitchCo should also ensure viewers are properly informed about switchover and its implications for them. The regulator should seek commitments from broadcasters and may consider including appropriate and necessary additional obligations for nationwide digital TV rollout in the new digital public service broadcasting licenses, which would be issued before switchover is complete. In some cases, the

role of SwitchCo can be played by a strong regulator, but in many cases it is preferable they are above the fray. A move from planning into implementation should happen as soon as possible.

3. *Transmission market review, state broadcaster review, and the setup of TransCo:* A market review of the broadcasting and broadcasting transmission market would be timely. As in most cases, only the state broadcaster would have transmission assets, and any market review will almost certainly result in it having significant market power (SMP) in transmission, which should automatically lead to remedies. Such remedies may include the hiving off of all its masts and transmission assets into a separate regulated new entity—TransCo—with TransCo charged to roll out as many masts and relays as possible by the broadcasters or MuxCos in order to increase the latter's coverage base. The state broadcaster itself will need to be reviewed and possibly split into a ContentCo and a TransCo, as happened in Tanzania—certainly its transmission assets will need to go into TransCo. The converged regulator should have the powers to ensure effective competition in this market and will seek to ensure that an agreement to extend DTT transmission networks does not result in broadcasters being charged excessive prices. This again proves the importance of a new regulatory regime set up in legislation.

4. *Redefinition of broadcasting and media market beyond TransCo:* Digital transition usually results in new market definitions. As noted above, new players emerge who do not exist in the analogue world, e.g., MuxCos or multiplex operators, both public service and commercial ones; EPGCo—the EPG provider for the platform; ServicesCo (both public and commercial); and content markets with likely quotas to meet certain plurality, location of origin, and other regulatory metrics. The market review will consider competition issues as well as decide on what the optimal market post the issue of the digital

licenses should look like. This would require a public consultation typically so that industry, not-for-profit sector, academics, likely investors, etc., can contribute ideas to the market structure post the issue of digital licenses. This may require new legislation and laws to enact them.

5. *Introducing spectrum fees—it sends a clear signal that spectrum is not free:* The government and/or enhanced regulator should consider imposing spectrum pricing to sharpen incentives to promote switchover. In most countries, commercial licensees typically pay for their licenses to broadcast, which include an implicit charge for spectrum. The regulator should ensure that licensees do not pay twice for the same spectrum. If spectrum pricing is introduced, charges could apply for the first time to the state broadcaster and other broadcasters by the end of switchover. By knowing they will be paying the market value of spectrum, they will not be wont to "wasting" or "hoarding" it. The key recommendation here is to ensure the government does not spend so much resources doing DSO just for the released spectrum to be hoarded or wasted by incumbents or new players.

6. *Costs of regulator-imposed obligations must be proportionate:* Some of the new and potential obligations (e.g., on coverage or content quotas or plurality of voices, etc.) could raise costs disproportionately for our fledgling state and commercial broadcasters. The regulator should be charged with taking account of additional burdens on these companies where appropriate as they regulate the sector.

7. *Government must impose some obligations on the state broadcaster:* As part of the review of the broadcasting and transmission market, the government/regulator may be minded to impose specific obligations to the state broadcaster's or newly created TransCo's current general obligations in order to

promote digital TV. They could/should include obligations on rolling out digital transmission nationwide in their new licences (which should go beyond similar obligations for commercial players), providing public information, continuing to provide its channels for free, and providing on-air marketing of digital TV on a platform-neutral basis.

Timing Issues

8. *Find out whether you are a 2015 or 2020 country:* For those countries yet to start their DTT migration planning in 2013/14, they should first check if they are a 2015 country or 2020 country. Even if they are a 2015 deadline country, the four myths noted above should give them some comfort not to panic and just carefully and deliberately follow the recommendations of this chapter on what to do next. For those with a 2020 deadline, they clearly have more time ahead of them, though they should not be complacent either.

9. *Government should set a firm roadmap, strategy, and timetable after consultation and hold firm to it:* Without a firm timetable for switchover, broadcasters and transmission companies will not be able to decide if and when the obsolete analogue equipment should be replaced. As soon as the technology platform for DTT is agreed, government should pass a law outlawing continuing sales of analogue-only TV receivers.

10. *Early announcement of date is preferable:* The benefits of an early announcement of a precise timetable are: certainty for consumers in their purchasing decisions; certainty for broadcasters, transmission companies, manufacturers, and retailers in investment decisions; and certainty for the regulator, SwitchCo, and the rest of government itself in implementing the regulatory framework for digital public service

broadcasting licences, the review of public service broadcasting, and spectrum pricing.

Consumer Information and Advice

11. *Consumers need information early:* Switchover will not hap-
    pen smoothly unless consumers also understand the benefits—
    and you do not want to lose their goodwill from recently
    acquired analogue equipment purchases which will be written
    off shortly.

12. *Mobilise a mass national advertising campaign well before the
    switchover date:* Well before switchover, a mass national ad-
    vertising campaign should explain to all households that swi-
    tchover is coming and should attempt to build public support
    for the objective. A new consumer labelling scheme and logo,
    e.g., Digital Tanzania as happened in Tanzania, should also
    be introduced to warn consumers that unconverted analogue
    equipment will not function past a set date. This needs to be
    implemented with the support of distributors and retail outlets.
    The funding requirements of consumer information and ad-
    vice would be significant.

13. *Further information around and after switchover date(s):*
    Around the switchover date in their region, consumers will
    require further information and support. The promotion drive
    should not just include on-air advertising on analogue TV, post-
    ers on billboards, etc., but also direct marketing, help lines, clear
    product labelling, and possibly in-home support. A regional
    communications campaign in the immediate run-up to analogue
    switch off will need to be developed with specially tailored ad-
    vice for households who are unable to receive digital terrestrial
    signals until switchover starts. After switchover is completed,
    continuing support will also need to be offered to consumers
    who remain hesitant or confused about the conversion to digital.

A Move from Planning to Implementation

14. *SwitchCo should be created after adoption of the DTTV action plan replacing the informal regulator-led grouping that most likely generated the DTT action plan:* This digital TV action plan, when delivered by the regulator and/or government, will be effective in delivering the preconditions and policy options for a government decision on switchover. However, a more active and well-resourced agency (SwitchCo) will be required to complete switchover effectively. SwitchCo is a child of both the public service broadcasters as well as the private ones and government of course. SwitchCo should highlight the benefits of switchover, provide public information, provide support at switchover, ensure clear labelling, liaise with other interested parties, report on progress made by them, attempt to maximise the number of digital options available, and ensure platform neutrality in the promotion of digital TV.

15. *SwitchCo must be adequately resourced:* The government, in collaboration with broadcasters and the enhanced regulator, should ensure SwitchCo is an adequately resourced body, which can gain the confidence of all parties. SwitchCo will require funding for running costs, marketing expenditure, and consumer support around switchover. Funding could come from a number of potential sources, including direct public expenditure, forgone future public receipts from broadcasting activities, an element of the TV licence fee, or private finance funded by foregone future spectrum revenues. Since the economy as a whole is the main beneficiary of switchover, the funding mechanism should not put a disproportionate burden on any interested party.

16. *A region-by-region switchover is less risky, starting from perhaps a second tier city in the country:* A gradual region-by-region switchover process is preferable, starting, arguably, from a second-tier city. You may be surprised by this

recommendation. In most European digital switchovers, they start from the smallest (border) villages and towns and end with the capital city. London was switched off in October 2012, well after the eastern borders of Scotland (Whitehaven and Selkirk), which was switched off at the end of 2008, almost four years earlier! Only seventy-five thousand homes were switched off by the end of 2008, compared to nearly nine million homes that were switched off (at the end) with the London switch off. Would you want to mess up London? It made sense to make mistakes in the small border regions, iron out all the processes and systems, and be in impeccable shape by the time it came to London's turn. And so it came to pass—London happened effortlessly and smoothly thanks to all the practice from other regional switch-offs over four years.

So why not just transpose this to Africa and emerging market countries? Doing so will demonstrate some lack of understanding of the continent and emerging economies. Tanzania started its digital switch off with Dar es Salaam, its capital city. It is not as crazy as it reads or sounds. However, I recommend the switch off starts with some second-tier cities for the following pragmatic reasons:

- There is more likely to be analogue TV viewership in the cities (first- and second-tier cities) that is worth switching off. There are virtually no TV viewers in most rural parts of Africa.
- Those in the cities can afford to buy and/or finance set-top boxes.
- There is electricity in the cities, compared to batteries or nothing elsewhere.
- Even if there was some TV in rural areas running off batteries, such rural areas would not be truly representative of the issues that will be faced when switching off a capital city like Dar es Salaam or Cairo.

- Since the quality of terrestrial TV was never that great across the continent, the middle class in cities like Nairobi already have satellite-based TV and so are not as reliant on terrestrial TV, like in developed economies.

For such pragmatic reasons as above, I recommend commencing with a second-tier city in the country as a starting point. Dar es Salaam switch off was clearly not a roaring success, but neither was it a disaster. However, it may have been better to start with a second-tier city first before getting to Dar es Salaam. Countries which decide to commence with their first-tier cities may be quite justified too for the reasons listed above.

International Issues

17. *Protect future use of released spectrum via international coordination Agreements with neighbours:* A key driver for switchover is the spectrum dividend. Every country's strategy for the UHF spectrum should be to seek to protect its DSO plan. It should also seek to protect its future use of the released spectrum for mobile broadband and any viable white space spectrum after switchover. This should be done through active international coordination agreements with neighbouring countries. It is also important in general to coordinate with other neighbours not yet switched on.

Affordability

18. *Consumers must have access to an affordable DTT kit (set-top boxes and TVs), and cooperation and harmonisation across governments and regulators throughout the continent and elsewhere is most important:* The transitional cost of conversion to digital would remain a significant barrier for many

households, and it risks leaving the vast majority of households excluded from TV after switchover. This will be a disaster for the future viability of the platform. The penetration of digital TV rises with household income, so transitional costs of switchover would fall predominantly on the poor. So the government and SwitchCo and other players must try and ensure affordable set-top boxes are available before and after switchover. Affordability is best driven by economies of scale across Africa and elsewhere from the harmonization on the same transmission and encoding standards, as well as avoiding taxing this equipment too.

Technology Choices and Decisions

19. *Early technology decisions on a plethora of digital options and technology pilots are absolutely vital:* Digital introduces a whole new bunch of technologies, transmission modes, codecs, frame rates, aspect ratios, antennae heights, transmitters EiRP, single frequency network vs. multifrequency network, etc. Along with chosen end user receivers, countries will need to pilot their optimum technology, transmitter, multiplexing, minimum receiver performance, and radio choices.

20. *Include at least a couple to several HDTV Services:* This ensures all receivers are ready for a few years down the line when HDTV becomes more ubiquitous. If one looks out to the 2020s, this is a sensible position to take

21. *Training, DTT network operation and maintenance, training of installers, ensuring availability of digital set-top boxes or TVs with in-built DTV tuners:* These are all vital to arrange via SwitchCo, MuxCos, and TransCo. Law makers also need training before legislation. Regulators may need training on a new converged regulatory regime.

Final General and Most Important Recommendation

22. *DTT migration must be policy and outcomes led, and it must be part of a wider TMT sector redesign in the country:* Perhaps the most important and final recommendation is this simple one going as far back as chapter 1. I make no apologies for emphasizing over and over again that DTT migration must be seen primarily within the wider context of the redesign of the TMT sectors in Africa and other emerging markets. They should not get caught up in the "silo" mentality of a big DTT engineering project. The DTT migration project releases much-needed spectrum which should/would be released for 4G mobile broadband, which—combined with all the submarine capacity being landed (and distributed) on the continent (and all national and regional backbone planning)—provides a golden opportunity to redesign the entire TMT sector. With this golden opportunity, affordability and reach/access must be the primary policy outcome drivers knitting all these projects. The blueprint proposed in chapter 3 underpins and underscores the sort of TMT sector redesign that a project like a DTT migration one truly triggers. This is the real context that any DTT migration project must be seen in—not the narrow technocracy that I see on several of the DTTV projects across the continent of Africa and some emerging markets.

23. Media (including TV) data and analytics are key: for an industry built on advertising and sponsorship, data and analytics is simply invaluable. An authoritative and credible player must emerge who measures and publishes such data and analytics. In the United Kingdom, an entity called BARB[12] provides the official source of TV viewing figures in the UK.

---

12 www.barb.co.uk

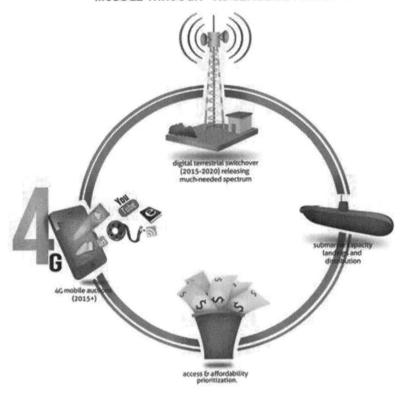

Figure 8 (unusually re-presented from chapter 1)—Digital TV Migration
Must Be Seen in the Wider Context of This Picture,
and *Not* as a Narrow Technocratic Project

SECTION V

TOWARDS *BETTER* AVAILABILITY OF AFFORDABLE FIXED LINES AND FIXED INTERNET

CHAPTER 10

TOWARDS *BETTER* AVAILABILITY OF AFFORDABLE FIXED LINE AND FIXED INTERNET

"It always seems impossible, until it's done."
—*Nelson Mandela*

"The man who removes a mountain begins by carrying away small stones."
—*Chinese Proverb*

Hopefully, you will empathise with this rather hopeful Nelson Mandela quote to begin this chapter on *better* availability of affordable fixed Internet on the continent of Africa in particular, but also in many other developing economies. It is a Herculean task, an almost impossible one, frankly—given where the African continent is today. This is the unashamed reason that you would have keenly spotted a different adjective describing the ambition of this chapter. It is *not* as with other sections and chapters in this volume aspiring "towards *widespread* availability of affordable *high quality*." Rather it is "towards *better* availability of affordable fixed line and fixed Internet." You are bound to ask, "Why such a brazen backing down and lowering of outcomes expected on this issue?" There are three reasons:

- Firstly, the fixed line and fixed Internet problem on the African continent (and many other emerging economies I have visited) is such a hard problem that it would be bluntly *unrealistic* to expect similar outcomes as are expected by this volume for the 2020s for mobile voice/data, mobile broadband, radio, digital TV, and other media.

- Secondly, in my defence as well, the recommended prioritization process in chapter 3 encapsulated by figure 27's straw man set of three- to five-years' priorities did not include the fixed line and fixed Internet problem. It is simply the case that most Africans will get to know the Internet first via wireless means, and it must be right that this is openly acknowledged and prioritized by decision makers. We will not be cabling fixed lines and fixed Internet to many significant African homes (to merit the adjective "widespread") anytime soon, even for the 2020s.

- Thirdly, there is a significant range of other "supply side" problems elsewhere to address to realize such a goal, including a much more sustainable solution to the power issue beyond diesel generators, revolutionary changes to town/city planning with named streets and cabling to homes, much denser regional and national backbone distribution which is very costly, etc. You can appreciate the size of these other "outside TMT" supply-side challenges for fixed line/Internet outcome to be achieved.

Why have this chapter at all given the reasons above then? This is a good question. Notwithstanding the three good "excuses" or reasons above, the straw man recommendations and the blueprint of chapter 3 (in general) still made clear recommendations under the "Competition" banner on "liberalisation of fixed" namely: "submarine capacity distribution" and "competition in fixed." These are tacit fixed-related activities and projects which if executed on properly, even though not as grand, would lead towards better availability of affordable fixed line and fixed Internet for the 2020s. Would they be widespread, high quality, and fully affordable over this period? Unlikely! However, any baby steps are better than none because all African countries must be charting their way to be on the path to knowledge-based economies, and fixed networks would be invaluable to such transformations. This is because, ultimately, radio spectrum is limited by Shannon's law, whilst fibre optic cable can provide virtually unlimited capacity with more fibre.

This is a rather shorter chapter too. Nevertheless, it attempts to address the following questions:

- After so many chapters covering wireless and other radio services, what, again, is *fixed* wireless?
- What is the size of the fixed challenge which makes it such a "Herculean" task that led me to back down on the ambitions vis-à-vis other sections of this volume? What are the fixed findings to date?
- What outcomes should be strived towards better availability of affordable fixed line and fixed Internet?
- What are the key initiatives towards better availability of affordable fixed line and fixed Internet?

10.1 Fixed vs. Fixed Wireless

As a reminder from chapter 2, fixed telecommunications refers to services provided over electronic communication networks which serve fixed locations. Fixed services are distinguished from wireless (mobile) services that can be used whilst on the move. Access networks are examples of fixed networks using copper lines or fibre optic cable networks, and so on. Though the term "fixed networks" is technologically neutral, it is usually taken to mean services over copper or fibre lines. This is distinguished from the term "fixed wireless," which is sometimes used to describe other forms of fixed service delivered by radio. Therefore, the precise meaning of the term "fixed telecoms" can vary in different contexts.

10.2 The Challenge of Fixed in 2013/14

It is only fair to quickly review where Africa is broadly on fixed, i.e., what is the scorecard to date. As you should expect from above, it is not good.

10.2.1 Comparing Fixed and Mobile Penetration in Africa

This subsection covers the stark comparison between fixed and mobile penetration across Africa. Though based on 2010 data by GSMA Intelligence (2011),[1] *not much* has changed on the fixed front; much of the changes are obviously happening with mobile penetration. Figure 59 shows the dire state of fixed penetration for twenty-five countries on the continent, which represent 91 percent of the continent's mobile connections in 2010. GSMA Intelligence (2011) argues that these markets are extremely diverse economically, culturally, geographically, and politically and are therefore a good representation of Africa as a whole.

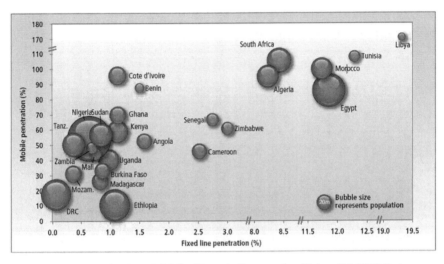

Figure 59—Fixed vs. Mobile (Percent Penetration Using Q4 2010 Data
for Twenty-Five African Countries, Which Represented
91 percent of Mobile Connections in Q4 2010)
(Source: GSMA Intelligence African Mobile Observatory 2011;
reproduced with permission of the copyright owner)

1 GSMA Intelligence *African Mobile Observatory 2011: Driving Mobile and Social Development through Mobile Services*, GSMA, http://www.gsma.com (accessed October 2013).

You may be concerned that the data shown with respect to fixed teledensity in figure 59 is dated being 2010 data—so was I. However, it is the most comprehensive and authoritative data and picture on the state of fixed in Africa, particularly sub-Saharan Africa (SSA). Nevertheless, I've since checked this 2009/10 data with more recent, though less comprehensive GSMA data (GSMA Intelligence, 2013b).[2] The new report finds the teledensity of Nigeria at 1.2 percent, Tanzania at 1.9 percent, Kenya at 2.3 percent, etc. The point here is a clear and simple one: the fixed data depicted in figure 59 has not changed significantly at all.

1. *Fixed teledensity for most Africans is below 3 percent, with many countries at less than 2 percent, and the quality is mostly awful:* Figure 59 clearly demonstrates the mobile story, which has improved considerably yet again. However, the real story of the figure which has not changed is that for fixed. Figure 59 clearly shows the clump of countries, sixteen in total (i.e., 64 percent of the twenty-five countries), having a fixed penetration of less than 2 percent, and nineteen of the twenty-five countries are under 3 percent. Cote d'Ivoire has a mobile penetration today in 2013 of circa 100 percent but with just circa 1 percent fixed penetration. Even the mighty South Africa— almost half the GDP of the entire continent in 2013—has a fixed line penetration of less than 10 percent. Africa, it goes without saying, has the worst fixed line penetrations in the world, and in most cases they are unreliable and of very poor quality.

---

2 GSMA Intelligence (2013b), *Sub-Saharan Africa Mobile Economy*, GSMA, http://www.gsma.com., http://www.gsmamobileeconomyafrica.com/Sub-Saharan%20 Africa_ME_Report_English_2013.pdf (accessed December 2013).

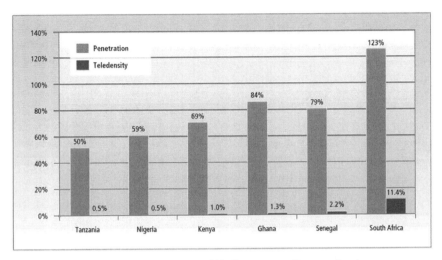

Figure 60—Fixed vs. Mobile Percentage Penetration in
Five Key SSA Markets and Senegal
(Source: GSMA Intelligence and Deloitte African Mobile Observatory 2012;
reproduced with permission of the copyright owner)

Figure 60 shows slightly more recent data but for just five key sub-Saharan markets and Senegal. At least it shows some good news of South Africa's fixed teledensity having increased from 8.62 percent (see figure 61 below) to 11.4 percent, but Nigeria seems to be getting worse.

2. *In sub-Saharan Africa (SSA) in 2010, there were twenty-eight mobile connections for each fixed line subscription* (GSMA Intelligence Mobile Observatory, 2012).[3] According to the respected ITU, there were only 12.3 million fixed lines in SSA in 2010, with nearly half of them located in South Africa.[4] This further confirms that mobile telephony is the key and often only provider of telecommunication services in the region. ITU put mobile penetration across the region at 54

3   GSMA Intelligence (2012), *Sub-Saharan Africa Mobile Observatory 2012*, http://www.gsma.com/publicpolicy/wp-content/uploads/2013/01/gsma_ssamo_full_web_11_12-1.pdf (accessed November 2013).
4   ITU, World Telecommunication/ICT Indicators Database, 2011 (accessed October 2012).

percent for 2010, with fixed teledensity at approximately 1.7 percent. Ergo, there are therefore twenty-eight mobile sub-scriptions for every fixed line in SSA, according to the ITU ICT Indicators Database in 2011. You can see from figure 60 that this 28:1 ratio flatters many countries. For Tanzania, it is more like 100:1 mobile subscriptions to fixed; for Ghana, 65:1; and for Nigeria, 118:1. These ratios highlight the impor-tance of mobile network infrastructure for voice, data, and Internet in the region.

	2007	2008	2009
Tunisia	12,65	12,18	12,45
South Africa	9,22	8,91	8,62
Botswana	7,24	7,41	7,4
Namibia	6,61	6,57	6,54
Senegal	2,26	1,95	2,22
Kenya	1,23	1,67	1,67
Cameroon	1,01	1,34	1,66
Benin	1,32	1,19	1,42
Cote d'Ivoire	1,23	1,73	1,34
Ghana	1,65	0,62	1,12
Ethiopia	1,12	1,11	1,1
Burkina Faso	0,83	0,95	1,06
Nigeria	1,07	0,86	0,92
Uganda	0,54	0,53	0,71
Zambia	0,75	0,72	0,7
Tanzania	0,4	0,29	0,4
Mozambique	0,36	0,35	0,36
Rwanda	0,24	0,17	0,33

(Source: ITU)

Figure 61—Number of Fixed Lines as a Percentage of the Population
(Source: ITU [courtesy of Calandro *et al.* (2010)]. Little changed since 2013.
Reproduced with permission of the copyright owner.)

3. *Fixed-line penetration is unlikely to grow further, not least because of the extensive infrastructure investments required:* Figure 61 shows a similar awful fixed line teledensity trends story for figure 59 showing Tunisia, South Africa, Botswana, and Namibia with the highest fixed teledensities. Calandro *et al.* (2010) attributes the higher teledensity for these countries partly to higher GDP per capita levels in these countries along with these countries having had strong fixed line incumbent monopoly operators. Figure 61 demonstrates two clear messages. First, there is no growth of note for fixed line teledensity across most of Africa. Second, and even more depressingly, fixed line teledensity actually declined as a percentage of population in all the countries in the period 2006 to 2008, bar Botswana, Burkina Faso, Cote d'Ivoire, Cameroon, and Kenya, though this decline started being reversed in 2009.

10.2.2 Implication of Nonexistent Fixed Infrastructure in Africa

There is one key obvious implication to this incredible state of poor infrastructure.

The lack of affordability, coverage, and reliability of fixed networks across the region means that mobile broadband is the only way for the vast majority of consumers to access the Internet: Given the poor state of fixed-line infrastructure, in sub-Saharan Africa in particular, wireless becomes the obvious means of communication. The lack of fixed infrastructure has therefore contributed to the rapid uptake of mobile services across the whole continent. Figure 61 shows a graphical implication of this, which proves the almost complete annhilation of fixed by mobile as the forecasts go out to 2016.

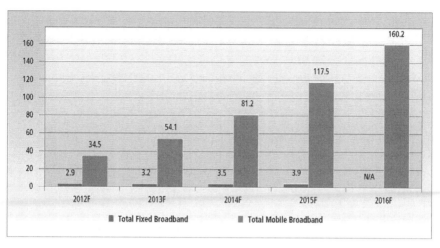

Figure 61—Number of Fixed Lines as a Percentage of the Population
(Source: GSMA Intelligence, Vodafone Public Policy Papers 2011
[as cited in GSMA Intelligence and Deloitte Mobile Observatory, 2012];
reproduced with permission of the copyright owner)

As we have seen in previous chapters, mobile/wireless plays a very large role in the total broadband provision in Africa because of the underdeveloped fixed access networks. GSMA Intelligence (2012) notes that, worldwide, the proportion of web browsing using mobile technology relative to that done across fixed lines is therefore the highest in sub-Saharan Africa. They cite for example, according to Statcounter, in Zimbabwe 58.1 percent of web traffic is mobile based, as is 57.9 percent in Nigeria and 44 percent in Zambia, compared to a global average of 10 percent. They note that this growth of mobile broadband can only be expected to continue, particularly amongst lower-income groups; overall, mobile Internet traffic is forecast to grow twenty-five-fold over the next four years. Mobile broadband connections are expected to increase almost four times from 2012 to 2016, increasing to over 160 million, as per figure 61.

You are, hopefully, now convinced from the above data of the sheer magnitude of the fixed challenge in Africa.

Here's another gentle reminder too, and yet again, about the four overarching challenges at the conclusion of chapter 3: Africa's sheer size, low ARPUs, sparse population distribution across the continent (compared to others), and the fact that 70 percent of Africans live in the rural parts. These add a new scale of challenge to the fixed problem.

10.2.3 The Baby Steps Fixed Outcomes Over the Medium Term

There are a few baby steps "outcomes" that feel appropriate for fixed networks over the next several years, i.e., the medium term which are covered in the next section, including privatisation of fixed incumbents; much better and effective regulation for fixed; regulation for national backbone networks; liberalisation of the fixed sector along with the injection of much-needed competition, including fixed-wireless operators; regulating for an open access fixed model; and more.

Now that the Herculean task is clear, indeed the seeming impossibility of it all, you can see why the chapter started by invoking Nelson Mandela. However, as the Chinese proverb at the start of this chapter notes, the man who moves the mountain started by taking away small stones. There are several to many small stones to take away as regards the fixed line and fixed Internet mountain in Africa and other emerging market countries.

The key and realistic short- to medium-term (i.e., up until 2020) fixed sector outcomes include the following:

- a state-wide widespread national (within country) fibre backbone ensuring most businesses and homes are within 10km of the nearest fibre point
- a regional (linking countries) fibre backbone and peering points to IXPs to peer intra-countries' traffic
- fixed wireless last mile connections to homes

- fixed (fibre) and/or fixed wireless last mile into businesses
- the privatisation of fixed operators across the continent
- the liberalisation of the fixed sector and injection of competition
- ensure that the current fallow fibre (in 2013/14) on the continent are put to good use

If these "baby outcomes" are achieved (or "small stones" taken away) in the medium term, Africa will be well on its way towards better availability of affordable fixed line and fixed Internet. In order to achieve these outcomes, the main recommendations following should be pursued.

Country	Name	Government Ownership %	Source
Benin	Benin Telecoms		
Botswana	BTC	100%	http://www.btc.bw/
Burkina Faso	Onatel	100%	http://www.mbendi.com/indy/cotl/tlcm/af/bf/p0005.htm
Cameroon	Camtel	100%	http://www.mbendi.com/indy/cotl/tlcm/af/ca/p0005.htm
Côte d'Ivoire	Côte d'Ivoire Telecom	49%	ttp://www.mbendi.com/orgs/cht6.htm
Ethiopia	ETC	100%	http://www.ethionet.et/aboutus/companyprofile.html
Ghana	Vodafone Ghana (Ghana Telecom)	30%	http://www.vodafone.com.gh/About-Us/Vodafone-Ghana.aspx
Kenya	Telkom Kenya	49%	http://allafrica.com/stories/200801080875.htm
Mozambique	TDM	100%	http://www.mbendi.com/indy/cotl/tlcm/af/mz/p0005.htm
Namibia	Telecom Namibia	100%	http://www.reuters.com/article/idUSLDE62I0WS20100319
Nigeria	Nitel (Transcorp)	25%	But 75% reclaimed in 2006 after failure of equity partners to meet obligations and currently bid by Omen International Consortium (Cellular News 2010)
Rwanda	Rwanda Tel		http://www.rwandatel.rw/?-History-
Senegal	Orange Senegal	17,28%	
South Africa	Telkom South Africa	39,80%	https://secure1.telkom.co.za/ir/sustainability/shareholding/shareholding.jsp
Tanzania	TTCL	36%	http://www.ttcl.co.tz/about_history.asp
Tunisia	Tunisie Télécom	100%	http://www.zawya.com/cm/profile.cfm/cid337471
Uganda	Uganda Telecom	31%	http://www.utl.co.ug/utl.php?l=75
Zambia	Yes	Yes	

Figure 62—Ownership of Incumbent Fixed Line Operator in Selected Countries
(Source: Calandro *et al.* [2010];reproduced with
permission of the copyright owner)

10.3 Recommendations Towards *Better* Availability of Affordable Fixed Line and Fixed Internet

Many of them should be familiar to you by now. You are also encouraged to revisit the recommendations in the fixed section in chapter 2. The set of recommendations following does not set out to repeat what is covered in there.

1. *Privatisation:* Almost all the thriving mobile operators on the African continent with the memorable exception of ETC (Ethiopia)—indeed across the globe—are private companies. There is a clue in here for governments in Africa with respect to the fixed problem! However, as figure 62 suggests, it is clear from these selected countries by Calandro *et al* (2010)—and not much has changed with them since today in 2013/14—that the privatisation process of these mostly comatose fixed incumbents is moving at a glacial pace.

   Some of them have been in the privatisation pipeline since 2000, e.g., Onatel (Burkina Faso) and CamTel (Cameroon), and others have gone through failed and/or contortious privatisation processes, e.g., Telkom South Africa or NiTel in Nigeria. The latter NiTEL was being liquidated at the end of 2013 (with massive debts owed to its suppliers) until the Nigeria Senate allegedly blocked it, ensuring a comatose incumbent lingers on. Instead and irrespective of the state-ownership percentage in the ownership column of figure 62, the state in most African countries continues *in reality* to dominate over fixed-line incumbent operators. Calandor *et al.* (2000) even go further to argue that states often create a structural conflict of interest in institutional arrangements in terms of their broader policy mandate for the sector and for their competitors. I agree. This is because this failure to privatise these fixed incumbents has extended monopolies and created conflicts with more nimble private new players, and there is a crystal-clear relationship between these extension of monopolies and low penetration rates. Is this not clear enough to decision makers? A less than 2 percent fixed penetration rate in most African countries is a textbook example of the failure of monopolies. These comatose so-called businesses should be 100 percent privatised as soon as possible, and if liquidation is required up front, so be it. All these countries should set themselves a three-year timetable to rid themselves of these incumbents or truly run it themselves like arms-length, regulated private businesses.

2. *Strong, independent, and effective regulation is an absolute must-have for a fixed sector turnaround*: The regulation of most incumbents on the continent has been incredibly ineffectual and nonexistent at best, to abysmal at worst. It is undoubtedly true that it is very hard work regulating big incumbents; I have seen this firsthand from the insides of an esteemed regulator how much resources are consumed by regulating a monopoly fixed-line operator BT plc in the United Kingdom. However, the prize to UK plc of the excellent regulation that Ofcom has achieved with BT has been a wonder to observe. A landmark 2005 review in the United Kingdom called the Telecoms Strategic Review (TSR) led to some truly innovative and sustained regulation of BT. Most African states are due their own equivalent TSR reviews in order to be crystal clear on short-, medium-, and long-term outcomes needed. What is not acceptable is governments doing nothing and strangling a sector as a result. This recommendation sadly goes back to an Achilles's heel of many African governments: their penchant to muzzle and not give free reign to their so-called independent regulators. A good test of how governments are allowing their independent regulators to "get on with it" with their sectors is how they allow strong regulators to emerge who can regulate the fixed sector properly and sustainably. There is much experience to learn from other countries on how this can or should be done.

3. *Technology and service-neutral licensing regimes are strongly encouraged*: This has stimulated investment and, along with markets policies, stimulated much-needed investment in the mobile sector. The same should apply to the fixed sector.

4. *Enabling a widespread national fibre backbone and a backstop national backbone provider (if necessary) via incentivisation, privatisation, and strong open access regulation*: National incumbents are in some countries dominant or have been mandated by state diktat to roll out invaluable national fibre backbones. This is not necessarily a good idea. In some markets like Nigeria, the private sector is beginning to take a leading role in the roll out of the national backbone network. This is a privilged position which other countries on the continent do not have, as Nigeria is the runaway biggest telecommunications market on the continent. Nevertheless even in bigger economies like Nigeria and South Africa, the laws of the market are already emerging. The backbone will emerge in areas where the private sector believes they will get a return on their investments for their shareholders and would not otherwise. What this means in practice is there may typically have to be a backstop national backbone provider. This does not mean the government should jump in and invest; rather, they should incentivize alongside sustained independent regulation from the regulator for the private sector to develop the backbone that ensures that the uneconomical parts of the country are also constructed.

A private player may choose to build such a network in exchange for long-term contracts from businesses and even the government. It could also be a regulated network as it may be the only one covering rural areas. Government intervention to construct and/or manage networks is not an effective or efficient substitute to private sector–owned and –managed networks. As an absolute last resort—when there is incontrovertible evidence of market failure—then and only then should the government step in to invest and build networks. Nigeria's communication regulator, NCC, is desperately attempting to coax the private sector to evolve just such a national fibre backbone network across Nigeria. The idea is to have a seamless backbone across the entire country by aggregating the fibre from all current private sector fibre. This fibre would be "open access" to all via appropriate enabling regulation so that small and large players alike are able to access the fibre at fair, reasonable, and nondiscriminatory (FRND-ly) prices. Where there are gaps, private sector companies would be incentivised to build fibre backbones, thereby achieving an end-to-end network across the country. Clearly, this is easier said than done, as the bigger players with significant fibre rollouts are already complaining of "free riding" advantages being accrued to their competitors.

This is where a combination of privatisation and truly strong, sustained enabling regulation is invaluable. Most African countries do not have incumbent fixed networks with large and expansive networks, like BT has in the United Kingdom or France Telecom has in France. Therefore the regulatory intevention needed in Africa is more for innovation, new infrastructure competiton, and rolling out widespread fixed networks, rather than for equality of access to existing networks, bottleneck access (i.e., to homes and businesses), and backhaul networks. These are the key issues of concern in Europe. African and emerging market governments should expedite truly strengthening their regulators along with privatising their fixed network incumbents. The empowered regulators must be charged by statutes to ensure the conditions for widespread backbone infrastructure deployment are in place and encourage public private partnerships to make such national backbone networks happen. It must be reemphasised that low fixed penetration rates in fixed and the resultant higher costs of bandwidth is due to limited backbone networks—particularly terrestrial backbone networks, as submarine capacity is now less of a problem on the continent. These largely derive from extant policies that have protected monopolies and the ineffectual regulation from weak regulators. With the right long-term regulatory frameworks in place, it is up to government to play its own key part in atracting private investors via PPPs, supplier concessions, supplier-provided loans at cheap interest rates, etc.

5. *Liberalisation and competition in fixed is critical, with the stick of "roll out or lose it obligations" (ROLIO):* Following on from the latter three recommendations must be one on the liberalisation and injection of competition into the fixed sector. The main takeaway as has been seen in the mobile sector on the continent is that liberalisation of the telecommunications sector has been a major success for mobile. It has increased competition, increased affordability, and increased choice, and it is constantly improving quality. It has also attracted oodles of investment. Why should fixed not have a share of these, albeit unlikely at the same level of success? Achieving just better fixed networks availability at affordable prices requires the liberalisation to continue. This is why the blue print in chapter 3 majors so much in several places on the benefits of liberalisation and competition; it's why figure 27's straw man makes recommendations on liberalisation and driving up competition in fixed networks. The more competition there is in markets—driven by the number of licensed fixed operators with the licenses having "roll out or lose it" obligations—and good sustained regulation, the better and more affordable services will become in the long term.

6. *The regulator and/or government must regulate and encourage more fixed/fixed-wireless operators via technological neutral regulations, IXPs, access to city ducts and poles, etc.:* As chapter 2's anatomy of fixed networks mapped out, there are many several facets to fixed networks: the most expansive of which is the access network to homes and businesses;

the national and regional backbones, city ducts, and poles city networks; core fixed networks; the international networks (and gateways that lead to them, i.e., the IXPs); and the submarine cables leading to the wider Internet. Perhaps the one that this recommendation singles out amongst all others is the access network. Clearly, coverage (as in the maximum possible amount of homes and businesses covered) is incredibly important. It is unlikely that the economics of backbone networks in most African countries would allow for cabling to homes. Hence, fixed-wireless networks become quite invaluable. The idea in this recommendation is not to be technology specific as in fixed-wireless networks. Rather it is to emphasise that though access networks in other parts of the world tend to use copper lines or fibre optic cable networks, etc., the term "fixed networks" must be regulator-technologically neutral. Whether the licensees choose to implement access networks using fixed wires or by radio (fixed-wireless) should be up to the operators. Fixed-wireless operators would be the natural way of choosing from technologies like LTE TDD, Wi-Fi, TV white spaces, WiMAX, and CDMA as the technologies options for access networks on the continent—and they must be encouraged via regulation and other government policies, including innovation policies, tax exemptions, etc.

7. *Evolving the right commercial models to obviate Africa's fibre remaining fallow and making them viable:* This is an important business model recommendation. As noted earlier, only 5 to 10 percent of landed fibre is being utilised today on the continent. One reason is clearly because this fibre has not been distributed across national backbones providing regional supply, which in turn can stimulate demand for their use. This has been addressed above. However, another arguably more important reason is the lack of the right commercial models that use these fibres for broadband services which makes them viable. It is the case that African governments and operators have funded massive roll out of fibre. Sadly, many of these projects

are commercially unviable because the business models and appropriate pricing models too are not in place to incentivise operators and other communication service providers to use them. There are many examples of best practice elsewhere in the world to draw upon to alleviate this situation, and the earlier this happens, the better. This will need partnership between governments, operators, and other communication service providers as national broadband initiatives are being discussed. Coordination failure is already evident in many fibre projects across countries wherein governments are using tax payers' monies to fund fibre routes which the private sector duplicates, resulting in a glut of capacity on those routes, such as Lagos to Abuja in Nigeria. Any government-funded fibre on such routes is bound to lay fallow. Best practice from the United Kingdom and elsewhere suggests the following, and Suveer Ramdhani rightly notes some of them in Africa Telecom & IT (September 2013 issue).[5]

- *Dark fibre should be laid down and made available.* Governments must realise it is easier, if the market does not deliver, for it to lay down just dark fibre. Alternatively, if the market is delivering, incentives should enable the widest possible dark fibre network possible. Access to dark fibre is important, whether it is overhead or underground, particularly where the dark fibre is owned by the government or by state enterprises but also by private enterprises. The regulator could define a product market specifically that comprises ducts, poles, and dark fibre and determine that some companies have or the government has dominance on some routes or areas. Passive infrastructure access (PIA) remedies could be imposed on such enterprises, guaranteeing access to competitors at cost-oriented prices to such assets. Having basic FRND-ly and guaranteed access at cost-oriented prices is a key first step.

---

5 "Make Africa's fallow fibre viable," *Africa Telecom & IT*, September 2013, p. 40.

- *Good regulation would facilitate optimal pricing for the benefits of consumers and businesses.* Dark fibre by definition is not lit, i.e., it is has not got electronics connected to both ends enabling its use. The owner of the fibre may want to provide the electronics at both ends and provide an *active* product and/or managed fibre services to other communication service providers. However, it is recommended that government or state enterprises do not try and do this. It is not the job of state companies to provide such services. However, private sectors companies may do so, and this may be economically beneficial to customers if many competitors want to use the same dark fibre. For example, competitors using passive remedies such as duct access or dark fibre would need to invest more in infrastructure and equipment than those that use regulated active products, increasing the static cost of competition. Fibre models in the United Kingdom showed that the static cost of competition to support four operators (the incumbent BT plc and three other competitor deployments) using BT's duct and poles infrastructure would double the cost per end user compared with competition based on the active BT's product. Good regulation can help optimize business models.

- *Distance-based pricing can also help make Africa's fibre more viable because it introduces the concept of variable pricing, rather than just massive up front fixed pricing.* PoP[6] to PoP pricing is resulting in very high pricing for short routes such as in the cities, making them unaffordable and them lying fallow in cities. Clearly, it is easier to build short routes which carry much traffic than long routes which carry little. This fact points again to some sort of distant-based pricing rather than pricing from one PoP to another, irrespective of distance. PoP to PoP pricing makes more sense for submarine cable pricing, and less so for terrestrial pricing.

---

6 Acronym for "point of presence."

- *Ramdhani suggests that changing the approach from leasing fibre infrastructure to providing indefeasible right of use (IRU) contracts would also help make Africa's fallow fibre viable.* Clearly, such IRUs can only be granted to creditworthy operators and communication service providers. Such rights relieve the burden of governments and tax payers to continue to operate, monitor, and maintain these complex fibre QoS systems and KPIs, assuming of course that government laid down the dark fibre. Rather, the private sector buys these rights to use the capacity of the fibre with up front monies which can be used to expand the fibre network even further.

Such best practice ideas and more would help make Africa's fallow fibre more viable and must be considered.

8. *Miscellaneous recommendations for mobile which also apply to fixed:* These include emphasising and addressing access and affordability concerns; reducing and/or eliminating the regressive telecommunication taxes (VAT, excise, custom, airtime, connection taxes, corporation taxes); alleviating power problems in order to support extension to rural areas; addressing rights of way blockages, etc.

9. *AU cooperation and other public private partnerships for a pan-African continental fibre backbone led by South Africa and Nigeria:* The development of an African continental fibre-optic backbone that interconnects Africa and all of the rest of the other continents via current and planned fibre cannot come any sooner. The African fixed telecoms infrastructure woes, the high costs of telephony to other African countries, the payments of six hundred million US dollars outside Africa (mostly to Europe) for intra-African Internet traffic, and the dependency still of some countries on expensive satellite VSAT will only be alleviated by a pan-African fibre backbone. Remember Sierra Leone having some of the highest satellite costs in the

world at four to five thousand US dollars for 1 Mbps (similar to South Sudan's bandwidth costs) compared to five hundred US dollars in east Africa. With such costs, broadband will never be affordable. The arrival of a functioning ACE should change this affordability equation in Sierra Leone. Also remember in chapter 2, we noted how the Liquid Telecom Group, for example, has constructed one of Africa's largest single fibre networks, spanning from north of Uganda down east Africa to Cape Town. This is the first fibre network to cross country borders, covering some of Africa's fastest growing economies, and capable of providing wholesale bandwidth to connect Nairobi (Kenya), Dar es Salaam (Tanzania), Kampala (Uganda), and Kigali (Rwanda). Liquid Telecom's pan-African fibre now totals 15,000 km as of 2013. Such Liquid Telecom's pan-African fibre totals need to be multiplied ten-fold, then a hundred-fold, and even some more. The initial business plan is simple: six hundred million US dollars outflow year in, year out. This last recommendation is quite a key important one, which needs to be engineered sooner later. It is difficult because coordination failure in such a project means no one leads. South Africa and Nigeria (as the two biggest telecoms countries) and key entrepreneurs on the continent can and must lead here. Public private partnerships brokered by AU and leading African countries are also possible.

Remember to revisit the fixed-related set of recommendations in chapter 2, which are not repeated here. The fixed line and fixed Internet problem is a much longer term one, but the baby steps towards better availability of affordable fixed line and fixed Internet covered in this chapter will definitely take us all in the right direction. These small stones need to be carried away before tackling the boulders later.

SECTION VI

REGULATION AS A CRITICAL SUCCESS FACTOR

CHAPTER 11

TMT REGULATION 101

The biggest two risks about investing in emerging markets and Africa in particular are the perception of political and regulatory risks.

"Practice without theory is blind. Theory without practice is sterile."

—Karl Marx

I have observed the above first truism multiple times over the years about the fear of international investors investing in emerging and African markets, and one which political and regulatory decision makers in these markets must fully appreciate. Most international investors worry about political and regulatory risks, or, more accurately, investors' perceptions of political and regulatory risks typically gate their investment decisions.

This volume has little to say on the perception of political risks beyond noting that the political situation in Africa has improved markedly over the last generation, i.e., twenty-five years. In 1979, there were only three democracies on the continent. In 2013, there are circa twenty-eight (out of fifty-four), depending on how you count them. The climate of constant coup d'états on the continent of Africa is hopefully behind us, and every time I hear of a coup in Africa—most recently the Malian coup d'état of March 2012 and the more recent instabilities in the Central African Republic still ongoing as at the end of 2013—I genuinely typically think, "There goes all investment in the country concerned for another ten years." Is it any wonder that Mali has arguably the poorest telecommunications network on the continent in 2013 (see figure 47)? Coups usually expose to all the underlying lack of political and other democratic institutions, as well as the lack of predictability that are prerequisites for international investment.

On the other hand, unlike with the perception of political risk, this volume has oodles to say about regulatory risk. Hardly any chapter has not touched on regulatory issues. All the outcomes that this volume promotes—*widespread* or *better* availability of *affordable* voice, data, broadband Internet, digital TV, radio, other media, and fixed Internet—require a significant dose of good, sustained, and predictable regulation to make these happen. This is why it is important that this volume provides an introduction to good regulation for the uninitiated. If you think I am overplaying the perception of regulatory risk in African and/or emerging markets, a lesson from Venezuela is very salutary.

In early 2007, the (now late) Venezuelan president Hugo Chávez suddenly announced his intention and plans to nationalise the local phone company, CANTV. The shares of the company dropped like a stone, by almost 50 percent, and this was before the details of Chavez's plans even emerged. Basically, international and national investors sold first and asked questions second. Perception is everything with political and regulatory risk. Worse for countries like Mali, international investors would just take them off their radars for years and, even much more worse, take other African countries off the radar with Mali too. Examples abound on the continent where the *perception* of the telecommunications regulatory environment is a clear indicator of both investment in and the health of the sector, whether it is about market entry, access to scare resources, interconnection, regulation of anticompetitive practices and tariffs, etc. These are excellently covered in Calandro *et al.* (2010).

Therefore, this 101 chapter impresses on governments in particular, but all the readers in general, on *why* good, predictable, transparent, objective, and independent regulation of the TMT sector is invaluable. It is not an option. It is mandatory unless the country concerned does not care about the consequences and opportunity costs:

lack of investment, poor innovation, poor quality TMT services, poor competition, monopolies, high and unaffordable prices, poor coverage, etc. This is not a good list!

This regulation 101 chapter attempts to address the following questions:

- What is regulation? Why regulate? What are the goals of regulation?
- Who regulates TMT? Why is converged regulation the way to go, and why have independent regulation? Indeed, what is an independent regulator, and how is it achieved?
- What are the bases of regulation, particularly the legal basis for regulation? Without a legal framework, a regulator and regulation would not exist. What are a typical TMT regulator's powers, duties, functions, and factors?
- What is the economic basis for regulation?
- How does good TMT regulation work in practice? What is the "balancing act," an art of TMT regulation?
- What are some of the key regulatory areas of concerns on the African continent today and other emerging economies?
- What are the main recommendations on regulation and regulators in Africa and other emerging markets?

11.1 What Is TMT Regulation, Why Regulate TMT, and What Are the Goals of Regulation?

Effective TMT regulation is ultimately about achieving efficient TMT markets. Simplistically, efficient markets are those that work well for consumers and citizens wherein prices are low and affordable, innovation is high, quality of TMT services are good, competition is rife, new entry by competitors is possible, coverage is widespread, switching to different suppliers is easy and straightforward, there is no market failure, anticompetitive market practices are stamped upon, scarce resources such as spectrum are fairly and transparently allocated, call termination rates are close to true costs, and so on.

TMT regulation is the prescription and implementation of rules and obligations, along with their implementation and enforcement, on how TMT markets should operate in order to achieve the above listed outcomes. It is easier said than done. There are almost no very few good TMT regulators on the continent of Africa, as the evidence from Calandro *et al.* (2010) attests, and anecdotal evidence suggests that the same applies to many other emerging countries too.

I can personally attest that good world class regulation is both a *science* and an *art*. The science bit comes from its legal and economic bases, both of which many African and emerging countries, in my experience, do not fully understand. This is why they are briefly covered in this chapter. The art bit comes from the quality of the interaction between the market's commercial (and other) players and the regulator. The trust between the regulated and the regulator is vital. Where it is in short supply, the growth of the TMT market will be stifled. Such trust is also quite fragile, and the regulator loses it at their peril, and once this happens, the resulting mistrust would breed uncertainty and unpredictability. This is why in several places in this volume, I have railed against governments undermining their TMT regulators, as has happened several times with Kenya's CCK—a truly emerging best-in-class TMT regulator on the continent. Once trust is lost between the regulated and the regulator, it takes so much time to recover—and this "lost time" means uncertainty, unpredictability, lost investments, poor competition, and so on. This art of regulation is equally as important as the science.

THE NEED FOR REGULATION (GOING FROM MONOPOLY TO FULL COMPETITION) SOURCE: ICT REGULATION TOOLKIT

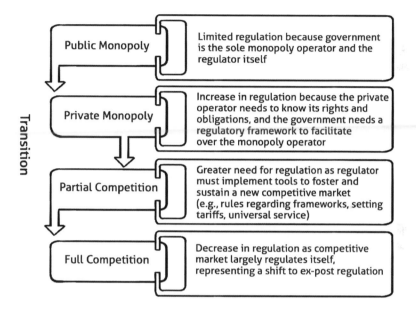

Figure 63—The Need for Regulation (Going from Monopoly to Full Competition) (Source: adapted from ICT Regulation Toolkit)[1]

Furthermore on the "Why regulate?" question, it is the case that the need for regulation varies from marketplace to marketplace. In most if not all countries, TMT subsectors began as state monopolies. That is, there are (or were) public monopoly telecommunications companies, e.g., Ethiopia Telecom for telecommunications or Ghana Broadcasting Corporation for broadcasting and so on. As figure 63 shows, countries would typically liberalise the sector, i.e., introduce some market-based principles, as well as create a regulator to oversee the sector, resulting in the replacement of the public monopoly, like Ethiopia Telecom still had been in 2013, with a private monopoly. Then, typically, another wave of liberalisation would follow wherein the government and/or

---

1 The ICT Regulation Toolkit, http://www.itu.int/itudoc/gs/promo/bdt/flyer/87876. pdf (accessed November 2013).

regulator authorises new entrants into the market to compete with the private monopoly. This would typically involve modifying the licensing framework to allow for such new entry, as well as the introduction of new fair and effective rules of competition for the new entrants to be able to operate in the marketplace. This would result in some form of partial competition where the private monopoly still has a period of grace of exclusivity. Even further liberalisation would ultimately usher in full competition when the private monopoly's exclusivity concludes. As the transition from monopoly to full competition progresses (as shown in figure 63), the need and the role of the independent regulator increases.

Many countries still need to take their broadcasting sectors, and in some cases, like Ethiopia's, their telecommunication sector, through the stages shown in figure 63. Nevertheless, regulation does not end when full competition is achieved. Even after "full" competition has been achieved, as in the case in some mobile telecommunication markets across Africa (e.g., Nigeria with four major players or Ghana with six as of 2013), regulation should persist as a vehicle for sustaining widespread and affordable access, effective competition, and consumer protection.

The ICT Regulation Toolkit (Infodev and ITU, 2012)[2] lists the following four key "steady state" goals of regulation:

- To avoid market failure: Market failure occurs where markets cannot or do not achieve a fully efficient allocation; we return to this concept later. This typically happens when the market is not fully competitive, and a monopoly provider may emerge.
- To foster effective competition: Effective competition or a true competitive market emerges when there is no super-normal profits being earned by any players because long run prices approximate average costs. For Africa and some

2 Infodev and ITU (2012), ICT Regulation Toolkit, InfoDev: 2121 Pennsylvania Avenue NW, Washington, DC 20433, USA. ITU: International Telecommunication Union (ITU) Place des Nations CH-1211 Geneva 20, Switzerland, http://www. ictregulationtoolkit.org/en/home (accessed November 2013).

emerging economies, fostering effective competition would include implementing regulation to support effective competition and efficient investment in 3G/4G mobile broadband. Another example drawing from the last chapter would be promoting regulating to promote investment in fixed telecommunications.

- To protect consumer interests: Most good regulators' primary role is mainly to deal with the protection of consumers and citizens in the presence of markets that may not be working well for them. This is the primary raison d'être for the existence of regulators. Markets typically have industrial private sectors with typically several big players, like Safaricom (Kenya), MTN, Orange, etc. Such players evidently do not need "protection" by the regulator against ordinary consumers and citizens. The protection needed is clearly the other way round. An example area to protect consumers would be to regulate to ensure they can switch between communication providers by removing unnecessary barriers.

- To increase access to technology and services: This is the clarion call objective of this entire volume—widespread availability/access and affordability of TMT services. You would be familiar with one of my key mantras by now: reach without affordability is futile; affordability without reach is sterile. Universal access and universal service provision as promoted by Universal Service Funds are typical policy tools to achieve this goal. This goal also covers regulating for innovation achieved often via tariff regulation in order to ensure inefficient old technologies do not dictate the price points in the market. Otherwise, new technologies are prevented or delayed from entering the market because the old incumbent firms price their substitute products such as to drive new entrants and technologies out of the market and then later increase their prices once the entrants exit the market. A good regulator would regulate the tariffs (or prices) of the incumbent at close to long run (incremental) costs (LRIC) such that competitors have a level playing field to compete.

As covered in chapter 3, I would also add the following important goal of regulation:

- Allocating and managing scarce resources in a FRND-ly[3] way: This typically refers to spectrum airwaves and telephone numbers. These are important national and scarce resources that need to be allocated and managed in such a manner as to maximise benefits to consumers and citizens. Chapter 5 (which covers auctions and other spectrum awards) covers the allocation of scarce spectrum resources. Chapter 3 and figure 27 note that allocation and management of such scarce resources are an important part of the blueprint.

11.2 Who Regulates TMT, and Why Converged and Independent Regulation?

Every TMT market must design and put in place a clear regulatory framework, including the establishment of a regulatory authority called the converged regulator. This regulator must establish transparent decision-making processes, clear accountability, and consumer protection and dispute resolution measures and enforcement powers. And the regulator must implement these even more efficiently.

All through this volume, I have argued strongly for converged regulation in the second decade of the twenty-first century. Nonconverged regulation no longer makes much sense. The case for converged regulation is summarised following:

- IP changes everything: The Internet Protocol (IP) technology—the foundation of the Internet and much else happening in broadcasting, media, and mobile—makes converged regulation inevitable. It is the case that more and more media will be consumed over IP platforms like the Internet. What sense would it make to have asymmetric regulation over different

---

3 Fair, reasonable, and nondiscriminatory (FRND)

platforms for the same content? So watching a Nollywood movie over the terrestrial broadcast platform is subject to a different regulation from watching the same movie over cable or fibre, or over the Internet? IP creates opportunities for differential and inconsistent regulation from disparate regulators. At the very least, a single converged regulator is a first step to addressing differential regulation by different entities before the converged regulator proceeds to harmonise regulations across different platforms which are all moving towards IP.

- Major policy projects to deliver major outcomes is more optimal with a single converged regulator: This volume has also made the case that trying to carry out a digital switchover project from analogue to digital, auctioning the spectrum through a 4G auction whilst driving up more take up of the Internet with two or more regulators is most suboptimal. In Cameroon in 2013, these outcomes would involve four regulatory and government agencies: the Ministry of Telecommunications (MinTek), the National Council for Communications (NCC), the National Agency for Information Technologies and Communications (ANTIC), and the Telecommunications Regulatory Board of Cameroon (TRB). This simply makes no sense. Confusion and inconsistencies would reign. In Nigeria at least two national regulators, NBC and NCC, would be involved along with the Ministry of Communications Technology (MoCT), who oversee spectrum across agencies. This is inefficient.

- New legislation also becomes more efficient: It makes more sense to have one government ministry (and one minister) which/who oversees the entire TMT sector to drive a "converged" TMT legislative bill with much internal consistency across telecommunications, media, and technology sub-legislations, and not split across two or more ministries. The government cannot possibly (in 2013 and beyond) be legislating for 4G for a national fibre backbone network and for liberalisation of moribund broadcasting sector in three different pieces of legislation sponsored by three different departments of state. This would be mad. Indeed, separate ministries of telecommunications, of ICT, of post, and of broadcasting makes little sense in 2013, yet alone going forward.

• Regional policy and regulatory coordination is more efficient with converged regulators: Throughout emerging economies and Africa, regional economic communities (REC) are increasingly focusing on ICT policies and regulatory developments in order to harmonise national ICT/TMT policies and legal frameworks within regional blocs. Clearly, regional harmonisation of policies and regulations is essential for regional economic integration. For example, the Central African Economic and Monetary Community (CEMAC) has developed a document proposing various harmonisation via six directives on ICT policy, universal services, interconnection, tariffs, and data protection (Calandro et al., 2010). It would be much more efficient for such needed harmonisation initiatives to happen with one converged regulator along with just one sponsoring ministry, and not several regulators per country along with several sponsoring ministries.

• Converged media organisations would be forced to carry much regulatory costs if regulations are not harmonised across platforms via converged regulators: In chapter 8, we saw the folly of not looking at regulation in a converged manner. We noted a scenario of an African broadcaster broadcasting a news item/bulletin on some national strike on its terrestrial platform, where it is subject to broadcasting regulatory rules from the broadcasting regulator in terms of "taste and decency" measures, news quotas, adverts quotas, etc. We noted how, if a newspaper organisation shot a similar news bulletin, probably of the same strike, and deployed its footage online, it would likely not be subject to the same regulatory constraints as its paper newspaper. We then imagined the broadcaster owned the newspaper organisation. The single "converged" terrestrial broadcaster who owns a newspaper group and online publisher would be subject to two or three separate regulations because they are operating on three different platforms. This organisation may also be subject to regulations from two or three regulators. These mean costs for the organisation and possibly inconsistencies and confusion.

Similarly, the volume in several places has espoused independent regulation. It has argued that effective regulators tend to be independent ones who play a FRND-ly role in regulating a liberalised market or assist in the transition from a public monopoly market to a liberalised one, as depicted in figure 63. It begs the question: What is an independent regulator?

11.2.1 What Is Independence, and How Is It Achieved?

Complete independence of a regulator neither is desirable nor is it really necessary. A regulator should not set and mark its own exam scripts, i.e., its own agenda; it must be subject to some minimal government oversight as well as some scrutiny. Independent regulation truly really refers to the following independent scenarios:

- independence from political influences and intervention
- independence from day-to-day meddling by civil servants and/ or routine government diktats
- independence from the private TMT sector industry, NGOs, and civil society
- independence from any short-term and expedient decision-making processes

Of course, the legislature of the day can and must have oversight of the regulators, and, sparingly, they may "direct" the independent regulator to achieve certain outcomes. However, the hurdle for directing the independent regulator must be very high—in the United Kingdom, this involves legislation requiring positive affirmative resolutions in both houses of Parliament. A sitting government does not choose to direct an independent regulator lightly. Once the regulator's duties, functions, and powers are prescribed and defined in statutes, it is up to the board of the regulator how to interpret them. It is also up to the board to decide on the (annual) priorities of the regulator in consultation with its stakeholders, and the board would typically take a long-term view. Therefore the regulator is an objective, impartial, nonpartisan implementer of statutes/laws, free of transitory governments.

The statutes are more enduring than governments This way, regulators are somewhat insulated from day-to-day governments and from ministerial control. The decisions of the regulator are not immune from legal scrutiny, as they must be taken within the laws of the land and may be appealed either on its merits (a merits appeal) or by challenging the process taken by the regulator to arrive at a decision, i.e., a judicial review. However, decisions of the regulator must be sacrosanct of government except via appeals to the courts based on current law or the high hurdle of changing existing legislation.

Appointments to the regulator bar a select few roles, e.g., the chairman or commissioners, must be open, impartial, and merit based and preferably under the auspices of the strong board. The regulator's funding must be adequate, reliable, and prescribed by law. Even better, the TMT regulator may levy the sector to fund its ongoing costs, thereby insulating itself from annual political meddle with government through the budgeting process. Salaries must be commensurate to attracting the best and must not be constrained by civil service bands.

The above and more help make regulators independent. Only such a confident, independent body can ensure and foster competition, implement a level playing field between dominant players and new and smaller entrants in a market. Only such an independent regulator can ensure a monopoly wholesaler TMT incumbent supplies to its competitors on the same fair, reasonable, and nondiscriminatory terms that it supplies to its own retail division. The regulator would have to build credibility over time with bold and objective regulatory decisions which attract the confidence of investors. How does the regulator build up such needed credibility? This is the subject of the ensuing section.

11.2.2 Principles of Independent Regulation

Independence is one thing. Using the independence to demonstrate effective and sustained regulation is something else. The esteemed UK regulator Ofcom has built up significant credibility and international reputation by religiously abiding by and living the following seven "regulatory principles" shown in figure 64. It appears to me that these principles would apply to most TMT regulators too, anywhere.

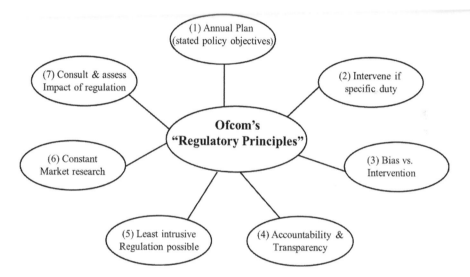

Figure 64—How Ofcom Regulates: The Seven Ofcom "Regulatory Principles"
(Source: Ofcom website)[4]

The seven Ofcom regulatory principles are the following (illustrated by a policy case example of achieving optimal mobile broadband access and affordability):

1. *Ofcom will regulate with a clearly articulated and publicly reviewed annual plan, with stated policy objectives.* One such policy objective, as noted earlier, may be to optimise access

---

4   http://www.ofcom.org.uk/about/what-is-ofcom/statutory-duties-and-regulatory-principles/ (accessed November 2013)

and affordability of mobile broadband within the market. See figure 28 for a reminder of what reporting against an annual plan looks like.

2. *Ofcom will intervene where there is a specific statutory duty to work towards a public policy goal which markets alone cannot achieve.* The market players deploying mobile broadband may not go beyond, say, 40 to 50 percent population coverage via 3G/4G. Therefore, if the regulator has a clear statutory duty to achieve widespread and affordable broadband coverage, the regulator may intervene to impose a coverage obligation which goes beyond where the market would go to, proportionally perhaps to, say, 60 percent.

3. *Ofcom will operate with a bias against intervention, but with a willingness to intervene firmly, promptly, and effectively where required.* This means intervention needs a high hurdle. Perhaps by license exempting some UHF spectrum for TV white spaces, the market may be able to go well beyond 60 percent of the population without the coverage obligation intervention to 60 percent, say, in which case the coverage obligation would be unnecessary.

4. *Ofcom will strive to ensure its interventions will be evidence based, proportionate, consistent, accountable, and transparent in both deliberation and outcome.* How does the regulator know 50 percent is as far as the market will go to in the first place and that 60 percent is an achievable and proportionate stretch target which will not bankrupt commercial players? These all emerge from evidence-based consultations, including detailed economic and technical analyses which are transparent, auditable, and defensible.

5. *Ofcom will always seek the least intrusive regulatory mechanisms to achieve its policy objectives.* A least intrusive mechanism in this case may be to license-exempt TV white spaces

and allow the market to go beyond where 3G/4G would go to. Alternatively, if a stretch coverage obligation is deemed necessary, it may be imposed on only *one* of several licenses, thereby ensuring the regulation is both least intrusive and proportionate.

6. *Ofcom will research markets constantly and will aim to remain at the forefront of technological understanding.* In this context, it is only through active research of markets that the regulator has understood the detailed pros and cons of TV white spaces, 2G/3G and 4G technologies, etc., and their capabilities. Without this understanding, competition could/would be skewed in favour of some players in the market.

7. *Ofcom will consult widely with all relevant stakeholders and assess the impact of regulatory action before imposing regulation upon a market.* This is important regulatory practice.

Independence and abiding by the above principles have enabled Ofcom (United Kingdom) to become one of the most respected regulators in the world. It can make a world of difference to African TMT regulators too.

11.3 The Legal Basis of Regulation

Regulation is rooted in an absolute legal basis. Without a legal framework, regulators would not exist. The legislature of the country (e.g., Parliament or Senate) crafts laws and statutes, including those that establish public bodies like regulatory agencies. Sometimes, the regulator emanates from one piece of statute or legislation, such as the Nigerian Communications Act of 2003 which founded and established NCC as the independent regulator in Nigeria.[5] Wikipedia defines a statute as a formal written enactment of a legislative authority that

---

5 Nigerian Communications Act, http://www.ncc.gov.ng (accessed October 2012).

governs a country or state; typically, statutes command or prohibit something or declare policy.[6] For example, the NCC Act commands the establishment of a regulator. Another example of a similar singlular legislation is the Communications Act of 2009 in Namibia, which founded and established the Communications Regulatory Authority of Namibia (CRAN).[7] In some other countries, particularly mature ones, the regulator's legal basis is founded in statutory duties contained in several pieces of legislation. Ofcom's (United Kingdom) legal basis derives from at least nine pieces of legislation: Communications Act (2003), Wireless Telegraphy Act (2006), Broadcasting Acts (1990, 1996), Competition Act (1998), Enterprise Act (2002), Postal Services Act (2000, 2011), and the Digital Economy Act (2010). Some of Ofcom's powers also derive from European Union legislation in just the same way that some African regulators' functions would derive from the African Union (AU).

11.3.1 Duties, Powers, Functions, and Factors

A regulator's legal powers typically come in the form of duties, powers, functions, and factors. Below is a list of commonsense-type distinctions and exemplars of these legal terms. I confess to being no lawyer whatsoever, though I am privileged to have worked with some of the brightest ones in the United Kingdom.

- *Duties*: Most regulators would have a duty to further the interest of citizens and consumers. The duty would specifically be something like to "protect the interest of citizens in all matters communications," whilst citizens would refer to "all members of the public in the said country." Duties tend to use words like "ensure" or "required to secure," which translate to verbs like "must" or "shall," as in the regulator "must do X" or the "shall

6 The word "statute" is often used to distinguish "law" made by legislative bodies from "case law" decided by courts and/or regulations made by government agencies/regulators.

7 Namibian Communications Act, http://www.parliament.gov.na/acts_documents/120_4378gov_n226act_82009.pdf (accessed November 2013).

do Y." Another two typical duties of most converged regulators are "ensuring the optimal use of electromagnetic spectrum" or "ensuring a wide range of TV and radio services of high quality and wide appeal." You can clearly note that the key objectives of this volume—towards widespread availability/access and affordability of TMT services including voice, data, mobile Internet, TV, radio, fixed Internet, and other media—have to be baked in legislation and statutes which a regulator interprets and regulates to make happen. You can now further attest why regulation is so vital to achieving the goals of this volume.

- *Powers*: Simplistically, regulators can *only* do what they have been given the powers to do. So, they can have duties above, but if they do not have the powers to achieve them, then the regulator would be toothless. Powers are instruments regulators "may" choose to use; they do not necessarily have to use them all the time. We have already seen earlier how a regulator's powers and functions are set out in statutes. For example, for a regulator to achieve being an evidenced-based decision-making body, it typically needs information-gathering powers written into legislation which enables it to formally request confidential information from private and public companies. For the regulator to carry out a competition assessment, the regulator would need access to such company-confidential information. Similarly, a regulator needs dispute resolution powers to be able to arbitrate industry disputes or enforcement powers to enforce their regulations.

- *Functions*: Any act establishing a new regulator is replete with many functions too, and as noted earlier, many functions are also derived from supranational entities like the African Union or the European Union. Typically functions would include

  ○ the granting and licensing of radio and TV licenses as well as licensing of digital services—without which digital switchover of TV will not be possible;
  ○ functions to promote competition;
  ○ functions to manage the use of spectrum;

- ○ functions to encourage innovation and investment;
- ○ functions to draw up codes of practice for "rights-of-way" access;
- ○ functions to protect consumers;
- ○ functions to regulate TV and radio; and
- ○ functions over the state broadcaster, etc.

You can surmise that, simplistically, functions combine powers and duties.

- *Factors*: Factors refer to important issues the regulator "must have regard to." Factors include issues like "taking into account" the "interests of consumers" or "different needs and interests of users of electromagnetic spectrum." They could also cover

  - ○ protecting vulnerable children;
  - ○ having regards to the needs of the disabled, elderly, and those on low income;
  - ○ having regard to ethnic communities and rural and urban areas;
  - ○ having regard to persons living in different regions of the country; and
  - ○ having regard to diversity and equality.

Duties, functions, powers, and factors are clearly germane to regulators, and regulators are absolutely essential to achieving the goals of this volume. Without what looks like a simple factor of "having regard to rural and urban areas," the regulator may have no basis to interpret its remit and regulate for rural broadband too.

This is why it is so vital that the legislative acts which create the new converged TMT regulators on the continent—needed to achieve the sort of TMT economies we deserve for the 2020s—fully understand (i) what outcomes are required such as those promulgated in this volume and (ii) how the powers, functions, factors, and duties are crafted in order to ensure the new independent regulator has the tools to attempt to deliver on these outcomes.

11.4 The Economic Basis of Regulation

As noted earler, the first role of most decent TMT-related regulators is to further (or maximise) the interests of their consumers and citizens in relation to communications matters. They also try and protect consumers in the face of markets that do not work effectively for them. This role—and not many regulators on the continent tend to realise it—is broadly informed by economic theories. Indeed, most TMT-related regulators, whether they realise it or not, are *economic* regulators. That is, they use (or are supposed to use) economic theories in their regulating, and such economic theories explain how scarce resources (e.g., spectrum or TV licenses) are allocated in society. They also explain how economic benefits (called "economic rents" by economists) are shared between consumers, producers, and other consumer groups. In addition to economic benefits/rents which consumers and producers enjoy, the protection of the interests and citizens in communications markets is also grounded in public interest goals (or factors as we saw earlier), such as diversity and equality.

Have you become slightly lost with the previous paragraph because of a change of gear into economics? Well, some basic economic concepts will clarify why regulators are really economic regulators and explain why economic theories actually help maximise the interests of consumers. Are you wondering what on earth could this mean? Let us revert to some basic economics.

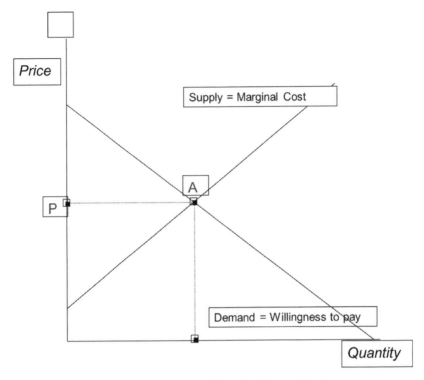

Figure 65—Demand and Supply Curves/Graphs

Figure 65 shows a market equilibrium price, P. This simple figure depicts how markets allocate scarce resources. And these are markets with decentralised agents pursuing their own self-interests. Let us explain some more. Imagine a scenario of production of mobile phones. (The same principle applies to other products too.)

The demand curve slopes downwards from top-left to bottom-right. If prices for the phones are high, economic activity is profitable, and entrepreneurs will invest and enter the market. If prices become too low, the entrepreneurs will exit the market and try and make their profits elsewhere. So the "demand" curve is equivalent to a "willingness to pay" curve: the higher the price of the phone, the less consumers are willing to pay, and hence the quantity demanded is less; the lower the price, the more consumers are willing to pay, leading to a larger quantity demanded.

The "supply" curve, on the other hand, slopes upwards from bottom-left to top-right. This is because as the price of the phone increases, suppliers are incentivised to enter the market in order to supply more phones. The supply curve is equivalent to the "marginal cost" curve. In plain English, this means the cost to produce the one hundredth mobile phone is lower than the cost to produce the ninety-ninth, assuming a perfectly competitive landscape. For example, suppose it costs $10,000 to manufacture 100 phones and $10,050 to manufacture 101 units. The average cost per unit is 10050/101 = $99.50. However, the marginal cost of unit 101 is only $50, i.e., $10,050–10,000. Suppliers will continue to supply more phones into the market as long as the marginal costs of the new units are less than the prevailing price. So if the marginal cost is $50 and the price is $70, suppliers will continue manufacturing phones because it is profitable for them to do so.

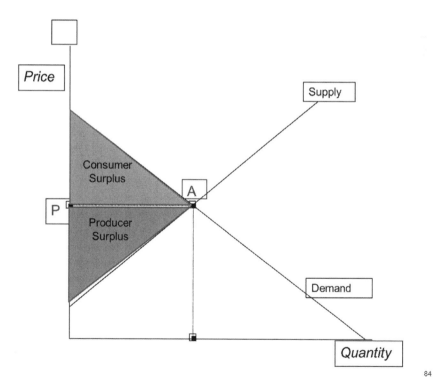

84

Figure 66—Producer and Consumer Surplus and Economic Regulation

The equilibrium position is defined by means of the equilibrium price. We are at the *equilibrium price*, when at this price the quantity of phones that buyers are willing and able to buy is equal to the quantity of phones that sellers are willing and able to sell—that is, the price at which demand equals supply. You should visualise supply (or marginal cost curve) is the sum total of all the supply curves of all the phone suppliers, and the demand curve is the sum total of all the demand curves for the various phones in that price range. The equilibrium price is also an average price point.

There are some people who would pay a lot more than this equilibrium price. Let us imagine there are ten buyers of these phones and the equilibrium price is $100. Let us suppose that a good 30 percent (i.e., three people) value the phone at more than $100 and would be prepared to pay more. The rest are only prepared to pay $100 maximum. So Customer A may be prepared to pay $150 (i.e., s/he is enjoying a surplus of $50). Customers B and C are prepared to pay $130 and $120, respectively, yielding further surplus of $50 between the two of them. Overall, there will be a consumer surplus of $100 from all ten customers.

The sum total of what customers are prepared to pay above the equilibrium price is called the *consumer surplus*, and it is shown by the green triangle in figure 66. Clearly, the more customers and citizens feel they are getting value from a product or service, the greater the value of the consumer surplus would be. The *producer surplus* (i.e., the brown box in figure 66) is also clearly the surplus above the marginal cost (i.e., supply) line. This is the sum total of the positive differences that customers pay above costs. In other words, this triangle represents the profits to the supplying firms.

11.4.1 Consumer Surplus, Producer Surplus, and Economic Regulation

Let us return to what all these demand and supply curves have to do with independent and economic regulation. You will notes we have made some minor amendments to figure 65, yielding figure 66 with some new terms: consumer surplus and producer surplus. What is their relevance to independent and economic regulation? The answer briefly follows. Only a flavour is provided here. There is much more to the following in the relevant economic textbooks.

It begins with how an independent regulator chooses to interpret its duties. Take one typical duty, that of promoting optimal use of spectrum. The regulator would independently[8] interpret this duty as promoting "efficient use of spectrum," and "efficient use" can be further interpreted as "maximising benefits to society from using spectrum, including broader social value." Economic regulation dictates that maximising benefits to society from using spectrum equates to maximising total surplus (TS), i.e., the consumer surplus (CS) and the producer surplus (PS). This makes sense because if customers all feel they are getting a good deal maximising CS, and producers are maximising their profits (PS), then society benefits optimally because both consumers and producers are happy.

This is how economic concepts are used to regulate, yielding economic regulation. Profits are easy to measure. However, measuring CS is complex but not impossible.

Therefore, to achieve optimal societal benefits (of some spectrum, say):

- An efficient allocation which maximises the sum of consumer and producer surplus needs to happen. So the spectrum goes to player(s) who would maximise their profits as well as maximise consumers' surplus.
- A free and competitive market would exist wherein purchasers who value the goods or services the highest (i.e., with the highest willingness to pay) get the goods. That is, the purchasers who value the spectrum the most should get the spectrum. Does this now make sense with respect to what we covered in the auction chapter (chapter 5)? Sure it does. Similarly, sellers with the lowest costs produce the goods.

There are many more economic concepts that are not covered here, including allocative efficiency, productive efficiency, and dynamic efficiency. Then there are other concepts too, including market failure, market power, dominance, and so on. These are important and relevant

---

8   The statutes do not stipulate how this duty should be interpreted by the regulator.

economic concepts behind the science of economic regulation. We just define them below but do not go into much detail.

Good regulation attempts to satisfy the three efficiency conditions of allocative, productive, and dynamic efficiency.

- *Allocative efficiency*: This is a static concept, and it relates to the optimal use of scarce resources. It requires that if a consumer is willing to pay an amount for a good that exceeds what it would cost society to provide her with this good, then that customer gets the good. Put another way, if she would pay twenty dollars for a good, and it would cost fifteen dollars to provide it to her, then she should get it over some other person who is only prepared to pay eighteen dollars. In even more plain English and relating it to regulation more, the good (e.g., the spectrum) should go to the person or firm who values it the most, as they are more likely to make the best use of it for society, i.e., they are more likely to drive up consumer and producer surplus (CS + PS in figure 66), or total surplus, with its use.
- *Productive efficiency*: This is also another static concept implying there is no waste in the supplying firm's productive process. This typically implies there is no (or little) technical waste, costs are minimised, and there is also no waste due to mismanagement. Take spectrum again. 4G is more productively efficient than 3G, which is more efficient than 2G. This is because for the same spectrum, a firm is able to get more capacity and throughput (measured in Mbps) from 4G than for 3G, say. It is akin to the spectrum being "less wasted" with better technologies, or, more accurately, the new technologies get more out of the same spectrum. Costs minimisation and lack of waste due to mismanagement clearly would drive *down* prices and drive up profits for the firm. In plain English, productive efficiency suggests the firm with the best technology who drives down costs and has the best management team should also be preferred to get the scarce resource/good (e.g., spectrum). They are more likely to drive up consumer and

producer surplus the most. Society should prefer such firms over other less productive ones.

- *Dynamic efficiency*: Dynamic efficiency is different from the above two (allocative and productive efficiency). Dynamic efficiency is achieved when resources move over time to their highest value uses. This means it involves the transition from one type of efficient use to another higher type of efficient use of the resource. Dynamic efficiency is at the economic heart of liberalisation and technology neutrality, the concept that regulators license spectrum but do not prescribe what technology the spectrum should be used for within limits. When spectrum is liberalised for a class of technologies (e.g., 2G, 3G, and 4G), it allows for dynamic efficiency because the firm who has the license for that spectrum may use it more efficiently over time by migrating its use to more efficient technologies.

  Indeed, even the digital switchover of some frequencies (where there is a wholesale move to more efficient digital transmission standards from analogue) is another clear example of scarce resources (TV frequencies) moving over time from inefficient analogue transmissions to their *highest value use*, digital transmissions in DVB-T2/MPEG4 (see chapter 9 on DSO). Even better dynamic efficiency also achieves the spectrum being released to transition to *higher value users* too, when the spectrum gets reassigned to mobile broadband, which typically would maximise consumer and producer surplus more than broadcasting does. Dynamic efficiency also relates to investment and innovation, i.e., both product innovation wherein the firm launches new services and process innovation where the firm improves on its processes increasing productivity and reduces costs over time.

These three efficiencies are important to economic regulation. They are at the heart of decisions made by regulators to allocate scarce resources. They (including the concepts of consumer and producer surplus) clearly show the importance of market-based thinking in the allocation of scarce resources and why regulators of such scarce resources are economic regulators. Hopefully you have now obtained a taste of the science of economic regulation. A flavour of the art follows next.

However, before that, there are some other economic terms to briefly explain to give you even more economic bragging rights (there are some serious regulatory implications behind them, hence why they are included):

- *Market failure*: Drawing from the above three efficiencies, market failure occurs where markets cannot achieve a fully efficient allocation. In other words, if the scarce resources (e.g., some spectrum bands) go to the wrong hands, which does not maximise consumer and producer surplus, this is not optimal for society. This is at the heart of why in earlier chapters I rail against CDMA spectrum not only arguably being the *wrong use* of 800 MHz frequencies today (there is much higher value use by 4G/LTE elsewhere) but, even worse, many 800 MHz spectrum bands are in the wrong hands. This is market failure, and it is the job of regulators to correct them, and they do this typically via intervention, explained briefly later.
- *Market power/dominance/anticompetitive behaviour*: This refers to the ability of a firm to maintain uncontested supernormal economic profits in the long term. This is clearly related to the concept of dominance in economic competition policy, i.e., the "ability of firms to behave to some extent independently of competitors, customers, and, ultimately, consumers." Evidently, this is not good.

  Our sector, partly due to its inherent network effect, is prone to firms evolving with market power. The sources of such market power are varied. It could be the nature of production or size, e.g., a mobile operator, A, with eight thousand base stations can "produce" (they have more coverage and capacity as in Mbps) than another operator, B, with only two thousand base stations. More calls which originate from B's network will terminate on A's network. Operator A therefore derives market power through sheer size. Market power could also derive from the fact that A would have more bargaining power with suppliers (and drive down costs further) than B can or that A has ensured (sometimes with political backing) a market structure with high barriers of entry. It is the job of the regulator to be very watchful for when market power and dominance occur in the market.

Dominance sometimes can be benevolent and benign. In itself, dominance is not a problem *per se*, but the abuse of a dominant position clearly is! If a dominant player starts displaying anti-competitive behaviour, the regulator must intervene, full stop.

- *Regulatory intervention:* Intervention by regulators is easier said than done. Most of the time, regulators try to intervene when firms are already so dominant and big with an army of lawyers and much more financial firepower. This is truly non-trivial for the regulator. A regulator may/would have to carry out a market review and make a determination or market findings and then move on to deciding what remedies it needs to put in place to correct the market failure in question.

11.4.2 Broader Social Value (BSV) and Economic Regulation

This concept of broader social value has been mentioned in several chapters of this volume, including this one. However, what exactly does it mean? It largely relates to total economic value framework, which I had the privilege of being exposed to at regulator Ofcom. It is briefly explained following.

As covered earlier, the statutory duties of a best-in-class communications regulator like UK's Ofcom require it to take account of the interests of both consumers and citizens. Believe me when I assert that this is easier said than done. How does the regulator prove that in arriving at policy choices it has taken into account citizen and consumer interests? In achieving the evaluation of policies and economic regulatory questions, Ofcom then needs to be able to demonstrate that the interests of consumers and citizens have been taken into account.

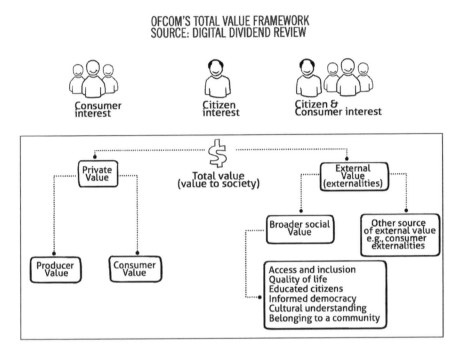

Figure 67—Ofcom's Total Value Framework
(Source: adapted from Digital Dividend Review)[9]

One of the ways in which Ofcom has addressed this problem is to define a "Total Value Framework," as shown in figure 67. The framework identifies the disparate and different types of economic value which may arise from the production and consumption of goods and services, and it shows how all of these amalgamate to yield the "total value to society," i.e., the sum of the consumer and citizen values.

9 Digital Dividend Review: A report of consumer research conducted for Ofcom by Holden Pearmain and ORC International, http://stakeholders.ofcom.org.uk/binaries/consultations/ddr/researchrpt.pdf (accessed October 2013).

As can be seen in the framework, total value to society (TVS) accrues from the sum of private value and external value. Private value is what we have covered above and consists of producer value or producer surplus + consumer value/surplus, i.e., PS + CS. The external value is similarly the sum of broader social value and other sources of external value. Broader social value (BSV)—we have seen before—refers to the interests of citizens (not consumers) that may be met by the production or consumption of goods or services. As TV/radio broadcasting is produced and consumed as noted earlier in this volume, there are vast numbers of people in society who do not pay for such services as *consumers* do via monthly subscriptions. This is because advertising pays for much of broadcasting. However, these people do derive value from such services as *citizens*. It could be an educational health programme or a national football match that one subscriber only is paying for on his/her TV set, i.e., there is a sole consumer, but a dozen other nonpayers watch. There is value to this *access* and how these dozen people feel *included* in seeing their national team play and them feeling like a community of nationals. There is value in these dozen people improving the quality of their lives via watching the educational health programme. There is much value in having educated citizens if they all watch factual and news programming, as well as having an informed democracy. These al contribute to BSV, and this example hopefully goes a long way to explaining why BSV for broadcasting usually dwarfs the private value.

Other sources of external value could be positive or negative. Such externalities refer to positive or negative value which accrues when the production or consumption of a good or service impacts those *not* producing or consuming that good or service. For example, an industrial plant may be manufacturing much-needed detergents but pollutes the air for miles and emits effluent (sewage) which make citizens living in the area feel sick. They have to go to the hospital to get treatment. Overall, even though there is good private value created here (i.e., PS + CS), there is also a negative value in the costs of such externalities.

Using such a total value framework, policies can then be assessed in terms of how well they might maximise total value to society or just private value.

This entire section 11.4 has covered enough on providing a flavour of what economic regulation entails. You can refer to other sources to get into much more depth on the theory of economic regulation.

11.5 A Flavour of the Art of Regulation: The "Balancing Act" of Weighing Up Conflicting Duties

Good (economic) regulation is ultimately a "balancing act." Drawing from my firsthand experience at Ofcom (United Kingdom), the objective of good regulation is to secure good regulatory outcomes for consumers and citizens. A good regulator like Ofcom abides by all the seven key principles noted earlier in concert with good economic regulation precepts whilst balancing, i.e., weighing up, sometimes truly conflicting duties.

Not all the duties that regulators get asked to perform are internally consistent. For example, duty to maximise broadband Internet availability comes up squarely against a duty to protect children/minors from the certain tasteless content which dominates the content online. Therefore, part of the art of good regulation lies in this balancing and in how the regulator marshals its arguments to optimally achieve its good outcomes whilst minimizing the unwanted ones. Figure 68 summarises pictorially just how Ofcom balances this art.

THE "BALANCING ACT" OF REGULATION—WEIGHING UP CONFLICTING DUTIES, FUNCTIONS, AND FACTORS

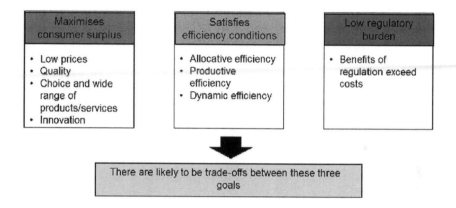

Figure 68—The "Balancing Act" of Regulation—Weighing Up
Conflicting Duties, Functions, and Factors

It depicts the use of the economic regulatory concepts discussed so far and how the *art* of world-class regulation also derives from (i) balancing the maximisation of consumer surplus (because regulators are there to look after consumer and citizen interests) (ii) whilst satisfying the above triumvirate of efficiency conditions and (iii) minimising regulatory burden. It is genuinely easier said than done. This balancing happens in concert with abiding by all the regulatory principles above, and the result is usually significant outcomes for consumers and citizens. It is clearly easier summarised here than done. Much expertise and experience is needed to execute this expertly.

11.6 Regulatory Concerns and Recommendations for Africa and Some Emerging Economies

This section draws unashamedly from Calandro *et al.* (2010),[10] as their comparative sector performance review of the ICT Policy and Regulation across seventeen countries on the continent is simply excellent. I cannot overemphasise how such analyses are vital and how every TMT regulator on the continent must read every word of such comparative analyses assiduously. Given that this report covers seventeen countries, I consider their findings quite representative of some of the regulatory ills on the continent and quite reflective of those in other emerging economies too that I know in other non-African markets. This section pulls out some key messages from Calandro and his colleagues' reports across several regulatory areas already touched on in chapter 3. All of the recommendations or their findings below are consistent with the other chapters of this volume, but it is still worth reemphasising from their perspective again.

1. *The African Union must lead regulatory policy and regulatory coordination based on a single economic market:* The harmonisation of ICT and TMT policy and legal frameworks is recognised by regional economic entities[11] and international donor communities as essential to regional economic integration, as well as the integration of regional economies into the global economy. The underlying principles around such harmonisation are to bring about and speed up competition in TMT, to interconnect national backbones into a seamless African backbone infrastructure, and to promote regional and

---

10 Enrico Calandro, Alison Gillwald, Mpho Moyo, and Christoph Stork (2010), *Comparative Sector Performance Review 2009/2010: Towards Evidence-based ICT Policy and Regulation*, Volume 2, Policy Paper 2, researchICTafrica.net.

11 The East African Community (EAC), the East African Regulatory, Postal and Telecommunications, the Economic Community of West African States (ECOWAS), the Southern African Development Community (SADC), the Economic Community of Central African States (ECCAS), and the Central African Economic and Monetary Community (CEMAC).

foreign investment. However, Calandro *et al.* rightly point out that these efforts are *not* driven by a single market philosophy like with the European Union. This is a mistake, as most African countries are frankly subscale from a TMT perspective. Regional regulator entities are all agreeing on recommendations, but they have no implementation powers, which all lie with national regulators. The fact that OHADA works demonstrates that where there is a will, there is a way. It is financed and supported by France. Therefore similarly, the Africa Union (AU) to the extent that it has any real use—it clearly has very little use in conflict resolution, as is evidenced by the case in 2012/13 of Mali which the UN is handling—must lead on a real single African economic market. I am very supportive of AU initiatives like HIPSSA,[12] and the AU must find a way to emulate the EU model of binding directives across all nations on the continent, and the support of the ITU is most welcome. Why HIPSSA is limited only to sub-Saharan Africa also passes me by.

2. *Regulatory institutional reforms ensuring true independent regulators on the continent are urgently needed:* This is yet another recommendation which this volume has been promoting across several chapters, including this one. Calandro *et al.* note that with 93 percent of African countries having established regulators, Africa as a continent now has more regulators than any other continent. Yet they note they are institutionally hampered by the absence of political autonomy to regulate independently. They further lament the poor levels of policy making and implementation across the continent, and governments undermine their regulators too. They cite Botswana, whose regulator issues licenses autonomously to operators but with the Ministry of Communications they are able to refuse or revoke the said licenses. Their analyses

---

12 HIPSSA, Harmonisation of ICT Policies in Sub-Sahara Africa, http://www.itu.int/en/ITU-D/Projects/ITU-EC-ACP/hipssa/Pages/default.aspx (accessed November 2013).

suggest that despite formal separation of powers in most west African countries, political pressure is frequently brought to bear on regulatory decisions. These all send terrible signals to international and national investors for such a key sector needing lots of investment. This chapter has made the case for true independent regulators. It just makes sense and must be heeded.

3. *Liberalisation and competition with converged regulators and the issuing of service/technology-neutral licenses must proceed across the continent:* This volume has noted this so often that there is a strong case to spare you this gospel here again. However, Calandro and his colleagues note that many African countries still neither have converged regulators nor unified licensing regimes. We saw earlier the economic regulatory case for *liberalisation* of licenses and making them *technology neutral*, as it allows the licenses to transition to higher productive efficiency uses and even to users who value it the most if trading of spectrum is also allowed. This drives up consumer and producer surplus, maximising welfare to society. Some countries like Benin or Ethiopia did not even have a regulator in 2013. Others, like Cameroon, neither have a converged regulator nor service/technology-neutral licenses.

4. *Privatisation of incumbent fixed line operators across the continent must be speeded up:* Calandro *et al.* note that this has been slow, leading to governments continuing to maintain dominance over fixed line incumbent operators whilst creating conflicts of interest for governments with these incumbents and their competitors. The woeful performance of fixed operators across the continent—see chapter 10, with most countries having fixed teledensities below 3 percent—cries out for privatisation and liberalisation of this fixed sector. The same applies to broadcasters.

5. *Spectrum policy and management should be improved across the continent:* It is fair to say—as was covered in the chapters covering spectrum (chapters 4, 5, and 6)—that the independent policy formulation and management of such an important national and natural resource across the continent leaves much to be desired. This volume has hopefully helped in this area. Calandro *et al.* highlight examples of countries not even having a spectrum policy (e.g., Ethiopia, still the case as of 2013), ineffective management of spectrum, compromising competition (e.g., Uganda), poor allocative efficiency of spectrum or spectrum in the wrong hands who do not use it (e.g., Ivory Coast), spectrum hoarding (e.g., South Africa), etc. I have trained several countries in this important area.

6. *Interconnection—Cost-based termination rates encourage competition and affordability and must be rolled out across all countries:* Call termination is a natural monopoly element of network operators. This is a key area where regulators truly make a difference. Moving towards pure LRIC-based mobile termination rates across the continent is vital to driving up affordability and driving up competition. CCK in Kenya has been at the forefront of driving for pure LRIC-based termination rates, to the extent that when Bharti Airtel acquired Zain Kenya in 2010, it immediately announced a reduction in prices by over 50 percent. This is competition in action. None of this would have happened without CCK's (Kenya's converged regulator) clear termination rates determinations and the glide path the regulator set for further year-on-year reductions. Figure 69 shows Calandro *et al.*'s termination rate findings for 2010.

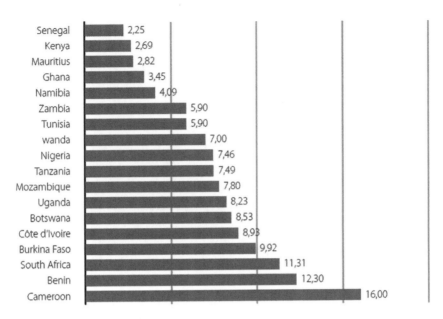

Figure 69—2010 Mobile Termination Rates in US Cents across Seventeen
Countries in Africa (Source: Calandro *et al.* [2010])

There have been some changes since, but not much. As of 2013,
it is still the case that my country, Cameroon, is still worst-in-
class with some of the highest mobile termination rates on the
continent. Is it any coincidence that as of 2013 it neither has
a converged regulator nor service and technology neutral licenses? Benin is still not much better. Is it any surprise since it
does not even have a regulator batting for Benin's consumers
and citizens? Even South Africa still has high mobile termination rates in 2013, leading to high telecommunications charges
in South Africa and muted competition. ICASA, its regulator,
could do much better. Is it any surprise today too that Kenya
and Senegal have arguably the most dynamic, innovative, and
competitive mobile markets on the continent in 2013/14? Good
regulation delivers good consumer surplus and therefore a
good deal for consumers and citizens. We could go on.

7. *Ending the roaming nightmare across the rest of the continent
as in the case of east Africa would be such a coup*: Calandro,

Gillwald, *et al.* note, "while Europe is struggling with the regulation of high roaming charges, in East Africa high tariffs and roaming charges are progressively being far more effectively addressed through competition in marginal markets."

East Africa is leading the world in using competition across borders to address cross border roaming, thanks to Bharti Airtel innovating with its "One Network" launch across Kenya, Tanzania, and Uganda. The then Zain increased its market share significantly via this move. MTN in Uganda and Rwanda, Safaricom in Kenya, Vodacom in Tanzania, and UTL in Uganda all had to respond and create their own seamless partner service, which they called Kama Kawaida.[13] The problem we have is the rest of Africa is not enjoying such roaming benefits.

8. *In general, the telecommunications regulatory environment (TRE) across all of Africa must be significantly improved:* What I love the most in the Calandro, Gillwald *et al.* (2000) report is their TRE assessment tool and their results. I love measurements and monitoring, and I hope that ICT Africa, led by Dr. Alison Gillwald, will continue to do such excellent work. It is a pity that most regulators across the continent, in my experience of having met almost 40 percent of them, do not seem to appreciate the gem in such work. The TRE instrument was originally designed to assess regulatory effects on investment but has subsequently been developed and adjusted for surveys in Latin America and Africa. The TRE methodology is a measure of perception that is affected by several different factors, including political and cultural ethos within the country. The overall TRE perceptions score of figure 70 below cover market entry, access to scarce resources, interconnection, tariff regulation, regulation of anticompetitive practices, universal service obligations, and quality of services.

---

13   Kama Kawaida is Swahili for "as usual."

Overall TRE 2009 Score

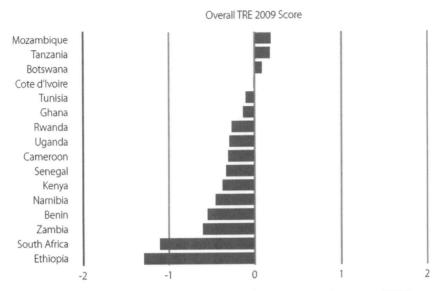

Figure 70—Overall Telecommunication Regulatory Environment (TRE)
2009 Score (-2 = Very Inefficient, +2 = Very Efficient)

The overall TRE scores speak for themselves, and the overall scores above flatter some truly much poorer scores across many of the classes, like access to scarce resources, regulation of interconnection, tariff regulation, and regulation of anti-competitive practices. Their high-level findings drawing from these perception analyses are most apt and are in quotes below, with my reminder of relevant recommendation/commentary following:

- *"Overall most countries are perceived to have inefficient regulatory environments."* In plainer English, most regulators are not doing a good job! Most countries need true converged regulators who are independent, along with significant capacity building across regulators on the continent.
- *"In most countries 'market entry' is perceived negatively as most countries have failed to open their markets sufficiently to enjoy the benefits of competition."* Liberalisation, privatisation, and competition are the key tools here to use here.

- *"The sub-optimal use of spectrum has impacted negatively on the service expansion capabilities of operators, the types of technologies deployed and the opportunities for innovation."* Spectrum policy and management must be improved across the regulators on the continent.
- *"High tariffs have been a major barrier to access telecommunication services and often a key indicator of the lack of competition."* Confident and true independent regulators must be true competition regulators too and must truly tackle high tariffs on the continent.
- *"Policy and regulatory developments in Africa are highly uneven, with considerable gains in some countries, such as the move towards cost-based termination rates, and continued political interference in the regulatory processes in others."* Cost-based termination rates drive competition as noted earlier, yet another reason to have true independent regulators.
- *"The majority of countries...were regarded as ineffective in the regulation of anti-competitive practices."* Again, regulators are clearly doing very poorly as competition regulators.
- *"Although several countries have established UAFs [Universal Access Funds] and often dedicated agencies to ensure their implementation, these have not yet yielded the intended results. Despite most of the African countries having liberalised their telecommunications sectors to some degree, access and affordability of services remain uneven and very low when compared with other regions of the world."* Regulating for access and affordability is a major contribution of this volume. TV white spaces for rural broadband (chapter 6) could make a big difference with UAFs too.

I could not praise enough the TRE tool and its applications.

11.7 Final Recommendations Towards *Better* TMT Regulation and Regulators in Africa and Emerging Economies

Hopefully, you can now attest that without regulation the goals of this book are unachievable. It is as simple as that. Three final recommendations to conclude the chapter follow:

1. *The TMT outcomes required must be "baked" into new statutes to be interpreted and enforced by their resultant independent and converged regulators:* It is now clearer that in order to achieve converged regulation, the legislatures of states of Africa and emerging economies need to be crystal on the TMT outcomes required—hopefully the outcomes highlighted in this volume and more. These outcomes would have to be baked too into powers, duties, functions, and factors of statutes. The resultant regulators are creations of statutes, and it is vital that the statutes are those necessary to realise the TMT outcomes desired. I cannot overemphasise this.

2. *Good (economic) regulation is both an art and a science. Good regulators should ensure they understand fully the science of economic regulation as well as its art:* This chapter has just provided a very brief flavour of what the *science* economic regulation entails by introducing the concepts of demand and supply graphs along with those of consumer and producer surplus. It has also introduced the *art* of regulation by describing the balancing and weighing across many duties, functions, and factors. It is recommended that middle-level and senior TMT regulators get the required training in economic regulation principles and praxis, as well as the art of good regulation too. The benefit of the investment in such training, along with contemporary case examples in their markets, is incalculable. Every time I have lectured and trained on such areas, participants mainly comment on how in the dark they have been as

regulators. Theory without practice is sterile. Practice without theory is blind. Karl Marx was right.

3. *Hold regulators to account for the growth of the TMT sector:* Regulators and governments must realise there is a clear correlation between how well the TMT/ICT sectors are regulated and the growth of those sectors. Legislatures and parliaments must genuinely see it as their responsibility to hold their TMT regulators to account for the growth of their sectors. They can commission analysis, such as the "Net Economic Value of Spectrum to the Economy" as shown in figure 33, to see how the spectrum regulator is furthering the interests of their consumers and citizens by optimising the use of spectrum. Similarly tracking the percentage contribution of TMT to GDP over a period, as shown in figure 2, could/should be commissioned and scrutinised. Poor regulators truly do incalculable damage to such an important sector, and they must be booted out. At best, the opportunity costs of bad regulators are too high, as many important regulatory decisions to realise important market outcomes are missed. At worst, bad regulators make barmy and nonsensical economic regulatory decisions, ensuring *suboptimal* allocative, productive, and dynamic efficience outcomes; indeed, they manage to achieve inefficient allocation of scarce resources. Such poor regulators are just bad news for the economy and for the nation's consumers and citizens.

Regulation is not only one of the main drivers of the TMT sector; it is also—as we have seen in this chapter—one of its main Achilles's heels too. Governments and ministers need to understand the true costs of poor regulation and/or their meddling in it. The costs are truly incalculable.

SECTION VII

TMT AND NEIGHBOURING SECTORS

CHAPTER 12

TMT, NEIGHBOURING SECTORS, AND CONCLUSIONS

"The one who says it cannot be done should never interrupt the one who is doing it."
—*Chinese proverb*

"The reasonable man adapts himself to the world; the unreasonable man persists in trying to adapt the world to himself. Therefore all progress depends on the unreasonable man."
—*George Bernard Shaw*

It feels most apt to use these quotes to start this last chapter which covers how TMT is underpinning, impacting, and influencing other neighbouring sectors of the economy and how TMT is providing (or would be providing) solutions to some real world problems in Africa and emerging economies across a whole host of sectors.

The spirit of including a chapter of this kind in this volume is threefold. First, policy makers and decision makers within the TMT sector must and should realize how much (whether they like it or not) they are gatekeepers to other sectors of the economy and how their actions—and, in many cases, inactions—have opportunity costs elsewhere in the economy. So, for example, if mobile data does not happen because an African or emerging market's lackadaisical regulator fails to release 4G spectrum early, many other sectors in the economy slow down or do not happen at all for several years: broadband/m-health, broadband/m-education, m-agriculture, etc. Essentially all applications that require more spectrum capacity than 2G/3G can handle are forfeited or postponed. It is the same argument that this book started with in the preface— railing against power and infrastructure issues on the African continent holding back TMT. As Calandro *et al.* (2010) note in the first paragraph of their report:

> The cost of wholesale telecommunication services as an input for other economic activities remains high, escalating the costs of doing business in most [African] countries. In addition the contribution of ICT to gross domestic product with some exceptions in North Africa, Senegal and the Indian Ocean island states, is considerably less than global averages and what it would be if it were being used more widely as a lever for economic growth on the continent.

This is the supply side of the story to both within and without the sector. If we in the TMT sector justifiably rail against the power sector for holding us back on the continent with their lack of supply of power, we all have responsibility too of not "holding up" other sectors where we are their dependent "suppliers."

Second, there is the demand side too. Those outside the TMT sector who understand their dependency on the TMT sector would be rightly demanding that the TMT sector delivers on widespread and affordable networks, broadband, fibre, TV, radio, etc., because it "oils the wheels" of their own sectors too.

Third, and more generally, a volume that focuses and impresses on access and affordability of telecommunications, media, and technology for Africans for the 2020s must also promote access and affordability of other equally important human right services, like education, financial services, health, etc., just as the Indaba declared broadband to be in 2012 (see beginning of chapter 7), not least as these services can/would be accelerated by TMT.

Fourth, broadband is the clear imminent growth enabler on the continent, and all sectors must evolve strategies to put as much pressure on governments to deliver on broadband, both in urban and rural areas. Better still, the governments' TMT strategies will accommodate for all their key sectoral broadband needs.

Fifth, and more specifically to financial services, financial exclusion is a clear risk for emerging countries financial systems, not least through a widespread use of cash only.

A more inclusive financial sector means more people feel included in the nation's financial stories, financial stability, integrity, consumer protection, reduction of the informal economy, and more. Mobile money (enabled via TMT) discussed in this chapter can help contribute to addressing this risk.

If TMT delivers on its side of the bargain, there is no telling the innovation that will be unleashed on the continent of Africa and in other emerging markets. It never ceases to amaze me, having spent the bulk of my career so far in Europe, the ingenuity of SMS-based, STK[1]-based, and USSD/SMS-based *narrowband* m-applications that have been developed in Africa covering many other sectors, including M-PESA in Kenya or even the iCow[2] application too from Kenya, WIZZIT from South Africa, and so on.

In this vein, it is truly a responsibility of those of us in TMT to do our bit and get out of the way and let innovation reign elsewhere. And when innovation is happening and in full swing, those of us who believe and say it cannot be done should get out of the way and not interrupt those doing it—as the Chinese proverb at the start of this chapter stipulates. If you as a TMT decision maker or policy maker are

---

1   STK: SIM Toolkit—STK is a standard from GSM to secure mobile phone applications, particularly for mobile banking and privacy using a passcode or PIN stored on SIM card. USSD: Unstructured Supplementary Service Data is different to SMS in that it informs the customer whether the message has reached the recipient or not, though this message is sent as an SMS.

2   iCow uses texts on mobile phones to educate rural farmers on how to look after the general wellbeing of their cows from birth to sale.

not moving with cautious haste, you are almost certainly part of the problem, not part of the solution. This is because there are thousands of would-be innovators and entrepreneurs—those "unreasonable" people, according to George Bernard Shaw—who persist on adapting the world to themselves and not adapting to the world. Two Google founder/entrepreneurs decided they would not adapt to the world as it was, and the rest is history. Africa and other emerging economies have many "unreasonable" people-in-waiting, hanging on TMT to deliver, in order for them to create brands in the TMT sector and beyond which may/would be as famous as Google.

So what are the questions this chapter seeks to answer? They include:

- What are some of the key neighbour sectors and services to TMT?
- Why are these sectors and applications and services important and timely now?
- What are some of their dependencies on TMT? What are some of the things TMT have to do to get out of their way?

The neighbouring sectors and application services covered include (they are by no means meant to be exhaustive):

- financial services, including, in particular, mobile money (or m-money) for financial inclusion
- education, including m-education
- government
- health, including m-health
- smart cities and big data
- agriculture, particularly m-agriculture

Apart from financial services, many of these sectors are only briefly mentioned without going into too much detail. The goal here is just to emphasise how dependent other sectors are on TMT and that citizens of these developing economies deserve to enjoy all these e-services/m-services in the 2020s. These neighbouring sectors are literally waiting on TMT. Then this proceeds to "round out" and conclude the book by mentioning other activities, such as incubation services, returning to the power problem, training, and capacity building, etc.—all prerequisites to a successful TMT sector in Africa and elsewhere for the 2020s.

12.1 Financial Services

Astonishingly, sub-Saharan Africa is the world leader in mobile financial services, particularly mobile money (m-money) initiatives, and the region led the development of more than fifty such programmes in 2011, compared to twenty in east Asia and fewer elsewhere, according to the GSMA. However, Africa is the runaway topmost leader in the league table of the unbanked, i.e., those without bank accounts. In Africa, only 20 percent of the population have bank accounts;[3] we return to this later. M-money refers to financial transactions undertaken using a mobile device, including mobile phones and tablets. The ITU defines and captures the three main types of m-money or mobile financial services as per figure 71 below.

---

3 Source: http://mobilemarketingandtechnology.com/2011/03/07/mobile-banking-in-africa-an-overview/ (accessed October 2013).

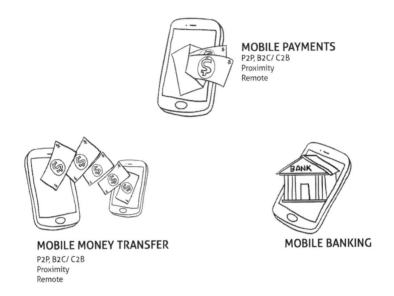

TYPES OF MOBILE FINANCIAL SERVICES
SOURCE: INTERNATIONAL TELECOMMUNICATION UNION (ITU-T, 2013A)

MOBILE PAYMENTS
P2P, B2C/ C2B
Proximity
Remote

MOBILE MONEY TRANSFER
P2P, B2C/ C2B
Proximity
Remote

MOBILE BANKING

Figure 71—Types of Mobile Financial Services
(Source: Adapted from International Telecommunication Union [ITU-T, 2013a])[4]

It shows the three main types of mobile financial services as mobile payments, mobile money transfer, and mobile banking. Mobile payments cover proximity payments at the merchant site (e.g., the customer paying at checking till or website) or transactions with a remote merchant. It could be a peer-to-peer (P2P) service, but it could also be a business-to-consumer (B2C) (e.g., a company refunding monies to a customer) or a consumer-to-business (C2B) service (e.g., a consumer paying his utility bill). Mobile money transfer is a broad term for the transfer of monies from one individual to another or a P2P pay which may be domestic or an international remittance. Mobile

---

4 ITU-T (2013a), *The Mobile Money Revolution, Part 1: NFC Mobile Payments*, ITU-T Technology Watch Report, May 2013, http://www.itu.int/dms_pub/itu-t/ oth/23/01/T23010000200001PDFE.pdf (accessed October 2013). This report provides an excellent review of the state of the art in near field communications mobile payments.

banking allows users to manage their bank accounts remotely from mobile devices. Mobile network operators (MNO) love m-money because it is increases the MNO's number of customers as well as its ARPU through taking a slice of the revenue generated by these payments in addition to other rental fees.

The full potential of mobile money is far from being realised in developing countries as of 2013/14. According to the GSMA Intelligence, 2.5 billion people in developing economies still lack a viable alternative to the cash economy and informal financial services, whilst 1.7 billion of them have mobile phones (di Castri, 2013). This GSMA report by di Castri asserts that the mobile money industry has found it very difficult to launch and scale mobile money solutions for the unbanked because many policy and regulatory environments are just not genuinely enabling to make this happen. As you will find out within the next few pages, I have much sympathy with this viewpoint. A combination of a more digitally financially included and cash-lite economy truly delivers key benefits: small and informal businesses suddenly become formal; customers of such businesses now can keep an electronic record of all their transactions; such records are gold because financial products and services can now be fashioned for such customers by microfinance institutions; customers and citizens can now be educated in matters financial; and women in particular in developing economies in Africa would become more financially independent, and hence more independent, etc. The broader social value to financial inclusion is humongous.

Kenya is the runaway global leader in mobile money transfer, mobile payment, and mobile banking services through M-PESA. M-PESA is by no means the only major mobile financial services application within Africa and Emerging markets. Others include WIZZIT (South Africa), MTN Mobile Money (used in several African countries), Airtel Money (used in India and fourteen African countries), T-Cash (Haiti), and Easypaisa (Pakistan)—see ITU-T (2013b)[5] for some more details on these.

---

5   ITU-T (2013b), *The Mobile Money Revolution, Part 2: Financial Inclusion Enabler*, ITU-T Technology Watch Report, May 2013, http://www.itu.int/dms_pub/itu-t/oth/23/01/T23010000200002PDFE.pdf (accessed October 2013).

However, the success of M-PESA *in Kenya* compared to these other m-money services is truly astonishing and worth studying some key lessons why. ITU-T (2013b) notes some key facts about M-PESA:

- an incredible 16 percent of adults report having used a mobile phone in the past twelve months to pay bills or send/receive monies, compared to less than 5 percent in all other regions;
- active bank accounts increased in number from 2.5 million in 2007 to more than 15 million in 2011;
- transactions via M-PESA exceed US$375 million each month;
- between 2007 and 2009, the percentage of M-PESA users who were unbanked doubled from 25 to 50 percent, showing it is attracting the unbanked in massive numbers—*a key metric for inclusion*;
- the number of M-PESA users living in rural areas increased from 29 to 41 percent between 2007 and 2009, too demonstrating M-PESA's ability to achieve access.

12.1.1 Towards Widespread and Affordable Mobile Financial Services

It is the case that different business models have emerged across all the different countries mentioned above, depending on regulatory regime, population size, and culture. The three mobile financial services business models are (ITU-T, 2013b): bank centric (i.e., bank led), MNO led (or nonbank based), or a partnership. MNO-led models tend to be prevalent in developing economies where financial services infrastructure is not well developed. Bank-led models, in contrast, occurs where there is good infrastructure and regulation. Partnerships would tend to happen in developed economies too.

Let us return to financial inclusion, which is simply defined as the absence of price or nonpriced barriers in the use of financial services (ITU-T, 2013b). It is the case that low levels of financial inclusion represent a barrier to socioeconomic development in developing economies. Mobile telecommunications is by definition a key dependency here.

Let us further consider the following two facts/propositions. First and interestingly, M-PESA has been implemented in other countries (including Tanzania, Uganda, South Africa, and Afghanistan) but not seen such success—by all comparisons so far—as in Kenya. Secondly, other countries have tried other business models, e.g., Africa's biggest telecommunications market, Nigeria, has experimented (and was experimenting as of 2013/14) with a bank-led model, and by all accounts, not promising to be as successful as Kenya. For example, several papers/publications in Nigeria ruled in September 2013 that mobile money had flopped in Nigeria.[6]

However, it is not simplistic enough to say it is the business model or size of a country (Nigeria is four times the population of Kenya), etc., that is key. It is a complex picture too that needs unpicking, and we use Kenya, Tanzania, and Nigeria as exemplars to illuminate some of the possible causes/reasons why Kenya is racing so far ahead in mobile financial services:

- Business Model: It is instructive to note that M-PESA is an MNO-led model, having been innovated and rolled out by Safaricom in Kenya before it got implemented in other countries. It is also an MNO-led model in Tanzania but with a much subdued level of success than in Kenya. This suggests the difference in success levels is not business model but something else. Nigeria, on the other hand, opted for a bank-led/ partnership business model. Simplistically, this is arguably an odd choice given the level of infrastructure and regulation in Nigeria. The result is that the MNOs are not leading mobile financial services in Nigeria; the banks are. Is this the killer reason why Nigeria was perceived to be flopping in mobile money as of 2013/14? This is a bit of rhetorical question, but it may be a key reason.

---

6   Business Day: http://businessdayonline.com/2013/09/why-did-mobile-money-flop-in-nigeria/ (*Business Day* is a daily business newspaper based in Lagos); TechPresident: http://techpresident.com/news/wegov/24319/why-did-mobile-banking-flop-nigeria (both accessed October 2013).

- Market Dynamics: There is no doubt that a well-funded, highly motivated, and dominant leading market player like Safaricom in Kenya would clearly do better than a less dominant, less motivated Vodacom in Tanzania. In Nigeria, the banks are leading, not the MNOs, and it is not clear why they would drive access and affordability better than MNOs who clearly have a financial incentive to drive up their ARPUs and number of subscribers. Nigeria's "open scheme" is also more likely to mean less leadership and no real responsibility on any real player to lead. Coordination failure appears to abound.
- Strategic Marketing: A potential explanation of the difference between Kenya and Tanzania thus far appears to be the much better strategic marketing by Safaricom in Kenya compared to Vodacom M-PESA in Tanzania, along with better cross-selling of airtime. Furthermore, the value proposition for M-PESA seems quite clear and simple, particularly in Kenya: "send money home." What is the simple and clear message for an "open model" bank-led approach in Nigeria? It appears to be a value proposition that benefits the Central Bank of Nigeria (CBN), who wants to manage Nigeria's cash supply and track money supplies too; but is it forgetting the customer?
- Network of Agents: Safaricom in Kenya has a well-developed network of agents converting cash into e-money and vice versa. It's more developed than in Tanzania and certainly much better than Nigeria too. Agents in Kenya handle cash in the context of financial transactions. In Nigeria, the banks do this.
- Regulation: Thanks to unique circumstances in Kenya, it did not issue any specific regulations even though it has allowed MNO-led models to proceed in the country on an *ad hoc* basis through "no objection" letters or conditional approvals which can be hardly reversed. Tanzania has some regulations and is working on more. Nigeria as of 2013/14 was working out what to do and had certainly signalled to the MNOs so far that they were not in the lead. There are other regulations, including cybersecurity, fraud, data protection, and cash handling. Then there is the biggie question of whether mobile money services

should be regulated as a bank. Kenya had ducked this question so far until 2013/14 with Safaricom, though the regulator (CCK) was thought/known to have some clear views. Nigeria had taken a clear stance that only banks (until date in 2013/14) had licenses to offer mobile financial services.

- Inter-Operability: This is important to drive up access and affordability (via scale economies). If different banks' and/or MNOs' financial software systems have to interoperate and "talk to one another," this creates an almightily large software systems project. A dominant Safaricom in Kenya does not face this problem, and a bank-led model of sixteen banks clearly presents some sort of an interoperability nightmare.

- Dominance: Safaricom's M-PESA is a clear success on many metrics, but at what cost? ITU-T (2013b) notes a key one: that Safaricom's market share has actually increased over time because of the lock-in attributes of MPESA. How do you regulate dominant players? Experience from mature markets like the United Kingdom show that once players become too big, they are a nightmare to regulate properly.

The above list of differences is not exhaustive, but it serves to illuminate some key messages.

12.1.2 Recommendations for Mobile Financial Services and TMT

We venture some recommendations from the lessons above.

Let us remind ourselves of the obvious: mobile financial services straddle the *outcomes* and *regulatory* spaces of both telecommunications and banking. Several of the recommendations below derive from this simple proposition.

1. *Agree joint sector outcomes across telecommunications and banking with determined facilitation:* The first and most important recommendation must be for two sectors (telecommunications and banking) to agree to joint outcomes. You are

509

now no doubt clear as to how outcomes driven I am. Chapter 3's blueprint is all about outcomes. It is patently clear that for the widest possible inclusion of mobile financial services to happen, there must be partnership and collaboration between these two sectors, ministries, ministers, joint policy formulation, etc. This is hard in developed economies, yet alone in developing countries. Both departments/ministries of state, i.e., finance and telecommunications(TMT), may have to employ strong facilitation via a good facilitator to achieve this. Opting for a bank-led model in Africa's circumstances of poor infrastructure and weaker regulation arguably, like George Bernard Shaw notes, is the right approach if one wants to adapt himself to the world *as is*. However, it appears to me that Kenya's M-PESA inadvertently (from a Kenyan policy perspective) took the "unreasonable" man approach by trying to adapt the world to Safaricom and, more importantly, to most of their customers—Kenyan consumers and citizens. Yes, there is also a clear competition risk with the Kenyan approach.

Therefore, there are three clear joint outcomes I suggest here, and they include:

a. to strive towards universal access to financial services, specifically payments, transfer, and banking for all
b. to ensure the access to financial services to all is affordable (remember, reach without affordability is futile; affordability without reach is sterile)
c. to ensure fair and open competition reigns driving costs down and minimising cybersecurity, fraud, etc.

These three outcomes are tricky to square. There may be other secondary outcomes, like managing the money or achieving a "cashless Lagos," Nigeria's "cash-lite" society, etc.—but such outcomes are either secondary to the above three or would be derived from them. Both departments must be open-minded as regards what tools/approach is/are best to achieve these outcomes, and I venture that TMT would have a pretty significant role in achieving it.

2. *Agree on provisional policies across telecommunications and banking and joint regulation; is there a role for extending the aims of Universal Service Funds?:* Partnership and collaboration across two key government departments (and possibly more) would possibly require joint policy formulation and sponsorship and also require enaction of jointly sponsored new legislation. One suggestion could be the extension of the role of the Universal Service Funds to include banking inclusion with sponsorship from the Finance Ministry too. Alternatively, the equivalent of Universal Service Funds for banking inclusion are also set up within the financial services sector. In terms of regulation, the set of joint outcomes would naturally lead to a way of achieving joint regulation to achieve these outcomes. A joint team across the banking and the telecommunications regulators may be charged with ensuring the joint regulation to achieve these important outcomes. New proposed policies are likely to emerge, including allowing telecommunications operators to enter nontelecoms activities, like mobile financial services as is exemplified by the one the GSMA (di Castri, 2013) asserts below:

> The basic proposition for mobile money to succeed is to create an open and level playing field that allows non-bank mobile money providers, including mobile network operators (MNOs), into the market. Anecdotal evidence, commercial lessons, and international regulatory principles all defend opening the market to providers with different value propositions. The prudential regulations of non-bank mobile money providers effectively mitigate the risk of mobile money customers losing the money they have stored in the system. The challenges of anti-money laundering and combating

the financing of terrorism (AML/CFT) compliance can be addressed by promoting risk-based know-your-customer (KYC) procedures. There are also cost-effective regulatory solutions in place to develop and set up distribution networks and accelerate customer adoption.

When both banks and non-bank providers, especially MNOs, are allowed to launch mobile money deployments, and when there are effective and proportionate mechanisms in place to manage the unique risks of this industry, mobile money has the capacity to significantly expand financial inclusion—through lower transaction costs, improved access to underserved areas, and higher levels of customer convenience.

The GSMA position is clear—that the risks to having a "more level playing field" is more that mitigated with current "prudential regulations on non-bank money providers." Such a position can be adopted provisionally and piloted within the countries to "prove" them.

3. *Piloting the emerging model and provisional policies between government, industry, and civil society is key:* There is unlikely to be a one-size-fits-all model that achieves the three outcomes suggested in all countries. Therefore, there must be a way to evolve and pilot how the partnership between government departments, industry, and civil society to achieve such financial inclusion. It is important to pilot (i) how joint regulation would work, (ii) interoperability across different stakeholder systems, (iii) testing cybersecurity measures, (iv) honing of regulations, (v) awareness creation, etc. How would telecommunications operators fare doing financials services? How can MNOs and banks co-lead along with civil society if this is how a model evolves? A cooperation model synthesising

banks, mobile network operators, cooperatives, and savings-led groups would probably have to emerge. These all need testing. I believe passionately in truly carrying out trials which puts tools in the hands of the "unincluded" and seeing what they make of it too.

4. *Adopt an innovation approach*: Indeed, there is a strong case not to regulate for mobile financial services too early. One of the lessons—surely—from the Kenyan exemplar is that the lack of formal regulation seems to be an asset so far. This is also something that may be piloted.

5. *Deregulation and liberalisation of financial services towards telecommunications and other civil society groups:* I venture that a likely outcome scenario would involve formal deregulation of financial and banking services towards telecommunications and other civil society groups in order to drive up financial inclusion as the GSMA prefers. What form they will take will vary from country to country. The real concern, arguably, should be whether the risks to such deregulations and liberalisation are clearly mitigated to ensure that unsuspecting consumers and citizens do not lose their hard-earned monies to unscrupulous firms.

Again, the above are a bunch of proposals and suggestions to stimulate debate amongst policy makers and decision makers on how to achieve financial inclusion in developing economies.

12.2 Other Neighbouring Sectors

12.2.1 Education

"I was raised to believe that excellence is the best deterrent to racism and sexism. And that's how I operate my life." —Oprah Winfrey

I could not agree more with Oprah Winfrey. I also believe Ms. Winfrey would also agree that what underpins this "excellence" is education, plain and simple. In my own miniscule way, this volume is about me striving to be "excellent." The role of education in achieving access and affordability cannot be overstated. Education is key to access and affordability! Only 27 percent of Africans have a second grade education and above. Similarly, the role of TMT could be invaluable, particularly m-education.

The challenges for education in developing economies (including Africa but other countries, like Pakistan and Bangladesh) include the following major ones:

- Millions of students and children are out of school. UNESCO estimates that 10.5 million students are out of school in Nigeria alone[7] and over 1.7 million in Ethiopia and 5.46 million in Pakistan as of 2011.
- Inadequate quality control. Teacher training is poor, class sizes are huge, and there is a dearth of instructional materials.
- Teaching methodologies need greater guidance and support.
- Curriculum in many countries is in desperate need of renewal.

E-education would be of immense help to address these issues. However and yet again, all the basic requirements for e-education all point to a resilient TMT infrastructure, colleges and institutions of learning being networked together, increased Internet bandwidth, increasing the number of affordable computers and phablets, and increasing and improving training in computer literacy and platforms. Such e-infrastructure not only includes mobile devices but also video-conferencing suites, e-learning management systems, CD-ROMs, DVD, audio radio platforms (FM and AM), TV platforms, and the Internet itself.

---

7 UNESCO Institute for Statistics (UIS), Schooling for millions of children jeopardized by reductions in AID, UIS Fact Sheet, June 2013, no. 25, http://www.uis.unesco.org/Education/Documents/fs-25-out-of-school-children-en.pdf (accessed December 2013).

E-education can help retain many of these dropouts from school for whatever reasons. The GSMA mEducation programme hopes to retain some 8 percent of dropouts across grades one to ten over the next five years in one African country.

M-Education would play an important role. M-Education is the application of mobile devices and services, in any education process, albeit in teaching, learning, assessment, and administration. Education is already happening on the continent, using mobile technologies to help support learning in schools, universities, and workplaces, helping to make leaning more personal. The mobile device is nothing if it is not personal. With the emergence of affordable tablets and phablets, institutions would benefit from more flexible delivery of education at reduced costs. "Bite-sized" lessons can be delivered via such a mobile platform, and a systematised approach to learning can be implemented via the mobile platform. M-education would provide cost-effective updates and up-to-date content and curriculum. It would provide students with opportunities to study from home and maintain their studies during periods of downtime. This would be possible because mobile devices provide ubiquitous access for teachers and trainers to be able to share experiences and curriculum plans.

The reality is that though the mobile platform and m-education would be important to developing economies, a mass platform like TV and radio (terrestrial or satellite) would also be invaluable to the widespread availability and affordability of electronic education and e-learning and, ultimately, the Internet. E-learning is the delivery of learning using interactive electronic technology, both online and offline.

The key dependency of education on TMT is for the latter to deliver on its various TMT platforms as described in the previous eleven chapters of this book. From the perspective of this volume, educational content generation and delivery would be both a key driver and beneficiary of the availability of widespread affordable Internet, other ICT infrastructure, fixed, TV, and radio. I have much confidence in entrepreneurs (in particular), progressive educational institutions, and educational public private partnerships (PPPs) in developing the requisite educational content across all these platforms if and when they become available.

12.2.2 Government

The best definition of e-government is arguably that of Jeong (2007), who defines it as the utilization of ICT technologies along with web technologies (e.g., the Internet) in order to improve and/or enhance the efficiency and effectiveness of the delivery of services in the public sector. E-government also refers to digital interactions between government and several other stakeholder groups as categorized below:

- government to citizens (G2C)
- government to businesses (G2B)
- government to employees (G2E)
- government to governments (G2G)
- citizens to government (C2G)

Government itself needs to be efficient. In most cases in developing economies, particularly those in Africa, they are bloated, bureaucratic, incredibly inefficient, and corrupt. It is a dream that the TMT infrastructure this book espouses would eventually be able to support e-government and cut out 50–80 percent of the human intermediaries who contribute to having such an opaque public sector in many African countries. Efficiency and transparency are urgently needed in interactions with governments, and only true e-government really promises to deliver this, in addition to improved services, better accessibility of public services, and accountability.

Indeed, an important aspect of the TMT business plan of some countries is the efficiency and costs benefits to be gained via going e-government. Nevertheless, the same civil servants and bureaucrats are the most likely encumbrances to change.

12.2.3 Health

E-health is invaluable for Africa and many other emerging economies, particularly as 70 percent of Africans live in rural areas. E-health refers to the application of ICT to healthcare, particularly, but not exclusively, the Internet. It covers the computerization of medical records, telemedicine,[8] healthcare telematics,[9] digital imaging and—yes, in the long term—the reorganization of the health sector around telematics. Improving access to healthcare using ICT/TMT technologies is now an International Telecommunications Union (ITU) resolution which was adopted at the World Telecommunications Development Conference in 2010 in Hyderabad—Resolution WTDC-65.[10]

M-health solutions truly provide an opportunity for health care providers to innovate in order to deliver more consistent, efficient, quality, and remote health care to millions. Even better is the potential of technology to empower individuals to take responsibility for their own health.

As is the recurring theme of this chapter of the book, TMT needs to deliver on all its platforms: TV, radio, improved fixed Internet, and mobile (data/Internet). If TMT does deliver these, many private commercial and civil society players will contribute meaningfully to national health objectives, albeit child mortality, maternal care, etc.

Like financial services, many e-health propositions would require clarity and/or definition of policy and regulatory frameworks that will govern and promote their use. This is because many innovations in this sector are in affordable devices (heart rate monitors, blood pressure monitors, skin sensors, etc.) that collect data from patients—in many cases they would be remote—and sent over various platforms. Clear regulations are needed here not least for privacy, empowerment of the patient, approval of medical devices (particularly high-risk ones), data protection, and security of data (to ensure they do not fall into the wrong hands). Many of the recommendations on how financial services sector and the telecommunications services sector should collaborate to make e-financial services happen would also apply to the e-health sector too.

---

8   Telemedicine is the use of telecommunications and information technologies to provide healthcare remotely or at a distance.

9   Telematics is just the fusion of telecommunications and informatics or ICT. Healthcare telematics refers to the fusion of telecommunications and ICT for healthcare.

10 Source: http://www.itu.int/ITU-D/conferences/wtdc/2010/pdf/WTDC10_Draft PreliminaryReport.pdf (accessed December 2013).

12.2.4 Smart Cities and Big Data

A "smart city" is simply one that makes extensive use of information and communications technology, including mobile, fixed, TV, radio, and Internet networks in order to improve the quality of life of its citizens. Examples include sensors in public car parking spaces,[11] intelligent sensors on roads and telemetry systems,[12] contact-free payments, intelligent traffic light systems, smart energy systems which minimize energy consumption, smart utility meters, contactless toll systems for cars, remote-controlled video cameras, central smart city operating centres, mobile networks, etc. It is obvious that all the major emerging developing economy capital and commercial hub cities need to be "smarter." You just have to visit Dhaka (Bangladesh), Lagos and Abuja (Nigeria), Douala (Cameroon), Cairo (Egypt), Nairobi (Kenya), Accra (Ghana), etc.—and suffer some of the traffic chaos in these cities—to agree that these cities must be planning now to be smart.

Smart cities force governments and cities to understand the concept of "big data." This refers to the concept of having to harness and combine information from several to many sources of smartly connected infrastructure and sensors to generate trends and insights that can be exploited to improve the "smartness" of the city.

The key dependency here again is resilient and dependable TMT and ICT infrastructure, as well as technology solutions to aggregate, analyse, and trend copious amounts of data. Most of the services required in smart cities are real-time services which would be nontrivial to deliver too.

---

11 Evidence suggests that 30–40 percent of traffic at most times consists of cars moving around, searching for a place to park!

12 Telemetry involves the automatic measurement via sensors and other measuring devices and the transmission of data by wireline, radio wave, or other means from remote sources, as from weather stations to receiving stations for recording and analysis.

12.2.5 Agriculture

TMT and ICT hold great promise for transforming agriculture in Africa and other emerging economies. GSMA (2013) notes that over 2.3 billion people (most in developing economies) live in poverty, and the majority of these people earn their living from small farms. In many of these countries, these farmers get information such as planting techniques, crop management, pesticide use, use of fertilisers, etc., from agricultural extension workers. Astonishingly, their evidence suggest that one extension worker may be expected to assist up to four thousand farmers, which clearly results in a most inefficient process because of long time delays between visits. However, these farmers need timely information as they face risks such as weather, pests, and diseases that can destroy their crops and harm their livestock (and hence their livelihoods) between these visits.

M-agriculture is the obvious answer here, as more and more of these farmers are availing themselves of mobile phones. Education and literacy are clearly important here for them to be able to read the information they get sent. This is an excellent case for having widespread availability of voice and some narrow band data—to enable the realization of m-agriculture. However, in the case of these farmers being illiterate, audio radio is the most entrenched ICT on the African continent, and this platform may be able to broadcast to these farmers in their own native dialects.

The iCow[13] application is just one example of m-application in the agriculture space. Yet again, the dependability of such a vital sector of our economy on TMT is clear to see.

12.2.6 Cloud Computing

The concept of cloud computing is relatively novel, and it specifically refers to users being able to run programs and/or applications on a network of distributed computers across a network, such as the

---

13 iCow uses texts on mobile phones to educate rural farmers on how to look after the general well-being of their cows from birth to sale.

Internet. In more common, everyday computing parlance, it refers to services that can be obtained over networks, i.e., network-based services. Consider a scenario where a user has his or her word processing document or spreadsheet on his computer and is able to write a book, as I was at some time in the past writing this page. I have these "fat client" applications like word processing software or PowerPoint presentation software on my personal computer to be able to pen this book. However, imagine a scenario where the user only has a small phablet or mobile device with not enough memory to store such fat applications on her client device. An alternative that presents itself is to have rather "smaller" applications on her small client device which runs the fat applications (like the word processing software network) on a network of computers or servers on the Internet and only delivers the results to the client device. These networks of servers will appear *virtual* to the user in the sense that though there are many physical computers running these fat applications, he/she would almost certainly have no idea *where* these computers are and *how* many of them are being used at any one time. The servers can be scaled up and scaled down depending on the complexity of the task. So if it is a complex mathematical set of computations like working out weather prediction using humongous sets of data from multiple satellites, hundreds of server computers could be involved in the solution to the problem of predicting Wednesday's weather.

Hence, cloud computing refers to network-based services that appear to be provided by a singular real hardware server, when, in reality, dozens to hundreds of servers may be involved. It is as if the solution is really being developed by the cloud,[14] as it were. Many "hosted" services are sometimes referred to as cloud services. Consider the case of where your company's website content is hosted. From your client browser on your device in Tunis (Tunisia), you are able to access your website content, which would almost certainly reside on multiple remote servers or mirrors (allowing for resilience and redundancy) on the Internet anywhere in the world. So cloud computing depends on shared distributed resources.

---

14 Read: "cloud" of servers or computers.

Why is moving to cloud computing relevant to Africa and emerging markets? Simply (and mainly though not solely) because moving to a cloud model means companies are able to move away from traditional capital expenditure (capex), where companies purchase dedicated hardware and fat clients software, and these capex depreciate over time. Moving to a cloud model using shared infrastructure means the business pays an operational expenditure (opex) cost, which is almost certainly going to be a much lower cash flow out of the business than the capex costs. The claim then of cloud computing is that companies are able to set up and run their business critical applications much faster and can grow their demand of these cloud services seamlessly as their business grows. In the recession too, they would use less resources and hence pay less rather than be lumbered with expensive hardware computers that are running well below their capacity.

Many small and medium enterprises in Africa and emerging markets would benefit from cloud services running off massive data centres—whether simple website hosting or running complex billing systems software in the cloud. Clearly, access to a widespread Internet of fixed networks and national fibre backbones connected to international submarine cable capacity is better here, though widespread, high-capacity wireless networks are also an alternative.

12.2.7 E-Commerce and M-Commerce

Electronic commerce (e-commerce) simply refers to the buying and selling of products and services over electronic platforms such as the Internet and other computer networks, including the cloud. M-commerce is clearly the equivalent of e-commerce over mobile platforms involving mobile operators, banks, merchants, and payment systems. According to Wikipedia, e-commerce can be divided into the following:[15]

- electronic retailing (e-tailing) or "virtual storefronts" on websites with online catalogues, sometimes gathered into a "virtual mall"

---

15 Source: http://en.wikipedia.org/wiki/E-commerce (accessed December 2013).

- buying or selling on various websites and/or online marketplaces
- the gathering and use of demographic data through Web contacts and social media
- electronic data interchange (EDI), the business-to-business exchange of data
- e-mail and fax and their use as media for reaching prospective and established customers (for example, with newsletters)
- business-to-business buying and selling
- the security of business transactions

Earlier on in chapter 1, it was noted that in the United Kingdom in 2011, one pound in every five pounds of sales took place online or through electronic means driven by purchases made on Amazon and eBay and business-to-business online purchases by SMEs and big businesses. I also reflected on how amongst seven middle-class and cash-rich managers of a prominent African regulator, none of them had ever shopped online up until July 2013. Clearly, e-commerce is enabled by widespread ICT, and this is clearly gating this important would-be growth sector.

12.3 Other Prerequisites to a Successful TMT Sector

As we "wind down" to the end of this entire volume, for the sake of completeness mainly, some other important prerequisites to a successful TMT sector are noted. They include mentioning other activities, such as returning to the power problem, training and capacity building, incubation services, and workshops, etc.—all prerequisites to a successful TMT sector in Africa and elsewhere for the 2020s.

12.3.1 The Need for Reliable Power and Electricity

The TMT revolution described in this volume would remain largely a dream unless the chronic power and electricity issues in emerging economies, particularly those in Africa, are comprehensively addressed. Most experts agree that the lack of power and electricity is a tremendous hindrance to the development of the African continent, particularly sub-Saharan Africa.

Furthermore, I hopefully live in the real world. It would have been remiss of me not to highlight the seriousness of the power issue so that the influential decision makers and entrepreneurs who happen to read this volume or chapter may be more informed. The reality of power/electricity issues on the continent of Africa in particular cannot be overstated. Much of the contents of this volume is predicated on power!

Power represents Africa's biggest infrastructure headache, with rural communities suffering the most. Many a time, I am *not* sure that African leaders realize that over six hundred million Africans are enslaved at night in their homes, using kerosene or candles. Some 85 percent of Africans in rural sub-Saharan Africa have no power. Those in the cities who can afford it buy and run diesel generators, as well as expensive fuel. The total costs of kerosene and candles in the rural areas and the diesel costs in the urban areas are out of all proportion to the energy delivered by them. In other words, this is very inefficient and costly power, which delivers miniscule productivity.

As I researched the power issue on the African continent, I frankly found myself being increasingly depressed. To get the dose of the depressing state of African power and electricity, you need look no further than reading chapter 8 of a World Bank publication,[16] *Africa's Infrastructure: A Time for Transformation* (World Bank, 2010). Below is a summary of some of the World Bank findings on power/electricity in Africa in 2010 reported in this 2010 book.

- Africa's generation capacity is woeful: the entire installed generation capacity of the forty-eight sub-Saharan African (SSA) countries in 2010 was just 68 gigawatts, no more than Spain's. About 44.3 gigawatts of this capacity needs refurbishment. Excluding South Africa, this total falls to 28 gigawatts.

---

16 Power: Catching Up, Chapter 8, *Africa's Infrastructure: A Time for Transformation (Africa Development Forum),* Washington, DC.: The World Bank. ISBN: 978-0-8213-8041-3, http://infrastructureafrica.org/system/files/Africa's%20Infrastructure%20A%20Time%20for%20Transformation%20CHAPTER%208%20POWER.pdf (accessed December 2013).

- Of this SSA capacity, 25 percent is unavailable because of ageing plants and poor maintenance.
- Of SSA population, 20 percent has access to electricity, compared to about 50 percent in south Asia and more than 80 percent in Latin America. Overall, 71 percent of households in urban areas have access to electricity, compared to just 12 percent in the rural areas. Only 15 percent of the rural population lives within ten kilometres of a substation. As much as 41 percent of the rural population is so isolated or remote from the grid that they are only reachable in the medium term via off-grid technologies, such as solar photovoltaic panels costing US$0.50–0.75 per kilowatt-hour. You can see why power in the rural areas is a major problem in Africa, and why solar panels (where possible) are being used in rural communication services.
- Since 1980, east Asia, Latin America, and the Middle East have all added about twenty percentage points to their rates of electrification, but in SSA it has been stagnant as population growth outpaces new connections.
- The costs of producing power in Africa are exceptionally high and rising because of increasing oil prices and lower availability of hydropower: $0.14 per kilowatt-hour compared to $0.04 in south Asia and $0.07 in east Asia.
- Incredibly, power consumption in Africa was found to be tiny and falling! Consumption in SSA, excluding South Africa, averaged only 124 kilowatt-hours a year, barely 1 percent of typical consumption in high-income countries.
- Power outages are rife: 25 days a year in Senegal, 63 days in Tanzania, and 144 days in Burundi 144. The economic costs of outages is almost 6 percent of GDP in South Africa and Uganda, almost 7 percent in Malawi, 5 percent in Tanzania, 2 percent in Kenya and Senegal, 1 percent in Cameroon, etc. The case for fixing power issues in Africa is clear.
- Backup generators represent an incredible 50 percent of the installed capacity in DRC, Equatorial Guinea, and Mauritania and 17 percent in west Africa as a whole. Backup generator

costs are circa $0.40 per kilowatt-hour, i.e., ten times the costs of south Asia's power costs. How can these countries compete against south Asian companies?

- An additional seven thousand megawatts of new generation capacity is needed every year, but only one thousand came online between 1990 and 2005. The bulk of this new capacity is needed by industry, including TMT. Without it, TMT is held back.

I do not delight in listing the above litany of woes. The motive is truly wholesome: to demonstrate that the lack of power should be seen by African leaders for the debilitating impediment it truly is on the continent of Africa, namely:

- It delays (at best) or outright inhibits investment.
- It limits productivity on the continent, as people can hardly work at night.
- Lifesaving vaccines cannot be stored in rural areas, where most Africans live without power.
- Students and pupils can hardly study after dark—more power will enable more time for productive work and study.
- Frequent power outages are the norm, meaning big losses in forgone sales, damaged equipment. As seen above, there is significant GDP impact on outages.
- The costs of most commodities (be it a bottle of water or other products) costs between 20 to 60 percent higher than what it should truly cost because of the absolute inefficiency and ineptitude of the power sector over the decades. We could go on.

The grid is expanding, but, in many countries on the continent, whatever grid electricity is generated is struggling to keep up with the increasing demands of the population with power (most of who live in cities), leaving little progress on the huge task of electrifying rural communities.

The good news for Africa is that SSA is well-endowed with both hydropower and thermal power resources, yet only a small fraction of its power potential has been developed. World Bank (2010) reports that of the forty-eight SSA countries, twenty-one have generation capacity of less than two hundred megawatts, well below what they term "minimum efficiency scale," resulting in costs of US$0.25 per kilowatt-hour, twice the $0.13 for the region's larger power systems.

There is also a not-so-well-understood virtuous circle at play with power too: power/electricity enables development that enhances the earning power that makes more electricity/power more affordable. The moral of the power story is simple—just plan for it, invest properly (ahead of demand), and ensure electricity for the majority of Africans as soon as possible, and the business case will pay for itself earlier.

12.3.2 TMT Training and Capacity Building

The TMT revolution described in this volume requires significant training and capacity building on the continent across businesses, mobile operators, fixed operators, regulators, governments, civil societies, universities, etc. The contents of this volume hopefully make a small, insignificant contribution in this regard. There is obviously much training to be delivered behind every chapter of the volume.

I plead with decision makers, in Africa in particular, to be humble enough to realize training and capacity building is invaluable to the growth of the TMT sector. In Africa in particular, there is the "*Oga*"[17] problem syndrome as regards training, wherein the senior staff and board members of key TMT institutions think it is beneath them to be seen in the same training room with their subordinates. Many a time, they would not even accept that they need training—period. This means that some of their progressive subordinates who decide to get the requisite training find themselves very frustrated with bosses who have no idea of the progressive ideas they are promulgating.

Furthermore, I come across numerous entrepreneurs on the African continent (as well as in other emerging market countries (like Haiti, Ethiopia, Tanzania and Bangladesh I have visited over the 3 months

---

17 Oga is a classic term referring to the "Africa big man," heard in Nigeria and other West African countries.

to January 2014) who really are clueless in running businesses. This is also another significant limitation.

Several chapters in this volume have already emphasized training and capacity building, and therefore there is no need to emphasise any more than above.

12.3.3 Incubators, Research Parks, and Techno Cities

Following on from training and capacity building above, the role of incubators, TMT hubs, and techno cities are very invaluable to Africa achieving the TMT sectors it deserves for the 2020s.

Well-run incubators are excellent vehicles that are proven to help grow Internet and other TMT-related businesses. I am privileged to have been a senior executive with a London-based incubator in the dot-com era of the late 1990s. A good incubator (typically run by experienced executives who have founded and/or run real businesses but who also know how to structure and invest in business) would typically offer the following:

- The incubator would invest capital in exchange for equity in the new company (NewCo) and raise further capital if necessary.
- The incubator would help recruit an excellent management team to run NewCo if they judge the founder(s) not right to run NewCo.
- The incubator management would advise NewCo on Internet marketing, TMT marketing, customer relationship management (CRM), public relations (PR), online branding, etc., as judged required by NewCo.
- The incubator would manage the entire scheme to deliver a working company in a defined time period, e.g., 180 days.
- The incubator could help use their networks to deliver key strategic alliances to NewCo.

Successful entrepreneurs on the continent, particularly those with experience in TMT, may want to set up, run, house, and incubate the next generation of TMT firms that Africa and emerging markets need. An incubator does not guarantee that the businesses incubated will all succeed; rather, it should help improve the chances of the businesses being successful.

Research Parks are also recommended as research facilities linked to major quality research universities. Africa has unique African problems too which need to be researched in order to yield solutions Africans need. America and Europe have hundreds of research parks that create links between a university, industry, and the community.

An even bolder move beyond research parks is the design and setup of techno cities. Techno cities are smart cities exploiting much TMT technologies that aim to be at the forefront of the technology-led business revolution that would transform Africa and other emerging economies. Typically techno cities would be master planned to attract international investment opportunities, to spur economic growth, and to create high-quality job opportunities. They would be endowed with the best connectivity and dedicated electricity and power. To attract investment, the government would establish the techno city, developing authority as a special purpose vehicle (SPV), and the city would be set up too with special economic zones (SEZ) acts allowing for a wide range of incentives being made available to investors. One of the best known emerging techno cities on the African continent is Konza techno city, and other countries would want to consider spurring the TMT growth for the 2020s using techno cities.

Incubators, research parks, and techno cities (run under SEZ) are all vehicles that would help catalyse TMT in Africa and other emerging economies.

12.3.4 TMT Leadership

As this insignificant volume comes to its conclusion with this subsection, there are many other prerequisites to a successful TMT sector in Africa and other emerging markets that could have been mentioned. However, in my humble opinion, one stands out without which the realization of everything recommended in this volume would come to nought: TMT leadership.

TMT leadership is no different from any other good true leadership. This sector, arguably more than any other sector of an economy, requires real and true authentic leadership. There must be hundreds of thousands of books and writings on leadership. However, at their essence, they all note that leaders shape the vision. Leaders shape goals and develop novel ideas. Leaders connect with others at an emotional level to ensure the vision, goals, and novel ideas are truly shared and owned.

Penning this last subsection on the same day that Madiba Nelson Mandela was being laid to rest made (and makes) this point truly poignant. You would be well aware of the true and authentic leadership of this remarkable African and world leader. TMT needs its mini-mini-Madibas too.

Perhaps the leadership model (out of dozens if not hundreds) of most relevance to TMT is the VCM leadership model. This model argues for three main traits of any good leader's personal profile: vision, commitment, and management skills. It posits that in addition to *vision* noted earlier, leaders demonstrate clear *commitment* to the vision and cause, and they must have the *management* skills to see the implementation through. All the vision in the world is no good without some of it, at least, being realized. Reflect again on Madiba Mandela's balanced leadership whilst he was president of South Africa: on his clear vision of a rainbow South Africa, with opportunities and a level playing field for all; on his clear and unadulterated commitment to the vision; and on his management via legislation, new laws, and their implementation in order to realize this vision.

Good TMT leaders in Africa and other emerging market countries need a similarly good balance of these three essential traits. Many ministers of ICT on the continent of Africa may be good managers who can solve day-to-day problems and climb up greasy political poles but who can hardly take on the true challenges of the TMT sector outlined in the volume. Those who have the authority and responsibility to appoint to these key positions must take this responsibility with the awe it entails. It is such TMT leadership that has delivered some of the most TMT-successful economies in the world, including South Korea, Japan, and Singapore.

It can also happen in Africa and other emerging economies. Indeed, it is. Returning to Rwanda, which was singled out in the preface of this book, there is some incredible leadership (including in ICT/TMT) happening there, personally led by current[18] president Paul Kagame. He is allegedly obsessed with the Singapore model of ensuring an entire new economy to be born in Rwanda. Everyone in his government uses tablets, ensuring that the ICT/TMT infrastructure must be (or would be) there in the first place. No one doubts President Kagame's ICT vision for Rwanda. Rwanda, in addition to having LTE rolled out to 90 percent of Rwandans to access 4G LTE broadband by 2015, is also driving a "one laptop per child policy"[19]—so not only will everyone in his government have tablets, but every Rwandan child too. What a vision! No one should doubt President Kagame's commitment either: a key mantra running all through Rwanda is "we have until 2017." This is the year when his presidential term runs out. This date is focusing the mind of all in Rwanda. Similarly, his management traits are also formidable: he allegedly works sixteen hours days and personally reviews ICT and other key milestones in Rwanda. He has a zero tolerance on corruption, encouraging international investors to invest with confidence in Rwanda.

In the preface, I noted that the TMT vision of this volume can be realized on the continent of Africa and in other similar emerging economies, like Bangladesh, Myanmar, and so on. Rwanda shows and is showing it can be done, and even Rwanda must upgrade its ICT vision to a full TMT one too. There are other pockets of excellent ICT leadership on the continent of Africa, including Minister Omobola Johnson[20] of Nigeria and President Jakaya Kikwete of Tanzania, to name a couple.

I saw this African proverb recently (November 2013) at the Oliver Tambo Airport in Johannesburg:

---

18 Paul Kagame has been president of Rwanda from 2000 till the time of this writing, December 2013. His term ends in 2017.

19 See http://rwandaolpc.wordpress.com/ (accessed December 2013).

20 Mrs. Omobola Johnson is the current (as per December 2013) minister of communication technology in Nigeria; she was appointed in 2011.

If you want to go fast, go alone. If you want to go far, go together.

What a profound, profound saying. Singular TMT leadership by the likes of President Kagame and Minister Omobola Johnson is just great. However, if more of their kind were going together, we would go further and faster with African TMT.

Lastly, it is my ultimate hope as an insignificant author that *some* of the musings of this similarly insignificant volume are adopted by true leaders of the ilk of President Kagame, Minister Johnson, and others. Better still, that even more authentic TMT leaders are identified to drive the vision, commitment, and management *together* towards the delivery of the TMT sectors that Africans and other emerging market citizens deserve for the 2020s.

JARGON BUSTER

1G: 1G is first generation mobile. It was analogue and is now obsolete and offered only 9.6 kb/s.

2G: Short for second generation mobile phone technology which succeeded the first generation (1G). Global System for Mobile Communications (GSM) networks are example of 2G networks, which became the de facto global standard for mobile voice communications with over 80 percent market share. Second generation (2G) systems, in contrast to 1G, are digital and to enable cross-border "roaming" and standardisation of frequency use was absolutely vital. Otherwise, we all would be using different phones/devices operating on different frequencies in different countries—a recipe for unmitigated chaos.

2.5G: Like with 2G GSM but with speeds from circa 56 to 115 kb/s.

3G: An ITU standard for third generation mobile phone technology standards that succeeds second generation (2G). 3G promises increased bandwidth of up to 384 Kbps to a stationary or moving device and up to 2 Mbps in fixed applications. An example of the implementation of 3G standard is the Universal Mobile Telecommunications System (UMTS), a 3G mobile technology.

4G: Fourth generation of mobile phone communication technology standards which succeeds third generation (3G) standards and second generation (2G). 4G differentiates itself by being designed for data. 4G provides for mobile broadband Internet access to laptops, smartphones, tablets, and other mobile devices. An example 4G system that implements the 4G standards is the Long Term Evolution (LTE) standard.

AM/FM: Amplitude modulation/frequency modulation. Modulation techniques are used to carry information in radio carrier waves, in the case of AM by varying the strength (amplitude) of the wave with respect to the information being transmitted; in the case of the FM, by varying the frequency of the radio carrier in relation to the information being transmitted.

ARPU: Average revenue per user, which is the monthly average takings per user earned from telecommunications customers.

costs orientation: The requirement (typically imposed by a regulator) that specific services be sold at a price that is derived from some measure of the cost to provide that service.

broader social value: The value accrued from intangible aspects like "access and inclusion," e.g., true mass broadcasting enables a country's citizens to feel included in that country and helps them feel they belong to that society. It fosters culture as well as enables an informed democracy. There is much social value here which are not easily "extracted" as profits.

bit: Shorthand for "binary digit." Communications on networks, at its most basic level, are a series of these binary digits of zeroes and ones which transmit all the voice and data information on these networks.

BWA: Broadband wireless access.

dual illumination: A special and transitory phase where the same channels are broadcast both in analogue and digital, and the analogue transmissions would be switched off at some time.

DVB/MPEG: Digital Video Broadcasting/Moving Pictures Expert Group. DVB-T2 stands for DVB-Second Generation Terrestrial and is a standard for digital transmission. DVB is already the dominant terrestrial digital terrestrial standard for ITU Region 1 that includes Africa and Europe. MPEG-4 is the most recent standard for compressing and encoding digital video and sound with minimum loss of quality.

DSL: Digital subscriber line. Cable is usually two or more metal wires running side by side.

EBITDA: Earnings before interest, tax, depreciation, and amortisation are subtracted. It provides a clear view of the profitability of a company's operational business.

femtocell: Small, low-power cellular base station typically designed for use in a home or a small business. It is normally used to augment poorer indoor coverage from the outside macro network and/or to provide more capacity.

fibre (optical): Optical fibre uses glass and transmits light between the two ends of the fibre carrying vast amounts of data. FTTC is fibre to the curb, whilst FTTP is fibre to the premises or to the home (FTTH).

FTTC: Fibre to the curb (kerb).

FTTH: Fibre to the home.

freeview: The digital terrestrial TV free to air platform in the United Kingdom.

FRND-ly: Fair, reasonable, and nondiscriminatory.

GDP: Total market value of all officially recognised finished goods and services in an economy of a country over a specified period of time.

gigabyte: 1 Gbps = 1 billion bytes per second = 10^9 bytes.

GSM: Global System for Mobile Communications. See 2G.

HD (and SD): HD stands for digital high definition standard, while SD depicts standard definition. HD provides for much higher quality resolution than SD, making for improved and better looking pictures, particularly on big, flat screen TVs.

ICT: Information and communication technologies.

IP/MPLS: In high-performance telecommunications networks, a way to be able to get data from one network node or network type to another based on short path labels rather than long and complex Internet protocol (IP) addressing. This reduces delay or latency.

interference: In layman's terms, when two or more waves (a wanted signal and at least one unwanted signal) interfere or "superimpose," resulting is a poorer wave. The same effect you have in a room full of people all conversing, and you are trying to listen to one person (the wanted wave signal), but you have to contend with much interference from all the others speaking too (the unwanted signals).

ISM: Industrial, scientific, and medical.

ITU: International Telecommunications Union is a specialised agency of the United Nations responsible *inter alia* to coordinate the shared use of global radio spectrum and shared use of satellite orbit slots in the skies, and it works to improve telecommunications infrastructure in the developing world.

IXP: Internet exchange point. These international gateway equivalents for the Internet are also called peering points (PPs).

license exemption: The approach to licensing spectrum wherein operators are able to operate electromagnetic communications equipment using frequency airwaves without having to hold a license from the regulator.

LINX: London Internet Exchange—much of the Internet traffic going in and out of the United Kingdom goes via this Internet exchange point (IXP).

LTE: Long Term Evolution. See 4G too.

MFN/SFN: A single frequency network (SFN) is an analogue or digital broadcast network where several to many transmitters simultaneously transmit over the same frequency channel. A multifrequency network (MFN), in contrast, is one in which multiple radio frequencies are used for broadcasting. One way to visualise it is to imagine a chessboard with a transmitter in each square. In an SFN, all transmitters will be using the same frequency, whilst in a MFN, no two same frequencies will be adjacent to one another on the chessboard. SFNs are therefore more efficient in the use of radio frequencies at the expense of likely self-interference, resulting in likely smaller coverage per cell/square due to the use of the same frequency in all cells.

M-PESA: *M* is for "mobile"; *pesa* is Swahili for "money." A mobile phone–based money transfer and microfinancing service for Safaricom and Vodacom, it is also the largest mobile network operators in Kenya and Tanzania. M-PESA is in other countries too.

mobile switching centre (MSC): MSC refers to that core of the network that sets up and handles calls made over a mobile network.

MVNO: A company without its own sprawling network which has made an agreement with an existing "real" mobile operator, like MTN, to carry services and products on its behalf. An MVNO will brand the product and services (and handsets) as if itself were operating a network. This may be a cost effective way for supermarket chains, music stores, and youth-related industries to move into the mobile service arena. A real operator may also make use of MVNO branding to target niche segments of the market, such as youth culture, gaming, etc.

network effect: Sometimes known as network externality, it refers to the phenomenon wherein the value of a product or service is dependent on the number of people using the service. A world with only one telephone is pretty useless—no one else to phone! A world with a thousand telephone lines is more valuable, as each can telephone 999 others. This is clearly more valuable. A network of one hundred million numbers is clearly exponentially more valuable—this is the essence of the network effect.

not spots: Areas where people cannot access mobile services due to lack of coverage.

peering points (PP): See IXPs.

picocells: Small cellular base stations which cover larger areas than homes or small business but with slightly larger radii, such as shopping malls, train stations, or airport perimeters.

PPP: Public private partnerships.

RAN: Radio access network is part of a mobile telecommunications system which implements radio technologies allowing users to have and share radio resources. Users via their devices are able to make calls via their access to the RAN network which sits between the users and the core network.

router: A device that receives electronic information message, notes the traffic condition on the network, and determines the best possible path for that message to get to its destination.

spectrum liberalisation: A process wherein licence holders can request a variation to certain licence conditions. In this way, licensees can change how they use their spectrum assignments subject to some constraints. A good example is where spectrum which was awarded just for 2G voice can, post liberalisation, be used for both 2G, 3G, and even 4G subject to meeting similar technical interference constraints.

TCP/IP: Transmission control protocol/Internet protocol—the communications protocol developed to enable computers of all kinds to share services and communicate directly as if part of a seamless network.

Terabyte: 1 TBps = one trillion bytes per second = 10^{12} bytes or one thousand gigabytes

terrestrial television: A mode of broadcasting television using radio waves from *land*-based transmission sites, transmitting and receiving via antennas and television antenna aerials, respectively.

TMT: Telecommunications, media, and technology.

Universal Access Policy: The implementation of the policy for the benefit of every person in society, including those in rural areas.

Universal Service Policy: The specific service that is delivered to all in society. It could be the main channel from the state broadcaster that broadcasts news, for example.

UMTS: See 3G.

VSAT: Very small aperture terminal. Most VSAT dishes or antennas are no more than 1.2 metres in diameter, and they are part of a two-way satellite communication with a satellite (or satellites) delivering typical data rates of 4 Kbps to 16 Mbps.

white space technology: A technology and approach pioneered by Google and Microsoft and others which promises affordable broadband to the masses using frequencies currently reserved for TV.

wired telecommunications activities (fixed telecommunications activities): Services provided over communications networks which serve *fixed* locations. Wired services are distinguished from mobile (or wireless) services, which can be used whilst on the move.

SELECTED BIBLIOGRAPHY

Beutler, R. (2012), The Digital Dividend of Terrestrial Broadcasting, Chapter 2, XVII, London: Springer Verlag, ISBN: 978-1-4614-1568-8.

Berger, Guy (2010) with contributions from Fackson Banda, Jane Duncan, Rashweat Mukundu, and Zenaida Machado, *Beyond Broadcasting: the future of state-owned broadcasters in Southern Africa*, Windhoek, Namibia: Fesmedia Africa Series.

Berger, G. (2010a), "Conclusion: Looking Forward," in Guy Berger (2010) with contributions from Fackson Banda, Jane Duncan, Rashweat Mukundu, and Zenaida Machado, *Beyond Broadcasting: the future of state-owned broadcasters in Southern Africa*, Windhoek, Namibia: Fesmedia Africa Series, pp. 85–89.

Berger, G. (2010b), "Introduction: Beyond Broadcasting," In Guy Berger (2010) with contributions from Fackson Banda, Jane Duncan, Rashweat Mukundu, and Zenaida Machado, *Beyond Broadcasting: the future of state-owned broadcasters in Southern Africa*, Windhoek, Namibia: Fesmedia Africa Series, pp. 7–19.

Calandro, E., Gillwald, A., Mpho, M., and Stork, S. (2010), *Comparative Sector Performance Review 2009/2010: Towards Evidence-based ICT Policy and Regulation*, Policy Paper Series Towards Evidence-based ICT Policy and Regulation, vol. 2, Policy Paper 2, researchICTafrica.net, http://www.researchictafrica.net/publications/Policy_Paper_Series_Towards_Evidence-based_ICT_Policy_and_Regulation_-_Volume_2/Vol_2_Paper_5_-_Comparative_ICT_Sector_Performance_Review_2009_2010.pdf (accessed July 2013).

Cave, M., Doyle, C., and Webb, W. (2007), *Essentials of Modern Spectrum Management*, Cambridge: Cambridge University Press.

CTO (2012), October, *The Socio-Economic Impact of Broadband in sub-Saharan Africa: the Satellite Advantage*, http://www.cto.int/wp-content/themes/solid/_layout/dc/ptojects/Socio-Economic_Impact_of_Broadband_The_Satellite_Advantage.pdf (accessed October 2013).

Di Castri, S. (2013), GSMA—Mobile Money for the Unbanked: Mobile Money: Enabling regulatory solutions, London: GSMA, http://www.gsma.com/mobilefordevelopment/wp-content/uploads/2013/02/MMU-Enabling-Regulatory-Solutions-di-Castri-2013.pdf (accessed December 2013).

Digital Dividend Review: A report of consumer research conducted for Ofcom, by Holden Pearmain and ORC International, http://stakeholders.ofcom.org.uk/binaries/consultations/ddr/researchrpt.pdf (accessed October 2013).

Duncan, J. (2010), "South Africa—Migration Underway," in Guy Berger (2010) with contributions from Fackson Banda, Jane Duncan, Rashweat Mukundu, and Zenaida Machado, *Beyond Broadcasting: the future of state-owned broadcasters in Southern Africa*, Windhoek, Namibia: Fesmedia Africa Series, pp. 69–84.

Egbon, M. I. (1982), "Origin and Development of Television Broadcasting in Nigeria," *Television Journal*, December, 4:4, pp. 27–28.

Fondufe, Clement, N., and Mansuri, Sara (2013), "Doing Deals in Africa—Reflections on What is Different and What is Not," *Business Law International*, vol. 14, no. 2, May 2013.

Gillwald, Alison (2013), "Innovation, Policy & Regulation," *Presentation at the CTO Forum*, Abuja, October, http://www.researchictafrica.net/presentations.php.

GSMA (2013), *Mobile Policy Handbook: An insider's guide to the issues*, London: GSMA, October 2013, http://www.gsma.com/publicpolicy/handbook.

Deloitte and GSMA Intelligence Report (2005), "Tax and the Digital Divide—How new approaches to mobile taxation can connect the unconnected," 2005.

GSMA Intelligence (2013), *Two thirds of Africans yet to join the mobile revolution: African mobile penetration set at 33%; multiple SIMs driving growth*, https://gsmaintelligence.com/analysis/2012/11/two-thirds-of-africans-yet-to-join-the-mobile-revolution/357/ (accessed September 2013).

GSMA Intelligence (2013b), *Sub-Saharan Africa Mobile Economy*, GSMA, http://www.gsma.com., http://www.gsmamobileeconomy africa.com/Sub-Saharan%20Africa_ME_Report_English_2013. pdf (accessed December 2013).

GSMA Intelligence & Deloitte (2012), *Sub-Saharan Africa Mobile Observatory 2012*, http://www.gsma.com/publicpolicy/wp-content/uploads/2013/01/gsma_ssamo_full_web_11_12-1.pdf (accessed September 2013).

Gunze, H. (2013), Tanzania Communications Regulatory Authority (TCRA), Country Status on Migration from Analogue to Digital Switchover, A Presentation to 8th CTO Digital Broadcasting Forum, February 12, 2013, Sandton, South Africa, http://www. cto.int/media/events/pst-ev/2013/DBSF-2013/Tanzania-Country-Status.pdf (accessed October 2013).

Handler, D., and Grossman, P., The Role of Income Distribution and Broadband Penetration in Developing Countries, http://www.cisco.com/web/about/ac79/docs/pov/Income_Distribution_POV_1123_1207FINAL.pdf (accessed October 2013)

The Harmonization of Business Law in Africa: Possibility or Fantasy? *The African Counsel,* vol. I, Issue 2, June 2009.

Infodev & ITU (2012), ICT Regulation Toolkit, InfoDev: 2121 Pennsylvania Avenue NW Washington, DC 20433, USA. ITU: International Telecommunication Union (ITU) Place des Nations CH-1211 Geneva 20, Switzerland, http://www.ictregulationtool-kit.org/en/home (accessed November 2013).

ITU-T (2013a), *The Mobile Money Revolution, Part 1: NFC Mobile Payments*, ITU-T Technology Watch Report, May 2013, http://www.itu.int/dms_pub/itu-t/oth/23/01/T23010000200001PDFE. pdf (accessed October 2013). This report provides an excellent review of the state of the art in Near Field Communications mobile payments.

Jeong, C. H. @Ibrahim (2007), Fundamental of Development Administration, Selangor: Scholar Press.

Lloyd, L. (2010), "Appendix 1: Public Broadcasting in Southern Africa: Beyond Protocols and Rhetoric. A Review," in Guy Berger (2010) with contributions from Fackson Banda, Jane Duncan, Rashweat Mukundu, and Zenaida Machado, *Beyond Broadcasting: the future of state-owned broadcasters in Southern Africa*, Windhoek, Namibia: Fesmedia Africa Series, pp. 90–101.

Machado, Z. (2010), "Mozambique—progress by many players," in Guy Berger (2010) with contributions from Fackson Banda, Jane Duncan, Rashweat Mukundu, and Zenaida Machado, *Beyond Broadcasting: the future of state-owned broadcasters in Southern Africa*, Windhoek, Namibia: Fesmedia Africa Series, pp. 35–44.

McKinsey (2010), *Lions on the move: The progress and potential of African economies,* McKinsey & Company: McKinsey Global Institute, June 2010.

Moyo, Dumisani, and Chuma, Wallace (2010) (Editors), *Media Policy in a Changing Southern Africa: Critical reflections on media reforms in the global age*, South Africa: Unisa Press. ISBN 978186888-569-5.

Mukundu, R. (2010), "Namibia—moving amidst uncertainties," in Guy Berger (2010) with contributions from Fackson Banda, Jane Duncan, Rashweat Mukundu, and Zenaida Machado, *Beyond Broadcasting: the future of state-owned broadcasters in Southern Africa*, Windhoek, Namibia: Fesmedia Africa Series, pp. 20–34.

Mwangi, Michuki (2013), Developing Internet Exchange Points in Africa, in *Africa Infrastructure Investment Report 2013*, Commonwealth Business Council, March 2013, p. 161; http://www.cbcglobal.org, p. 169.

Mytton, Graham (2003), *A Brief History of Radio Broadcasting in Africa,* http://www.transculturalwriting.com/radiophonics/contents/usr/downloads/radiophonics/A_Brief_History.pdf (accessed September 2013).

Mytton, Graham (2000), "From Saucepan to Dish: Radio and TV in Africa," in *African Broadcast Cultures*, edited by Richard Fardon and Graham Furniss, Oxford: James Currey, 2000.

Ndukwe, Ernest (2011), *The Telecommunication Revolution in Nigeria*, 2011 Igbinedion University Convocation Lecture, December 2, 2011.

Nwulu, N. I., Adekanbi, A., Oranugo, T., and Adewale, Y. (2000), "Television Broadcasting in Africa: Pioneering Milestones," Telecommunications Conference (HISTELCON), *2nd IEEE Region 8 Conference on the History of Telecommunications*, Madrid, Spain. November 2010.

Ofcom's Second Public Service Broadcasting Review: Putting Viewers First, Statement, 21 January 2009, http://stakeholders.ofcom.org.uk/binaries/consultations/psb2_phase2/statement/psb2statement.pdf (accessed October 2013).

Ofcom, *New News, Future News: The Challenges for Television News after Digital Switch-over*, an Ofcom Discussion Document, June 26, 2007, http://stakeholders.ofcom.org.uk/binaries/research/tv-research/newnews.pdf (accessed October 2012).

A Guide to the Spectrum Framework Review (SFR), September 2005, Office of Communications (Ofcom), www.ofcom.org.uk; http://stakeholders.ofcom.org.uk/binaries/consultations/sfr/annexes/sfr_guide.pdf (accessed August 2013).

Sanou, Brahima (2011), Measuring the Information Society 2011, published by the International Telecommunications Union (ITU), http://www.itu.int/ITU-D/ict/publications/idi/index.html (accessed October 2013).

Schumann, R. (2013), Case Study of Digital TV Switchover in Tanzania, http://www.analysysmason.com/About-Us/News/Insight/Case-study-of-digital-TV-switchover-in-Tanzania/#.UjhvE8bWR5I (accessed September 2013).

SoS Report (2004), Driving Digital Switchover: A Report to the Secretary of State, Office of Communications (Ofcom), April 5, 2004: http://stakeholders.ofcom.org.uk/binaries/research/tv-research/dso1.pdf (accessed October 2013).

Starks, Michael (2004), *Report of the Digital Project, Version 6*, November 2004, http://www.kigeit.org.pl/FTP/kl/DICE/Report_of_the_Digital_Television_Project_UK.pdf (accessed October 2013).

Thanki, Richard (2012), The Economic Significance of Licence-Exempt Spectrum to the Future of the Internet, June 2012.

The State of Broadband 2013: Universalizing Broadband, a report by the Broadband Commission, September 2013, http://www.broadbandcommission.org/documents/bb-annualreport2013.pdf (accessed September 2013).

Toure, Hamadoun (2013), Investing in Broadband Infrastructure, in *Africa Infrastructure Investment Report 2013*, Commonwealth Business Council, March 2013, p 164; http://www.cbcglobal.org, p. 169.

Umeh, C. C. (1989), "The Advent and Growth of Television Broadcasting in Nigeria: Its Political and Educational Overtones," *Africa Media Review*, vol. 3: no 2., pp. 54–66.

World Bank (2010), *Africa's Infrastructure: A Time for Transformation (Africa Development Forum)*, Washington, DC: The World Bank, ISBN: 978-0-8213-8041-3.

INDEX

ON THE AUTHOR

Professor Hyacinth. Sama Nwana CEng FBCS CITP FIET, (aka H) is founder and CEO of Atlantic Telecoms & Media, a UK-registered telecommunications, media, and technology (TMT) consultancy firm specialising in advising African and emerging economies but also doing TMT consultancy in mature economies.

He was until September 2013 group director of Spectrum Policy at Ofcom, United Kingdom, from August 2009, where he was responsible for overall leading of the recent 4G spectrum auction in the United Kingdom that raised billions of pounds sterling. He oversaw all UK airwaves for broadcast, mobile, and other communications services. He has also led significantly on spectrum clearances, including the analogue to digital switchover (DSO) in the United Kingdom. Before that, he worked at the £800-million UK transmissions firm Arqiva as managing director for four years. Before Arqiva, he was an executive managing director at Quadriga Worldwide, where he took digital hotel entertainment services across Europe. He was a venture capital investment professional (two years) and a senior manager at BT plc (five years). Before BT, he was an academic teaching and researching computer science at the Universities of Keele and Liverpool (United Kingdom).

Dr. Nwana holds an MA from Queens' College Cambridge, a first degree in computer science and electronic engineering from the University of Birmingham, an MSc in computer science, and a PhD in artificial intelligence/computer science from Aston University, Birmingham. He also holds an MBA *with distinction* from the London Business School, University of London.

He is visiting professor of telecommunications at the University of Bristol and visiting professor of computer science at Brunel University in West London. He is also visiting professor of telecommunications to the American University of Nigeria, Yola. He has published several scientific tomes and is well cited.

He is on the board of Breezie Ltd., advises the Commonwealth Telecommunications Organisation (CTO) based in London, is a trustee of various charities, and is a consultant to various international TMT companies. He has trained senior regulators and advised ministers on TMT issues. He has recently led a consortium to winning a £2 million digital TV switchover advisory project for an African country.

Professor Nwana, a devoted pan-African, is married with three children.